Commando

FOR ACTION AND ADVENTURE

BATTLE OF BRITAIN
70th
ANNIVERSARY

BATTLE of BRITAIN SCRAMBLE!

Published in 2009 by Carlton Books Limited
An imprint of the Carlton Publishing Group
20 Mortimer Street
London W1T 3JW

COMMANDO is a trade mark of and
© DC Thomson & Co. Ltd. 2009
Associated characters, text and artwork
© DC Thomson & Co. Ltd. 2009

A catalogue record for this book is available from
the British Library.

ISBN 978-1-84732-421-4

Printed and bound in Thailand

10 9 8 7 6 5 4 3 2 1

BATTLE of BRITAIN
SCRAMBLE!

THE 10 BEST COMMANDO
BATTLE OF BRITAIN COMIC BOOKS EVER!

FOREWORD BY CALUM LAIRD, COMMANDO EDITOR
INTRODUCTION BY GEORGE LOW, FORMER COMMANDO EDITOR

CARLTON
BOOKS

Contents

THE FLYING AVENGERS

What does a pilot do when his plane is shot down from under him, his airfield bombed to pieces and his country invaded? Jan Lubanski knew of only one answer — keep fighting. And that's what he and his fellow airman, Nik Czaja do, wherever and whenever they could. The enemy may have conquered Poland but they hadn't even dented the surface of Poles like Jan and Nik.

UPSIDE DOWN ACE

Alan Burnett and Colin Harvey flew as the crew of a Defiant night-fighter. They shared the same room and spent almost every second of every day with each other … yet the very air round them seemed to vibrate with the fierce hate they had for each other. But, despite their bickering and brawling, they had the highest score of kills in the Group. How they managed it was their own special secret …

BATTLE OF THE BOFFINS

Tony Ansell had always envied his cousin's exciting role as a pilot compared to his own job as a dull scientist. So he was delighted when he got the chance to fly in an Avro Anson – even if it was only as a passenger. Then, when the sinister shape of an enemy fighter-bomber latched onto the tail of the unarmed reconnaissance plane, Tony would have given anything to have both feet firmly on the ground.

WINGED WOLVES

In two wars the families of Von Stellen and Page had clashed in the air. Both fathers had already proved their skill and courage, and their sons were now showing that they had inherited these same qualities. But the Germans had always come off second best in the bitter duels, a fact which left the eldest son, Carl, with a burning desire for revenge. He was determined to settle the score — whatever the cost …

DANGER BELOW

When Flight Lieutenant "Patch" Probin was posted to R.A.F. Venshaw, a top-secret radar station and fighter base in the south of England, he was shaken rigid to find the fighter-pilots crashing, one after the other, for no apparent reason. Had the Nazis developed a new secret weapon? Or worse still, was it sabotage? Was there a traitor on the base?

CZECH MATE

The fighting Czech just HAD to prove himself! When the Germans marched into his stricken country in 1938, he escaped — determined to fight them in the air one day. Flying didn't come easily to him at first, but he persevered. He just HAD to become an ace, because, after all, his name was RICHTHOFEN!

"SQUADRON-SCRAMBLE!"

All that stood between Britain and defeat by the mighty Luftwaffe in the high summer of 1940 were the brave young pilots of R.A.F. Fighter Command. They could be expected to fly several sorties a day and had to be ready for take-off at a moment's notice, constantly on the alert for that stomach-churning call to arms — "Squadron-Scramble!"

NO MERCY

Otto Meitzel was one of the top fighter-pilots in the Luftwaffe. He knew it, and he made sure everyone else knew it, too. He was a Nazi to the core, cruel and arrogant. But then one day, in a dog-fight over the Channel, he was shot down by a complete beginner! Meitzel swore that if he ever met the Englishman again he would kill him. And fate played into his hands, for eventually the young pilot became his prisoner …

SPITFIRE SPIRIT

Major Kurt Krantz was a Luftwaffe ace, one of Germany's top fighter-pilots. The leader of the famous "Black Eagles" squadron had no equal — except for one man. That man was Harry "Handlebar" Hanley of the R.A.F., the only pilot ever to hold his own against Krantz. Then one day Harry found himself alone against six Black Eagles. They blasted the Spitfire full of holes, and Krantz was sure his enemy would trouble him no more. But he was going to find out that the Spitfire spirit doesn't die so easily …

DEATH of the COBRA

Kurt von Schlange was his name, and a scarlet cobra was his badge — a badge of shame! For Kurt von Schlange, Luftwaffe pilot, was no ace. Far from it … he was a murderer who sneaked up on damaged aircraft with wounded pilots, just to add to his tally of kills. But time was running out for Schlange, because Flight Lieutenant Brian Craig was on his tail. And Brian had a very special debt to clear up …

Foreword

SLAMMING THE DOOR BEHIND HIM, JAN RACED ACROSS THE AIRFIELD. HE HEARD SHOUTS, AND THEN THE HARSH WAIL OF AN ALARM KLAXON.

I HOPE THE FENCE ISN'T TOO FAR AWAY!

HE HAD A DEFINITE PLAN IN MIND — A VERY CLEVER ONE AT THAT.

Put yourself in the role of Editor of Commando (good feeling, isn't it?). A writer contacts you to say that he has a great idea for a story about the Battle of Britain.

You've heard that before and been disappointed, so your reaction is guarded. How will it be possible to come up with an original storyline based on one of the most studied and written about confrontations in the history of war? How will someone be able to look at the events of those few short months in 1940 and put a new twist on them?

So you ask them for a short synopsis of what they have in mind. Lo and behold, the idea comes in, fleshed out and in detail. You realise that writers can, and do, take a few events, known so well by so many, and mould them into a fresh narrative.

Partly that's because the story won't necessarily be just about the Battle itself. That may be the beginning of the tale. Or the end. It will likely range over time and location but the Battle will be the crux of the matter.

Partly it's because every writer has a different outlook, a different take on what might seem familiar territory. And a little bit of storyteller's magic too.

Later, when you read the completed script, you imagine it drawn up. Illustrations of Hurricanes, Spitfires, Dorniers and Heinkels flash past in your mind's eye. Guns blaze, aircraft burn, pilots parachute to safety … or not.

FROM THE CLUMSY WAY VON SCHLANGE AVOIDED BRIAN'S FIRE, IT WAS PLAIN HE HAD NO REAL ABILITY. AS ALWAYS HE TURNED TO FLEE, BUT BRIAN WAS ON HIM.

THAT'S WINGED HIM, BUT HERE COME HIS BULLY BOYS. SOMEBODY GET THESE TWO OFF MY BACK!

WHEN CONTACT WAS MADE WITH A BUNCH OF UNESCORTED HEINKEL
BOMBERS TRYING A SNEAK RAID, PETER WENT FOR THEM LIKE SOME
BLOOD-THIRSTY TIGER.

You must, though, remember not to get carried away with the illustrations, for a Commando story is much more than a collection of pictures. In a Commando you get inside the characters' heads, find out what drives them, find out what lengths they'll go to in order to get their way. The writer will have put that in too.

So you send all this out to an illustrator wondering if he can match the pictures in your head to his drawings on his paper. When those illustrations arrive you realise that you shouldn't have worried, his drawings are always miles better than your mental pictures!

This magic happens with every Commando story whether it be set on land, at sea or in the air. If you don't believe me, read the tales from the Battle of Britain in this collection, 10 of the best air-action stories ever.

Fortunately, for the Commando editor, that's not the end of the story. Commando has run since 1961, its heroes and villains battling for supremacy on its pages just as the pilots of R.A.F. and Luftwaffe did in 1940. Long may they continue to do so.

Calum Laird,
COMMANDO EDITOR

Introduction

PIECES FLEW OFF THE MESSERSCHMITT AS JOSEF CLOSED THE RANGE, THEN IN A DELUGE OF SPURTING BLACK OIL, ITS ENGINE BURST INTO FLAMES.

THAT'S FOR MARCHING INTO CZECHOSLOVAKIA!

Just imagine for a moment that you are serving in the Royal Air Force in Britain on 13 August 1940. You maybe haven't been in uniform long, but you know that a massive air struggle has been going on since 10 July as Nazi Germany tries to defeat your country in the skies above. You also know that most of Europe lies under the boot of the Nazis and that the British army escaped by the skin of its teeth earlier in the year from the Dunkirk beaches in France.

There isn't much good news around and maybe worse is to come. What you don't know is that this will be what the Germans have code-named "*Adlertag*" … "Eagle Day" to you and me … and their hostile fighters and bombers will fly almost 1,500 sorties today in an attempt to pound Britain into submission.

All your fellow warriors will play their part … not only the pilots in their Spitfires and Hurricanes, but also the hard-pressed ground crew working round the clock to keep those aircraft flying, as well as the anti-aircraft gunners scanning the skies for any targets. And don't forget the men and women behind the scenes who are helping to plot the enemy's threatening moves, calling on vital information from the newly built radar stations protecting the coast which are themselves a target for destruction.

ANTON CONGRATULATED HIS FRIEND ON HIS VICTORY BUT WAS SUNK IN GLOOM WHENEVER HE CONSIDERED HIS OWN PERFORMANCE.

GERMANS THREE . . . ME NIL. I'LL NEVER HAVE ANY SUCCESS AS A FIGHTER PILOT.

NONSENSE, ANTON. YOUR CHANCE WILL COME.

GUNS HAMMERING FURIOUSLY, THE TWO AIRCRAFT SCREAMED TOWARDS EACH OTHER, NEITHER PILOT GIVING WAY.

It won't be easy and the damage will be severe, but the Luftwaffe will learn that they won't win the Battle of Britain today … or even on 15 August when their aircraft will take off in a massive strike from bases stretching from enemy-occupied Norway to Brittany in Nazi-held France … dogfights soon raging from Scotland in the north right down to the south coast.

The air struggle won't officially finish until 31 October but on September 15th, what we now recognise as Battle of Britain Day, the enemy will finally realise that this is a fight that they can never win. The R.A.F. has been hit hard, but the Luftwaffe losses of air crews and machines are much higher and they have failed in their attempt to beat down Britain.

The war is far from over, though, and it will be five long, hard-fought years before Berlin instead of London is in ruins and the Third Reich has been toppled. Just maybe one of the first steps on the road to victory was made by all those who played their part in the Battle of Britain … on the air or on the ground. Heroes all …

George Low.

George Low,
FORMER COMMANDO EDITOR

ROYAL AIR FORCE AIR SEA RESCUE LAUNCH

The motto of the crews of these high speed rescue launches made by the British Power Boat Company was "The Sea Shall Not Have Them", and they lived up to that claim wherever possible. It was vital to save downed airmen from either death or capture in the waters around Britain in the Second World War, and the nine-man crews of these fast craft could be relied on to play their part.

63 feet long
500 mile range
36 knots top speed
3 x .303 machine-guns
for anti-aircraft protection

Commando

THE FLYING AVENGERS

EVEN WITH ALL THE SKILL AND COURAGE IN THE WORLD, IT'S AN IMPOSSIBLE TASK TO FACE UP TO ENEMY FIGHTERS WHICH ARE BETTER ARMED AND CAN FLY MORE THAN A HUNDRED MILES PER HOUR FASTER. THAT WAS THE DAUNTING TASK CONFRONTING THE POLISH PILOTS WHEN THE NAZIS INVADED THEIR HOMELAND IN NINETEEN-THIRTY-NINE AND THEY FOUND THEMSELVES OUT-NUMBERED AND OUT-GUNNED.

YET THEY NEVER FLINCHED AND FOR MANY THEIR SOLE AIM BECAME TO ESCAPE TO BRITAIN TO FIGHT ON AGAINST THE INVADERS. AND THIS TIME THEY'D HAVE THE AIRCRAFT TO MATCH THE MIGHT OF THE LUFTWAFFE!

THE POLISH P.Z.L. P-11 SINGLE-SEATERS WERE NO MATCH FOR GERMAN Me109s. JAN AND NIK, BOTH EXPERIENCED PILOTS, HAD THEIR WORK CUT OUT JUST TRYING TO STAY ALIVE AS THE GERMAN FIGHTERS SWARMED ALL OVER THE SKY.

THEY CALLED IT DOING BATTLE, BUT IT PROVED TO BE A MASSACRE FOR THE DEFENDERS.

THIS IS SHEER SUICIDE! BUT AS LONG AS WE HAVE PLANES AND GUNS WE MUST FIGHT!

INFERIOR PLANES AGAINST SUPERIOR NUMBERS — THIS WAS THE STORY AS THE GALLANT POLES DID THEIR BEST TO HALT THE GERMAN ONSLAUGHT.

LOOK AT CAPTAIN LUBANSKI'S MACHINE. I HOPE HE'S IN BETTER SHAPE!

AND IT GOT WORSE AS THE DAYS PASSED. THERE WERE NOT MANY AIRCRAFT LEFT IN JAN'S AND NIK'S SQUADRON. AND THOSE THAT WERE WERE NOT REALLY IN ANY CONDITION TO FLY AND FIGHT.

WE MUST BE LIVING ON BORROWED TIME!

YES, BUT WE MUST FIGHT ON . . .

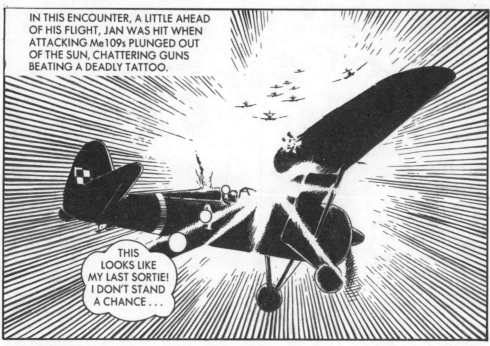

IN THIS ENCOUNTER, A LITTLE AHEAD OF HIS FLIGHT, JAN WAS HIT WHEN ATTACKING Me109s PLUNGED OUT OF THE SUN, CHATTERING GUNS BEATING A DEADLY TATTOO.

THIS LOOKS LIKE MY LAST SORTIE! I DON'T STAND A CHANCE . . .

A HAIL OF GERMAN LEAD STITCHED A RAGGED PATTERN ALONG THE WINGS OF THE P.Z.L. AND STRUCK THE BRISTOL MERCURY ENGINE. THE AIRCRAFT WAS FINISHED BUT MIRACULOUSLY JAN WAS UNHURT.

FAR TOO CLOSE FOR COMFORT . . .

RELIEF FLOODED THROUGH HIM AS THE PARACHUTE SNAPPED FULLY OPEN, ALTHOUGH NOW HE FEARED THAT THE ENEMY MIGHT OPEN FIRE AT HIM AS HE DRIFTED DOWN.

BUT A CERTAIN AMOUNT OF THE OLD CHIVALRY STILL EXISTED AT THAT EARLY STAGE OF THE WAR AND HE LANDED SAFELY.

HE HAD COME DOWN QUITE CLOSE TO HIS BASE. SOON HE WAS WITHIN SIGHT OF IT.

AS HE REACHED THE FIELD, HE REALISED WITH HIS PILOT'S INSTINCT THAT A NEW DANGER THREATENED. SCANNING THE SKY ANXIOUSLY, HE WAS THE FIRST TO SPOT AN APPROACHING ARMADA OF JUNKERS 87s.

AND IT WAS TO PROVE EVEN EASIER FOR THE LUFTWAFFE TO DESTROY THE P.Z.L. FIGHTER PLANES ON THE GROUND THAN IT WAS IN THE AIR.

THERE WILL BE NOTHING LEFT AFTER THIS. I PRAY ONE DAY I CAN MEET THESE BUTCHERS ON EQUAL TERMS!

THE GERMAN BOMBS STITCHED A PATTERN OF ALMOST TOTAL DESTRUCTION ON THE POLISH AIRFIELD. RESISTANCE WAS POINTLESS.

GET DOWN, OR WE'LL ALL BE BLOWN TO BITS LIKE THE PLANES!

WHEN THE STUKAS HAD COMPLETED THEIR WORK, THE
MESSERSCHMITTS CAME IN TO STRAFE THE FEW REMAINING
TARGETS.

LIEBER
GOTT, THEY HAVE
LEFT NOTHING FOR US TO
DO BUT SHOOT AT A FEW
MISERABLE AIRMEN!

BUT THE FIGHTER SQUADRON HAD THEIR ORDERS,
AND THEY WOULD CARRY THEM OUT.

SHOCKED AND DEAFENED BY THE DIVE-BOMBER RAID,
THE POLISH AIRMEN WERE TOTALLY UNPREPARED FOR THE
ATTACKS WHICH FOLLOWED . . .

. . . AS THIS SQUADRON OF Me 109s, EVERY
AIRCRAFT SPORTING A FEROCIOUS LEAPING
TIGER EMBLEM, CAME IN FOR THE KILL.

THEY STRUCK AT EVERYTHING WHICH MOVED AND AS THE RAIDERS SPED ON THEIR WAY, JAN DRAGGED HIMSELF FROM THE GROUND. HE KNEW HE WOULD NEVER FORGET THAT HATED DESIGN.

MURDERERS! I SHALL KNOW YOU WHEN WE MEET AGAIN!

IT WAS A BITTER TALE HE HAD TO TELL WHEN THE FEW SURVIVING PILOTS, NIK AMONGST THEM, LIMPED BACK TO THE BLITZED BASE.

A FEW HOURS LATER THE COMMANDER CALLED ALL HIS OFFICERS TOGETHER WITH SAD NEWS.

GENTLEMEN, WE HAVE NO AIRCRAFT LEFT WITH WHICH TO OPPOSE THE NAZI INVADERS.

I HOPE YOU DON'T MEAN SURRENDER, SIR? WE MUST FIGHT ON!

IT WAS JAN WHO HAD SPOKEN UP, BUT THAT WAS THE OPINION OF
EVERY OFFICER PRESENT, A DETERMINATION WHICH MADE THEIR C.O.
GLOW WITH PRIDE EVEN AT THIS DESPERATE TIME.

NO ONE IS SUGGESTING
SURRENDER. WE ARE ORDERED
TO JOIN UP WITH OUR ARMY
TO FIGHT IN THE FRONT-
LINE OF THE DEFENCE.

THE OFFICERS AND MEN OF THE
SQUADRON WERE ARMED AND DRIVEN
WESTWARDS TOWARDS THE FRONT-LINE
WHERE THEIR COUNTRYMEN FOUGHT
DESPERATELY AGAINST THE STEAM-
ROLLER ADVANCE OF THE WEHRMACHT.
ALSO ON THE ROAD WERE MANY UNITS
OF POLISH CAVALRY.

MEN ON HORSES?
DON'T THEY KNOW
THEY WILL BE FACING UP
AGAINST GERMAN
TANKS?

WHEN
IT IS ALL WE
HAVE TO FIGHT WITH,
WE MUST DO THE
BEST WE CAN.

THE NAZI PILOT WAS GOOD AT HIS JOB. HE PROVED THAT WHEN HE
LANDED HIS PLANE ON ITS BELLY AT THE EDGE OF THE CORNFIELD
BESIDE THE FARM WHERE JAN AND NIK WERE IN COVER.

SOME OF THE POLES WERE INCLINED TO LEAVE
THE GERMAN TO ROAST IN HIS PLANE, BUT JAN
COULD NOT, DESPITE HIS HATE OF THE NAZIS.

THE TWO POLISH OFFICERS MANAGED TO OPEN THE COCKPIT HOOD. THEY DRAGGED THE UNCONSCIOUS MAN CLEAR.

HEAVE AWAY AT HIM, NIK. THE FUEL COULD EXPLODE ANY SECOND!

JUST IMAGINE BEING KILLED TRYING TO SAVE THE LIFE OF A NAZI!

AND WHAT A NAZI THIS ONE WAS GOING TO TURN OUT TO BE.

AS THEY PULLED THE UNCONSCIOUS GERMAN TO SAFETY, JAN NOTICED THE SQUADRON EMBLEM ON THE MAN'S OVERALLS. FIERCE RAGE GRIPPED HIM —

LOOK, IT'S THE LEAPING TIGER! THE SAME AS ON THE PLANES THAT MACHINE-GUNNED OUR AIRFIELD!

WE OUGHT TO HAVE LEFT HIM TO THE FLAMES!

ESCORTED BY SOME SOLDIERS, JAN AND NIK TOOK THEIR PRISONER
TO A BARN BEHIND THE CORNFIELD. HE SOON CAME TO HIS SENSES,
ARROGANT DEFIANCE MIRRORED IN HIS EYES.

WHO ARE YOU?
WHAT IS YOUR
SQUADRON?

I HAVE
NOTHING TO SAY
TO YOU!

JAN HAD A WAY OF MAKING THE GERMAN CHANGE HIS TUNE. A PISTOL TO THE
MAN'S TEMPLE AND THE MENACE IN THE POLE'S VOICE WAS ENOUGH TO PERSUADE
EVEN THIS MOST ARDENT NAZI TO TALK.

YOU WILL
SPEAK, OR I'LL BLOW
YOUR HEAD OFF!

I AM LEUTNANT
GUNTHER OBERWESEL,
AN OFFICER OF THE
LEAPING TIGER
STAFFEL . . .

THE PRISONER WENT ON TO REEL OFF
THE SQUADRON'S NUMBER AND
LOCATION.

NOW JAN KNEW ALL HE WANTED ABOUT THE HATED SQUADRON. HE WASN'T MUCH INTERESTED IN OBERWESEL AS AN INDIVIDUAL AND TURNED HIM OVER TO THE SOLDIERS.

TAKE HIM BACK WITH YOU. TURN HIM OVER TO THE PRISON AUTHORITIES!

I WILL NOT BE A PRISONER FOR LONG. MAYBE WE SHALL MEET AGAIN!

THE BLUSTER DIED ON OBERWESEL'S LIPS AS JAN GLARED AT HIM.

MEANWHILE DAY AFTER DAY THE TERRIBLE ADVANCE CONTINUED. NOTHING COULD STOP THE MIGHTY GERMAN ARMY . . .

. . . AND THE END WAS IN SIGHT FOR POLAND.

FURTHER RESISTANCE WOULD ONLY MEAN TERRIBLE SUFFERINGS ON THE PART OF CIVILIANS. SURRENDER WAS THE ONLY CHOICE, ESPECIALLY WHEN THE RUSSIANS NOW ATTACKED POLAND FROM THE EAST.

THUS THE FIRST CAMPAIGN OF THE WAR CAME TO AN END.

A COMMAND FROM THE FARMER SILENCED THE DOG.
HE EYED THE INTRUDERS CAUTIOUSLY —

WHAT ARE YOU DOING HERE?

WE ARE OFFICERS OF THE AIR FORCE, ESCAPING FROM THE GERMANS.

JAN SAW NO POINT IN TELLING LIES AND HIS STRATEGY PAID OFF . . .

. . . FOR THE FARMER WAS A LOYAL POLE, ONLY TOO WILLING TO HELP AND FEED THEM.

IF WE CAN REACH A PORT WITHOUT BEING CAPTURED, WE STAND A CHANCE OF ESCAPING ABROAD TO CONTINUE THE FIGHT.

YOU WILL BOTH NEED CLOTHES. I HAVE SOME THAT ARE OLD, BUT THEY WILL SERVE.

AFTER A GOOD MEAL, A SOUND SLEEP, AND A CHANGE OF CLOTHING, JAN AND NIK WENT ON THEIR WAY BY DAWN.

THE FARMER SAYS THE NEAREST PORT IS ALREADY OCCUPIED BY THE GERMANS.

WE STILL HAVE OUR GUNS. IF IT COMES TO A FIGHT, WE CAN TAKE A FEW OF THEM BEFORE THEY GET US!

THEY REACHED THE PORT SAFELY. MANY FOREIGN SHIPS WERE BLOCKADED THERE BY THE WAR, WAITING FOR GERMAN CLEARANCE AND THE CHANCE TO SAIL HOME.

WE'LL DO THE ROUNDS OF THE DOCKSIDE CAFES, AND TRY TO GET BERTHS ABOARD A SHIP SAILING FOR A NEUTRAL COUNTRY.

THERE ARE A LOT OF GERMANS ABOUT. TOO MANY FOR MY LIKING!

... OBERWESEL, THE PILOT THEY HAD RESCUED FROM HIS BURNING MESSERSCHMITT. AND THE GERMAN'S MEMORY HAD BEGUN TO STIR AS WELL.

I KNOW YOU, DON'T I? WHERE HAVE WE MET BEFORE, POLE?

YOU MUST BE MISTAKEN . . .

THEN THE NAZI REMEMBERED. HE SEIZED JAN BELLIGERENTLY.

YOU'RE THE CURSED POLE WHO PULLED ME OUT OF MY PLANE AND HAD ME KICKED INTO PRISON CAMP!

TAKE YOUR HANDS OFF ME!

SNARLING, THE GERMAN REACHED FOR HIS LUGER.

ALL EYES WERE ON JAN AND OBERWESEL NOW. NO ONE WATCHED NIK AS HE DREW HIS PISTOL FROM INSIDE HIS JACKET.

SAY YOUR PRAYERS, POLE. YOU'RE ALREADY ON YOUR WAY TO YOUR MAKER!

I'VE GOT TO CAUSE A DIVERSION . . .

ONE BULLET, SMASHING OUT THE ONE LIGHT IN THE DIMLY-LIT BAR, WAS ALL NIK NEEDED.

RUN FOR IT, JAN. WE'LL MEET UP OUTSIDE.

IN THE CONFUSION JAN AND NIK SLIPPED OUTSIDE, BUT THE NAZI WAS QUICKLY AFTER THEM WITH HIS MOB.

DON'T LET THEM GET AWAY!

NEARLY EXHAUSTED BY NOW, JAN CLUNG TO THE RUDDER OF A CARGO SHIP, THE NUMBING COLD GNAWING AT HIS BONES AS HE KEPT TO THE SHADOWS WHILE HIS PURSUERS TRIED TO SPOT HIM.

I CAN'T SEE HIM. I RECKON HE'S DROWNED.

WHO CARES, HE'S ONLY A POLE. LET'S FIND A BAR AGAIN!

LUCKILY THE FANATICAL OBERWESEL WAS NOT WITH THIS GROUP TO SPUR THEM ON TO SEARCH FURTHER.

JAN HEARD THEM GO, YET DARED NOT MOVE IN CASE IT WAS A TRICK. IT SEEMED THAT HOURS PASSED BEFORE A VOICE HAILED HIM FROM THE DECK OF THE CARGO SHIP AND A ROPE TUMBLED DOWN TOWARDS HIM.

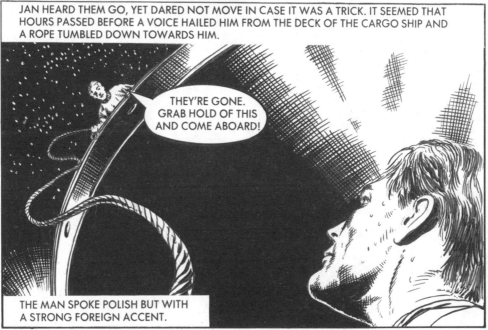

THEY'RE GONE. GRAB HOLD OF THIS AND COME ABOARD!

THE MAN SPOKE POLISH BUT WITH A STRONG FOREIGN ACCENT.

HOW HE MANAGED TO RETAIN HIS HOLD ON THE ROPE HE WOULD NEVER KNOW, BUT AT LAST JAN WAS ON DECK. HE TRIED TO EXPLAIN HIS PREDICAMENT BUT THE SAILOR CUT HIM SHORT.

THE SHIP WAS A DANISH FREIGHTER. HER HOLD EMPTY, SHE HAD BEEN PERMITTED TO SAIL BY THE GERMANS. THE CAPTAIN, LIKE THE FIRST MATE, WAS MORE THAN READY TO HELP JAN ESCAPE. AND BY DAWN . . .

BY THE TIME JAN HAD RECOVERED, HE WAS
TAKEN UNDER ARMED ESCORT TO A REFUGEE
INTERROGATION CENTRE.

IF YOU WANT MY
OPINION, I RECKON
HE'S A SPY.

NEVER. HE KEEPS
SAYING SOMETHING THAT
SOUNDS LIKE POLAND.

JAN MADE A MENTAL NOTE THAT THE FIRST THING HE
MUST DO WAS TO LEARN TO SPEAK ENGLISH.

AT THE INTERROGATION CENTRE, HE WAS QUESTIONED FOR
HOURS ON END BY POLISH-SPEAKING OFFICERS.

IF I
MENTIONED THE
NAME OF LIEUTENANT
NIK CZAJA, WOULD
YOU KNOW IT?

BUT OF COURSE. NIK
AND I WERE TOGETHER
IN POLAND!

IF JAN SOUNDED A BIT ANGRY IT WAS DUE TO THE FACT THAT
THIS INVESTIGATION HAD BEEN GOING ON FOR WEEKS.

NOW IT WAS ABOUT TO END AS ONE OF THE OFFICERS PRESSED A BELL AND NIK SWEPT INTO THE ROOM.

HELLO, JAN. I KNEW YOU'D MAKE IT IN THE END.

NIK — I THOUGHT THE GERMANS MUST HAVE GOT YOU!

THE BRITISH WERE SATISFIED. THE TWO POLISH AIR FORCE OFFICERS KNEW EACH OTHER, AND THEIR STORIES MATCHED IN EVERY DETAIL.

LATER, NIK TOLD JAN THAT WHEN THEY HAD BEEN SEPARATED, HE HAD FOUND A SHIP WILLING TO TAKE HIM DIRECT TO ENGLAND BEFORE GOING ON TO ITS HOME NEUTRAL PORT.

I'VE BEEN HERE A LONG TIME. THEY HAVE PROMISED ME A PLACE IN THE R.A.F.

PERHAPS WE CAN JOIN TOGETHER . . .

WITHIN A FEW WEEKS THE TWO YOUNG MEN WERE ENLISTED IN THE R.A.F. AS AIRCRAFTS-MEN SECOND CLASS.

PLEASE, WE ARE POLISH . . .

WE'VE BEEN EXPECTING YOU — FOLLOW ME.

NOTHING LASTS FOR EVER, NOT EVEN SQUARE-BASHING. AT LAST THEIR FLIGHT PASSED OUT, AND WERE FULLY TRAINED AIRMEN.

HEY, WHAT PRICE THAT OLD MISERABLE SERGEANT NOW, EH?

IT IS GOOD THAT WE SOON PART COMPANY WITH HIM, I THINK.

AND TO ADD TO THEIR PLEASURE WAS THE EAGERLY AWAITED NEWS THAT THEY WERE TO GO ON TO FLYING SCHOOL FOR PILOT TRAINING.

UNFORTUNATELY IT MEANT STARTING AT THE BEGINNING AGAIN AND JAN AND NIK WERE IMPATIENT. THEY KNEW ALL THIS WITHOUT BEING TOLD — AND THE OLD HAWKER FURY THEY WERE TO TRAIN ON WAS YEARS OUT OF DATE ANYWAY.

YOU TWO, PAY ATTENTION. HAVING FOUGHT JERRY IN POLAND DOESN'T MAKE YOU KINGS OF THE CLOUDS, YOU KNOW!

THESE ENGLISH — THEY DO NOT EVEN ACT AS THOUGH THEY ARE FIGHTING A WAR!

JAN HAD SET OUT TO PROVE THAT HE DIDN'T
NEED ANY TRAINING WHEN IT CAME TO FLYING.

NOW MAYBE THEY'LL REALISE THAT WE POLES ARE ALREADY TRAINED PILOTS!

HE WAS NOT BEING BOASTFUL. HE FELT HE WAS WASTING VALUABLE FIGHTING TIME —
ALL HE WANTED WAS TO BE SENT TO A FIGHTER SQUADRON AND SEE ACTION.

WHAT HE DID SEE HOWEVER WHEN HE CLIMBED OUT OF THE
COCKPIT WAS THE ANGRY FACE OF THE CHIEF INSTRUCTOR.

WELL, SIR, WHAT DID YOU THINK OF THAT, PLEASE?

I THINK IT WAS DISGRACEFUL. YOU'RE ON A CHARGE!

SO ENDED JAN'S FIRST SOLO FLIGHT WITH THE R.A.F.

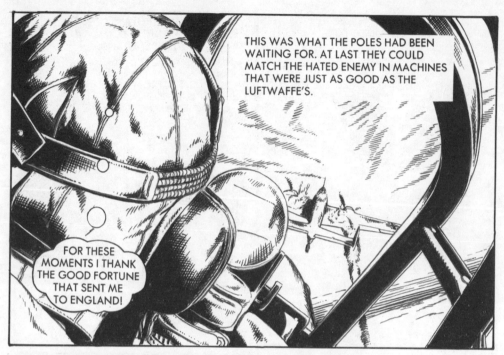

THIS WAS WHAT THE POLES HAD BEEN WAITING FOR. AT LAST THEY COULD MATCH THE HATED ENEMY IN MACHINES THAT WERE JUST AS GOOD AS THE LUFTWAFFE'S.

FOR THESE MOMENTS I THANK THE GOOD FORTUNE THAT SENT ME TO ENGLAND!

AND THERE WERE TIMES WHEN THE ENTHUSIASTIC PAIR DISOBEYED ORDERS IN THEIR EAGERNESS TO DESTROY THE LUFTWAFFE HORDES, BREAKING FORMATION TO CLASH WITH ANY ENEMY AIR ARMADA.

WHAT ARE THOSE TWO IDIOTS UP TO NOW? THEY THINK THEY CAN TAKE ON THE ENTIRE GERMAN AIR FORCE ALONE!

THEIR C.O., SQUADRON-LEADER WYATT, MADE ALLOWANCES FOR THE POLES, KNOWING THEIR HATRED OF THE GERMANS. BUT HE HAD TO EMPHASISE TO THEM THE NEED TO OBEY ORDERS.

EVERY MAN IN THIS SQUADRON HAS A JOB TO DO, AND WE DO IT AS A TEAM, NOT LIKE A HERO OF THE COWBOY FILMS!

YES, SIR. WE UNDERSTAND.

AFTER DUNKIRK CAME THE BATTLE OF BRITAIN. FLYING ALONGSIDE BRITISH PILOTS, MEN OF MANY NATIONS TOOK TO THE SKY TO SMASH THE MENACE OF GOERING'S LUFTWAFFE.

AAGH!

THE POLES HAD DONE SOME CRAZY THINGS IN THE PAST, BUT THIS TIME THEY HAD REALLY BLOTTED THEIR COPYBOOKS BY TAKING OFF WITHOUT BEING ORDERED TO DO SO.

THE OLD MAN WILL GIVE 'EM A ROUGH TIME FOR THIS.

ROUGH TIME? THOSE TWO WILL FIND THEMSELVES ON KITCHEN FATIGUES FOR THE REST OF THE WAR!

KEEPING THE SUN BEHIND THEM, JAN AND NIK RAPIDLY GAINED HEIGHT UNTIL THEY SPOTTED A FORMATION OF HEINKEL BOMBERS ESCORTED BY Me 109s.

THERE THEY ARE, NIK. TALLY-HO, AS OUR BRITISH FRIENDS SAY!

I'LL COVER YOUR TAIL AS YOU GO IN!

JAN AND NIK WERE SOON HAVING A FIELD DAY. THEY HAD CAUGHT THE ENEMY UNAWARES AND POUNCED ON THE NEAREST FIGHTERS RIGHT AWAY.

ONE TO YOU, ONE TO ME, NIK!

WITH FUEL RUNNING LOW, AND AMMUNITION SPENT, THE TWO PILOTS ESCAPED BEFORE THEY SUFFERED ANY SERIOUS DAMAGE AND CAME HOME IN THE HAPPIEST OF MOODS. THIS WAS WHAT THEY WERE IN THE R.A.F. FOR.

THEY WON'T BE ABLE TO TELL US OFF FOR THIS. FIVE ENEMY PLANES BETWEEN US — NOT A BAD SCORE!

THEY RETURNED TO THEIR FLIGHT HUT — TO FIND IT DESERTED, EXCEPT FOR ONE OF THE GROUND-CREW.

WHAT HAPPENED TO EVERYONE, RONNIE?

ORDERS TO SCRAMBLE TEN MINUTES AFTER YOU TOOK OFF, SARGE. THE SQUADRON-LEADER SAID HE WANTS TO SEE YOU BOTH AS SOON AS HE GETS BACK!

WHEN WYATT LED HIS SQUADRON BACK TO BASE, THE TWO POLES WERE UP BEFORE HIM IMMEDIATELY. THE C.O. WAS LIVID —

I COULD HAVE YOU BOTH COURT-MARTIALLED! THE PLANES YOU ATTACKED WERE ONLY A DIVERSION — THE MAIN ATTACK WAS ON SOUTHAMPTON, AND I LED THE BOYS TO INTERCEPT THEM!

JAN AND NIK WERE CRESTFALLEN. THEY REALISED ONLY TOO WELL THAT THEY HAD MADE A MISTAKE.

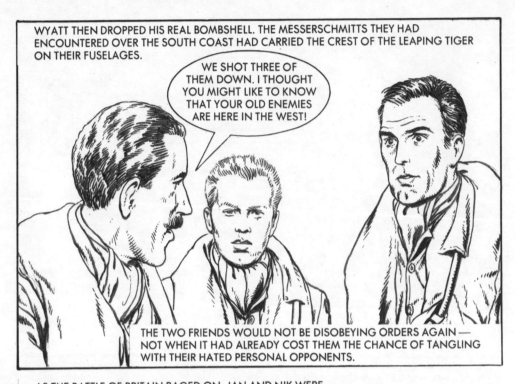

WYATT THEN DROPPED HIS REAL BOMBSHELL. THE MESSERSCHMITTS THEY HAD ENCOUNTERED OVER THE SOUTH COAST HAD CARRIED THE CREST OF THE LEAPING TIGER ON THEIR FUSELAGES.

WE SHOT THREE OF THEM DOWN. I THOUGHT YOU MIGHT LIKE TO KNOW THAT YOUR OLD ENEMIES ARE HERE IN THE WEST!

THE TWO FRIENDS WOULD NOT BE DISOBEYING ORDERS AGAIN — NOT WHEN IT HAD ALREADY COST THEM THE CHANCE OF TANGLING WITH THEIR HATED PERSONAL OPPONENTS.

AS THE BATTLE OF BRITAIN RAGED ON, JAN AND NIK WERE SOON TO GET THEIR OWN CHANCE TO ENGAGE THE LEAPING TIGERS.

BANDITS AT FOUR O'CLOCK. LET'S GO, CHAPS!

TENSELY JAN GRINNED AS HE SAW THE EMBLEM HE LOATHED SO MUCH ON THE NAZI FIGHTERS WHICH ROSE TO MEET THE HURRICANES.

HIS HURRICANE WAS BADLY HIT. OUT OF CONTROL AND DIVING, HE LAUNCHED HIMSELF INTO SPACE, CURSING HIMSELF.

I WON'T MAKE THE MISTAKE OF FOLLOWING MY KILL DOWN NEXT TIME — IF THERE EVER IS A NEXT TIME!

MINUTES LATER HE LANDED IN THE WATER. AND IT WAS COLD —

I WON'T LAST LONG IN THIS!

IT FELT AS THOUGH HE WAS IN THE SEA FOR HOURS, AND YET HE WAS PICKED UP WITHIN HALF-AN-HOUR OF BAILING OUT.

OVER HERE!

TOO LATE HE REALISED THAT HIS RESCUERS WERE NOT BRITISH. HE WAS PULLED OUT OF THE DRINK BY THE CREW OF A GERMAN S-BOAT.

NO. NO. TAKE YOUR HANDS OFF ME!

IT'S A HOLIDAY IN GERMANY FOR YOU UNTIL WE WIN THE WAR!

THESE GERMANS WERE VIGILANT BUT THEY TREATED HIM VERY WELL.

HOURS LATER THE VESSEL CAME BACK TO ITS BASE IN A FRENCH PORT, BRINGING JAN WITH IT AS A PRISONER-OF-WAR.

WITH LUCK THE WAR WILL SOON BE OVER, AND YOU WILL BE SET FREE TO GO HOME.

THANK YOU, BUT I HOPE TO BE FREE LONG BEFORE THEN!

ALREADY ESCAPE WAS HIS MAIN PRIORITY.

WHEN THE CRAFT FINALLY DOCKED, JAN SAW THAT A LUFTWAFFE RECEPTION COMMITTEE WAS WAITING FOR HIM.

WHY THE WELCOME?

WE SENT A SIGNAL OF YOUR RESCUE. THE LUFTWAFFE IS OBVIOUSLY WAITING TO TAKE YOU TO THE STATION WHOSE PILOT SHOT YOU DOWN. IT IS A CUSTOM.

THE OFFICER IN CHARGE OF THE LUFTWAFFE ESCORT PROVED TO BE FRIENDLY. BUT JAN COULD NOT HIDE HIS TRUE FEELINGS AT MEETING UP WITH ANY MEMBER OF THIS SQUADRON.

WELCOME TO FRANCE, AND WELCOME TO THE LEAPING TIGERS STAFFEL. ONE OF OUR PILOTS SHOT YOU DOWN.

I AM SORRY, BUT I DO NOT SHARE YOUR ENJOYMENT!

TWENTY MINUTES DRIVE BROUGHT JAN AND HIS GUARDS TO THE AIRFIELD FROM WHICH HIS HATED ENEMIES NOW OPERATED. THE ESCORTING OFFICER HAD IGNORED JAN'S ATTITUDE, PUTTING IT DOWN TO ANGER AT BEING CAPTURED.

I AM TO TAKE YOU TO THE MESS, SERGEANT. IT IS THE TRADITION OF THE MEN WHO FLY.

I AM NOT UNAWARE OF THE TRADITIONS, LIEUTENANT!

TIGHT-LIPPED AND INWARDLY SEETHING, JAN WAS INTRODUCED TO THE PILOTS WHO BORE THE LEAPING TIGER EMBLEM ON THEIR FIGHTERS.

YOU WILL DRINK WITH US BEFORE YOU GO TO A PRISON CAMP?

THANK YOU.

A FEW DRINKS LATER JAN, AS THE GUEST, WAS ASKED TO PROPOSE A TOAST.

TO WHAT DO WE DRINK, SERGEANT?

TO ANY MAN WHO CAN BRING DOWN YOUR AIRCRAFT!

THE ANNOUNCEMENT WAS FOLLOWED BY A HORRIFIED SILENCE.

ANOTHER LUFTWAFFE PILOT CAME IN THEN AND PUSHED HIS WAY THROUGH TO STAND FACING JAN. THE RECOGNITION WAS MUTUAL.

I KNOW YOU — IN POLAND — YOU PULLED ME FROM MY PLANE WHEN I LANDED!

AND I ESCAPED FROM YOU AND YOUR THUGS SHORTLY AFTER!

THERE WAS NOTHING BUT HATRED IN THE EYES OF OBERWESEL, THE NAZI JAN HAD ALREADY CLASHED WITH ON TWO BITTER OCCASIONS.

AND OBERWESEL HAD NOT CHANGED IN THE LEAST. HE
SNEERED AS HE CUFFED JAN AS HARD AS HE COULD.

THE OTHER LUFTWAFFE PILOTS HAD WATCHED IN SILENCE, BUT
NOW ONE OF THEM INTERRUPTED.

AS THE TWO MEN ADVANCED CAUTIOUSLY TOWARDS EACH OTHER, OBERWESEL SNARLED AND PULLED THE TRIGGER. JAN WENT CRASHING BACK.

ARGHH!

YOU'RE DEAD, POLE!

AT THE GERMAN'S SHOUT OF TRIUMPH, THE OTHER YOUNG FLIERS CAME RUSHING IN. ALL WERE FLUSHED WITH THIS LATEST VICTORY.

WHERE IS HE, GUNTHER?

OVER THERE, BY THE WORK-BENCH!

DROPPING TO HIS KNEES HE BEGAN TO BURROW UNDER THE PERIMETER FENCE, BLESSING THE FACT THAT THE EARTH WAS SOFT.

I'VE GOT TO MAKE A GOOD JOB OF THIS . . .

BEFORE THE GERMANS ARRIVED ON THE SCENE, JAN HAD FINISHED THE HOLE . . . BUT HE DIDN'T ESCAPE THROUGH IT. INSTEAD HE DOUBLED BACK INTO THE SHADOW OF A GERMAN FIGHTER.

THIS IS WHERE HE GOT OUT. HE'S AWAY ACROSS THE FIELDS. AFTER HIM!

WHY RUN ACROSS FIELDS WHEN YOU CAN FLY OVER THEM?

HIS DECEPTION HAD WORKED. THE SEARCH PARTIES SWARMED OUTSIDE WHILE HE LAY IN COVER IN THE ENEMY LAIR UNTIL DAWN BROKE.

BY THEN THE MECHANICS WERE WARMING UP THE FIGHTER ENGINES, READY FOR THE FIRST BOMBER ESCORT DUTY OVER ENGLAND — JUST AS JAN HAD RECKONED THEY WOULD.

HE CHOSE HIS MOMENT WELL WHEN ONLY TWO MECHANICS WERE BESIDE THE CLOSEST KITE.

THE TWO MECHANICS WERE TOO TAKEN ABACK TO ARGUE. JAN KEPT THEM WITH HIM UNTIL THE LAST MOMENT. HE WANTED TO BE AIRBORNE BEFORE THEY RAISED THE ALARM.

THE TWO GERMANS REMAINED MOTIONLESS AS JAN TAXIED HIS FIGHTER OUT ONTO THE RUNWAY. NOT UNTIL HE WAS ALMOST AIRBORNE DID THEY SHAKE THEMSELVES OUT OF THEIR TERROR, RACING TOWARDS THE NEAREST OFFICER.

ACHTUNG, SOMEONE HAS STOLEN OUR PLANE. HE IS TAKING OFF!

WHAT'S THAT IDIOT SHOUTING?

MORE FOUL-TEMPERED THAN EVER AFTER A NIGHT OF FRUITLESS SEARCHING, OBERWESEL WAS WITH THESE OFFICERS. HE GRABBED AT THE NEAREST MECHANIC AND RAPIDLY DESCRIBED JAN.

JAWOHL, THAT IS THE ONE. HE HAD A LUGER!

AND THE PISTOL HAD ONLY ONE BULLET, BUT THE MECHANICS WEREN'T TO KNOW THAT.

THE GERMAN PILOTS DIDN'T NEED OBERWESEL TO PUSH THEM INTO ACTION. THIS POLE HAD MADE THEM LOOK FOOLS — AND NOW HE HAD STOLEN ONE OF THEIR PLANES INTO THE BARGAIN.

WE'VE GOT TO GET HIM BEFORE HE CROSSES THE CHANNEL!

IF WE DON'T, THE C.O. WILL HAVE OUR HEADS!

JAN HAD A GOOD LEAD, AND HE INTENDED TO KEEP IT.

THE CHANNEL, AND NO SIGN OF THE GERMANS YET. I'VE MADE IT.

FAMOUS LAST WORDS . . . FOR THE PURSUING NAZIS HAD BEEN FLYING LOW TO AVOID THE BRITISH RADAR. NOW THEY SOARED HIGH, RIGHT ON JAN'S TAIL.

THEY'RE GAINING ON ME . . . ONLY ONE WAY TO PUT A STOP TO THAT!

HE BANKED TO GAIN HEIGHT AND DIVED BACK AT THE ENEMY.

ACTUALLY JAN WAS BEGINNING TO ENJOY HIMSELF AND HE WENT AFTER ONE OF THE FIGHTERS AS IT CLIMBED ALMOST VERTICALLY. HE DID NOT KNOW THAT THE PILOT OF HIS QUARRY WAS OBERWESEL.

NUMBER TWO RIGHT IN THE SIGHTS — HERE GOES!

THE HARSH BITE OF BULLETS SHOOK THE MESSERSCHMITT AND THEN THE NAZI'S ENGINE SEIZED UP. OBERWESEL BEGAN TO FALL CLEAR AS THIS LATEST KILL MARKED JAN OUT TO THE OTHER GERMANS.

LOOK, THERE'S THE SCHWEIN . . .

AND NOW THE REST OF THE LEAPING TIGERS WERE RAGING FOR VENGEANCE.

AT THAT MOMENT THE ROYAL AIR FORCE JOINED THE BATTLE. A SQUADRON OF SPITFIRES HURTLED DOWN OUT OF THE RISING SUN WITH CHATTERING GUNS.

THE R.A.F.! AS FAR AS THEY KNOW I'M JUST ANOTHER GERMAN, AND I CAN'T DO A THING TO DEFEND MYSELF AGAINST THEM!

JAN WAS ONE OF THE FIRST CASUALTIES, OIL SPATTERING HIM AS HIS ENGINE WAS BADLY HIT. NOW HE MUST TRY TO BRING HIS PLANE DOWN TO DITCH IN THE WATER.

THE ONE THING I FORGOT WAS A PARACHUTE!

THE FIGHTER HIT THE SURFACE IN ONE PIECE, AND JAN FELT HIMSELF GOING DOWN WITH IT AS IT BEGAN TO SINK ALMOST AT ONCE.

I'VE GOT TO GET OUT!

BENEATH THE WATER HE FREED HIMSELF, AND STRUCK OUT FOR THE SURFACE WITH BURSTING LUNGS.

EVEN AS HE STRUGGLED TO GET HIS BREATH, AN AIR-SEA RESCUE LAUNCH WAS COMING HIS WAY.

OVER HERE — CAN'T YOU SEE ME?

WHEN THE LAUNCH ARRIVED BACK AT BASE, GUARDS WERE WAITING FOR OBERWESEL WHOSE ANGER HAD INCREASED BY THE SECOND.

I DEMAND THAT WE FIGHT ANOTHER DUEL. YOU TRICKED ME THE LAST TIME!

DEMAND ALL YOU LIKE. I'VE DECIDED TO END MY DUELLING DAYS. YOU CAN PRACTICE YOUR DUELS IN A PRISON CAMP!

JAN SAW THE NAZI OFF TO CAPTIVITY WITHOUT THE BENEFIT OF A DRINK AT ANY R.A.F. MESS. HE HIMSELF WAS SOON LIVING IT UP BACK WITH NIK AND HIS OTHER FELLOW PILOTS.

I GIVE YOU A TOAST. THE DEFEAT OF THE LEAPING TIGERS!

AND THEN CAME SQUADRON-LEADER WYATT WITH SOME GREAT NEWS FOR THE POLES. AN ALL-POLISH SQUADRON WAS ABOUT TO BE FORMED —

YOU WILL BOTH BE TRANSFERRED TO IT WITH YOUR ORIGINAL RANKS IN THE POLISH AIR FORCE. CAUSE FOR A DOUBLE CELEBRATION!

IT WAS INDEED. THE LEAPING TIGERS COULD NOT BE A MENACE FOR A LONG TIME TO COME. AND NOW JAN, NIK AND THEIR COUNTRYMEN WHO HAD ALSO ESCAPED THE NAZI OCCUPATION WOULD BE FLYING UNDER THE BANNER OF THE POLISH EAGLE.

Commando THE END

HEINKEL 111 H-6

Aircraft of the Second World War — No. 3

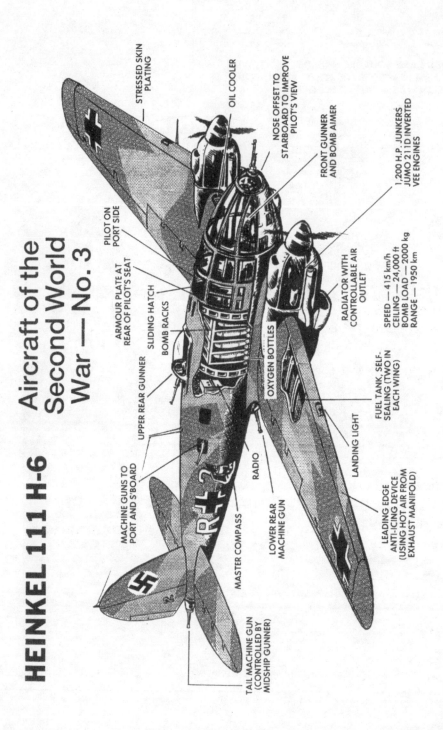

STRESSED SKIN PLATING

OIL COOLER

NOSE OFFSET TO STARBOARD TO IMPROVE PILOT'S VIEW

FRONT GUNNER AND BOMB AIMER

1,200 H.P. JUNKERS JUMO 211D INVERTED VEE ENGINES

PILOT ON PORT SIDE

ARMOUR PLATE AT REAR OF PILOT'S SEAT

SLIDING HATCH

BOMB RACKS

UPPER REAR GUNNER

OXYGEN BOTTLES

RADIATOR WITH CONTROLLABLE AIR OUTLET

SPEED — 415 km/h
CEILING — 24,000 ft
BOMB LOAD — 2000 kg
RANGE — 1950 km

MACHINE GUNS TO PORT AND S'BOARD

RADIO

LANDING LIGHT

FUEL TANK, SELF-SEALING (TWO IN EACH WING)

MASTER COMPASS

LOWER REAR MACHINE GUN

LEADING EDGE ANTI-ICING DEVICE (USING HOT AIR FROM EXHAUST MANIFOLD)

TAIL MACHINE GUN (CONTROLLED BY MIDSHIP GUNNER)

ONE of Germany's best aircraft, the Heinkel 111 played many roles during the war — glider-tug, mine-layer, torpedo-carrier, rocket-launcher. It was also the plane that tried to flatten London during the terrible time of the "blitz".

Compared with our Lancaster or Halifax it was only a medium bomber, but it was extremely reliable and saw service from the blistering heat of Africa right up to arctic Russia.

FROM A DISTANCE IT LOOKED LIKE A HAWKER HURRICANE, SO ENEMY PILOTS THOUGHT THEY'D BE SAFE IF THEY STAYED BEHIND IT. THEY NEVER GOT THE CHANCE TO THINK AGAIN, FOR THIS WAS A BOULTON PAUL DEFIANT — THE ONLY SINGLE-ENGINED FIGHTER IN THE WORLD WITH A FOUR-GUN TURRET!

AUTUMN, 1939. AT A TRAINING AIRFIELD IN THE SOUTH OF ENGLAND, TWO WORRIED MEN WATCHED A TIGER MOTH TAXI OUT TO TAKE OFF. THEY WERE THE CHIEF INSTRUCTOR AND ONE OF HIS STAFF.

THIS IS HIS LAST CHANCE, SIR. I'VE TRIED EVERYTHING. NOW IT'S UP TO HIM.

I KNOW, PETER. PRAY HEAVEN HE DOESN'T BREAK HIS NECK.

NO LESS WORRIED WAS ALAN BURNETT, THE CADET PILOT AT THE MOTH'S CONTROLS. THIS WAS HIS FIRST SOLO, AND COULD VERY WELL TURN OUT TO BE HIS LAST.

WELL, I'M ON MY OWN NOW. I MUST GET IT RIGHT THIS TIME.

THE ENGINE ROARED, AND THE LITTLE BIPLANE ROSE SMOOTHLY INTO THE AIR.

NICE TAKE-OFF.

HE HAS THE MAKINGS OF A GOOD PILOT, BUT HE JUST CAN'T LAND.

AS SOON AS HE ATTEMPTED A LANDING, ALAN WAS LOST. HE BOUNCED, GROUND-LOOPED, AND SEVERAL TIMES DISASTER HAD ONLY BEEN AVERTED BY PROMPT ACTION BY HIS INSTRUCTOR.

I'M HOPING THAT WITHOUT ME IN THE OTHER SEAT TO GET HIM OUT OF TROUBLE, HE'LL PULL HIMSELF TOGETHER.

HE'S ONLY GOT TO PULL OFF ONE DECENT LANDING AND HE'LL HAVE NO MORE TROUBLE. HERE HE COMES. WE'LL SOON KNOW...

THE CHIEF INSTRUCTOR HIMSELF COULD NOT HAVE BETTERED ALAN'S APPROACH. GENTLY THE MOTH LOST HEIGHT, ENGINE TICKING OVER. THEN IT HAPPENED — THAT AWFUL TIGHTENING SENSATION WHEN ALAN'S HANDS AND FEET REFUSED TO OBEY HIM.

GOT TO GET HOLD OF HER, MUSTN'T LET THE NOSE COME UP.

IT WAS NO USE. THE MOTH STALLED, THE HUM OF THE WIND IN THE WIRES DIED AWAY, AND SHE DROPPED TWENTY FEET TO BOUNCE ON THE HARD TURF.

OH MY LORD, HE'LL HAVE THE WHEELS THROUGH THE TOP WING AT THAT RATE.

OPEN UP AND GO ROUND AGAIN, YOU CHUMP!

BUT THE TIGER MOTH SAGGED DOWN AGAIN. THEN THE UNDERCARRIAGE COLLAPSED AS THE LITTLE BIPLANE GROUND TO A HALT ON HER BELLY.

AT LEAST HE REMEMBERED TO CUT THE IGNITION. A FIRE WOULD HAVE BEEN THE END OF HIM.

IT'S THE END OF HIM AS A PILOT ANYWAY.

SHAKEN BUT UNHURT, ALAN KNEW HE HAD FAILED AND THE DISAPPOINTMENT WAS HARD TO BEAR. HIS ONE AMBITION WAS TO BE A FIGHTER PILOT AND NOTHING ELSE WOULD DO.

I CAN'T SPARE ANY MORE TIME ON YOU. I'M SORRY, BUT THERE'S A WAR ON.

THERE ARE OTHER FLYING JOBS, LADDIE. HOW ABOUT TRYING FOR NAVIGATOR? HE'S KEY MAN ON A BOMBER. THE PILOT'S JUST THE DRIVER.

ALAN'S NATURAL COCKINESS AND SELF ASSURANCE WAS ALREADY ASSERTING ITSELF. HE BRUSHED ASIDE THE OLDER MAN'S SYMPATHY.

SIT DOING SUMS WHILE EVERY-BODY ELSE GETS THE EXCITEMENT? NO THANKS! I'LL GO AS AN AIR GUNNER. I WANT TO DO SOME SHOOTING IN THE WAR.

IF THAT'S WHAT YOU WANT, I'LL FORWARD YOUR REQUEST.

SADLY THE SQUADRON-LEADER REALISED THE COCKY ALAN WOULD SUFFER MORE DISAPPOINTMENTS BEFORE THE WAR WAS OVER.

BUT NOT YET. ALAN TOOK TO AIR GUNNERY LIKE A DUCK TO WATER. A NATURAL SHOT, HE HAD BEEN A MEMBER OF A RIFLE CLUB IN CIVILIAN LIFE. HE SAILED THROUGH THE GROUND TRAINING AT THE TOP OF HIS COURSE.

RIGHT, YOU LOT, TODAY YOU'RE GOING TO TRY TO HIT A MOVING, AIR-BORNE TARGET. WE'LL BE OVER THE SEA, SO YOU DON'T DO TOO MUCH DAMAGE TO LIFE AND PROPERTY. JUST REMEMBER THE TOW PLANE IS PULLING THE TARGET, NOT PUSHING IT!

SO SEVERAL OXFORDS TOOK OFF, FOLLOWING THE TARGET TUG. OVER THE SEA THEY TOOK TURNS TO SHOOT AT THE CANVAS DROGUE. ALAN WAITED IMPATIENTLY. HE WAS IN THE LAST OXFORD FROM WHICH THE INSTRUCTOR HAD BEEN WATCHING HIS CLASS PERFORM.

RIGHT, BURNETT. LET'S SEE IF YOU CAN DO ANY BETTER THAN THESE OTHER CROSS-EYED HAMFISTS.

ACTUALLY THE TOUGH FLIGHT SERGEANT WAS DELIGHTED WITH HIS PUPILS' PERFORM-
ANCE, BUT HE WOULD SOONER DIE THAN TELL THEM. AS ALAN SETTLED IN THE TURRET,
OTHER EYES WERE WATCHING FROM ABOVE.

THE JUNKERS 88 WAS RETURNING FROM AN ANTI-SHIPPING PATROL. IN THE OXFORD,
THE SHARP-EYED FLIGHT SERGEANT SPOTTED THE BLACK-CROSSED MACHINE
SWOOPING DOWN AND HURRIED AFT.

HOLDING HIS FIRE SPLENDIDLY, HE WAITED UNTIL THE JUNKERS WAS AT POINT-BLANK RANGE. THEN —

BULL'S-EYE!

HIS STARBOARD ENGINE TRAILING SMOKE, A MUCH CHASTENED GERMAN PILOT HEADED FOR HOME.

PITY WE CAN'T FOLLOW AND POLISH HIM OFF.

NOT BAD FOR A BEGINNER. YOU'RE LEARNING.

THANKS TO HIS COOLNESS AND ACCURACY, ALAN MADE LIGHT WORK OF HIS COURSE. PROMOTED TO SERGEANT, HE WAS SENT TO A SQUADRON NEWLY EQUIPPED WITH BOULTON PAUL DEFIANTS — A FIGHTER FITTED WITH A POWERED GUN TURRET.

FOUR LOVELY GUNS AND ALL MINE.

BIT HARD ON THE PILOT, THOUGH, JUST BEING THE DRIVER.

AT THAT MOMENT ANOTHER SERGEANT, WEARING PILOT'S WINGS, WALKED UP AND EYED THE DEFIANT WITH UNDISGUISED DISGUST.

JUST MY ROTTEN LUCK. I SWEAT BLOOD TO GET POSTED TO FIGHTERS, AND NOW LOOK WHAT I'M LUMBERED WITH.

YOU'LL BE MY CHAUFFEUR I SUPPOSE. DON'T TELL ME YOUR NAME'S JAMES.

THE OTHER MAN'S JAW TIGHTENED.

IT'S COLIN HARVEY, ACTUALLY. AND I SUPPOSE I'M LUMBERED WITH YOU?

DON'T TAKE IT TOO HARD...

COLIN HAD A SHORT TEMPER AND FORMIDABLE FISTS WHICH HE WAS NOT SLOW TO USE.

LOOK, CHUM, I'M NOT IN THE MOOD FOR CLEVER REMARKS!

OK, OK. IF YOU CAN'T TAKE A JOKE, LET'S GO AND SEE ABOUT OUR QUARTERS.

THEY TURNED TO MEET THE COLD GAZE OF THE UNIT WARRANT OFFICER, "BASHER" CRAIG, SO NICKNAMED BECAUSE HE HAD ONCE BEEN A TOP BOXER AND COULD STILL HANDLE HIMSELF.

SAVE YOUR ENERGY FOR JERRY. ALL AIRCREWS ARE TO ASSEMBLE IN THE BRIEFING ROOM. AND TIDY THIS PLACE UP. IT LOOKS LIKE A WIRE-LESS MERCHANT'S RUBBISH TIP!

IN THE BRIEFING ROOM THE COMMANDING OFFICER, SQUADRON-LEADER LARKIN, WELCOMED HIS CREWS AND OUTLINED THE JOB AHEAD.

WE HAVE NO PAST EXPERIENCE TO DRAW UPON SO WE MUST WORK FROM SCRATCH. BUT BOTH PILOT AND GUNNER MUST LEARN TO ACT AS ONE – READ EACH OTHER'S MIND ALMOST.

AN AIR FIRING EXERCISE WAS LAID ON THAT SAME AFTERNOON. COLIN, NOT YET FAMILIAR WITH HIS NEW MOUNT, MADE A RATHER BUMPY TAKE-OFF.

ALAN HONESTLY THOUGHT HE COULD, AND KEPT UP A STEADY FLOW OF CRITICISM AS THEY FLEW TO THE TARGET AREA.

ALAN WOULD NOT LET HIS PILOT ALONE. THE DEFIANT CURVED IN TOWARDS THE TARGET SLEEVE.

THE RESULT WAS BULLETS SPRAYED OVER A LARGE AREA OF SKY, NONE OF WHICH WENT THROUGH THE TARGET. LARKIN'S EXASPERATED VOICE CRACKLED IN THEIR HEADPHONES.

FUMING WITH RAGE, COLIN SNAPPED OFF THE INTERCOM SWITCH.

THERE, SMARTY BURNETT. NOW I'LL BRING HER IN MY WAY WITH NO CHAT FROM YOU.

REALISING HIS NAGGING HAD FLUSTERED COLIN, ALAN NOW KEPT HIS ORDERS SHORT AND CRISP, UNAWARE THAT HE WAS TALKING TO HIMSELF.

MORE THROTTLE, THAT'S BEAUTIFUL. KEEP HER COMING...

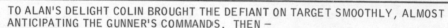

TO ALAN'S DELIGHT COLIN BROUGHT THE DEFIANT ON TARGET SMOOTHLY, ALMOST ANTICIPATING THE GUNNER'S COMMANDS. THEN —

THAT'S HOW IT SHOULD BE DONE!

BACK AT BASE THEY LEARNED THEY HAD ACHIEVED THE BEST SCORE OF THE ENTIRE SQUADRON.

YOU MESSED UP THE FIRST PASS, BUT YOUR SECOND WAS SUPERB. YOU'VE REALLY GOT THE IDEA OF WHAT I WANT — PILOT AND GUNNER WORKING AS ONE.

I'LL TRY TO KEEP IT UP, SIR.

AFTER LARKIN LEFT —

TRUST YOU TO TRY AND GRAB ALL THE CREDIT. NOW YOU CAN SEE I CAN LINE HER UP WITHOUT YOU YAPPING IN MY EAR ALL THE TIME. ON THE SECOND RUN I SHUT OFF THE INTERCOM.

YOU WHAT? BUT YOU REACTED EXACTLY AS I WANTED, ALMOST BEFORE I SPOKE.

THE TWO LOOKED AT EACH OTHER IN ASTONISHMENT. COULD IT BE THEY REALLY WERE READING EACH OTHER'S MINDS?

THE FEELINGS JUST CAME TO ME AS I WATCHED THE TARGET AND WORKED OUT YOUR ARC OF FIRE.

BUT YOU MOVED AT EXACTLY THE SAME MOMENT I WANTED. WHAT A POSER. MUST HAVE BEEN A FLUKE, BUT STILL...

BUT NEITHER WANTED TO TALK ABOUT THIS ANY MORE. IT WAS SOMEHOW TOO EERIE AND STRANGE.

THEY SOON FORGOT IT AS LARKIN WISHED TO DECLARE HIS SQUADRON OPERATIONAL AS SOON AS POSSIBLE AND HE KEPT HIS CREWS HARD AT WORK EVERY MOMENT OF THE DAY.

I'M BUSHED, AND THE C.Q. WANTS US UP AT DAWN TO-MORROW. WE'D BETTER GET AN EARLY NIGHT.

I'LL JUST HAVE AN HOUR ON THE RADIO. MIGHT PICK UP SOMETHING INTERESTING.

COLIN EXPLORED THE AIR WAVES BUT ALL HE HEARD WAS SQUEAKS, GROANS AND CRACKLES. GRATIFYING TO HIM, BUT NOT TO ALAN WHO WANTED TO SLEEP.

IF YOU CAN'T FIND SOME MUSIC, THEN TURN IT OFF. YOU MAKE A FIST OF EVERYTHING, WORKING A RADIO OR FLYING AN AIRCRAFT.

YOU'RE ALWAYS MOANING ABOUT MY FLYING. IF YOU'RE SUCH AN EXPERT, WHY AREN'T YOU WEARING PILOT'S WINGS?

THAT TOUCHED ALAN ON A VERY SORE SPOT. HE LUNGED OUT OF BED AND COLIN WAS READY FOR THE CHALLENGE WHEN A SHARP VOICE STOPPED BOTH OF THEM IN THEIR TRACKS.

WHAT ARE YOU TWO SHOUTING AND BAWLING ABOUT? I CAN HEAR YOU AT THE OTHER END OF THE CORRIDOR.

IT WAS PART OF WARRANT OFFICER CRAIG'S DUTIES TO EXAMINE THE DOCUMENTS OF ALL PERSONNEL. HE KNEW VERY WELL WHY ALAN WORE NO PILOT'S WINGS.

BURNETT, YOU MUFFED YOUR PILOT'S COURSE, SO QUIT TELLING OTHERS HOW TO FLY. HARVEY, PLAY WITH YOUR TOYS SOME TIME WHEN OTHER PEOPLE AREN'T TRYING TO SLEEP. UNDERSTOOD?

BOTH NODDED GLUMLY AND WENT SILENTLY TO BED AFTER CRAIG LEFT.

NEXT DAY CAME REAL ACTION. THE DEFIANTS, ESCORTED BY SPITFIRES, WERE SENT TO PATROL THE DUTCH COAST AND ATTACK ANY ENEMY SEEN.

FIREDRAKE LEADER TO SKITTLES LEADER. IS THAT DESTROYER BEING SHELLED OR BOMBED?

LOOKS LIKE BOMBS. WE'LL TAKE A LOOK.

THEN HE SPOTTED AN ANGULAR SHAPE CLIMBING AWAY FROM THE DESTROYER.

AND THERE'S THE BIRD THAT LAID THE EGGS. WE'LL TAKE HIM. OK, FELLOWS, LET'S SEE HOW WELL WE'VE LEARNED OUR LESSONS.

THE DEFIANTS QUICKLY OVERHAULED THE FLEEING JUNKERS. BUT THE GERMAN CREW WERE SEASONED FIGHTERS, AND EASILY EVADED OR BEAT OFF THE CLUMSY ATTACKS OF THE DEFIANTS.

OUR TURN. THIS BLOKE KNOWS HIS STUFF.

HE'S GOT PLENTY OF GUNS, BUT NOT IN TURRETS. OUT ON HIS BEAM THEY WOULDN'T BEAR.

BEFORE ALAN COULD SPEAK, COLIN WAS ABREAST OF THE JUNKERS, WINGTIPS ALMOST TOUCHING.

GET THOSE POPGUNS GOING!

HE'S TURNING, STAY WITH HIM!

DODGING AND WEAVING, THE GERMAN TRIED TO SHAKE OFF HIS TORMENTOR.

LOVELY GRUB. ONE MORE SQUIRT WILL FINISH HIM.

ALAN KNEW HIS JOB TOO. HE SNAPPED OFF SHORT MURDEROUS BURSTS WHICH CUT THE JUNKERS TO RIBBONS. THE END CAME QUICKLY.

NICELY DONE. WE WERE JUST COMING DOWN TO POLISH HIM OFF FOR YOU.

TWO HEADS ARE BETTER THAN ONE, YOU KNOW.

LARKIN ADDED HIS CONGRATULATIONS WHEN THEY RETURNED TO BASE.

SMART TACTICS, LADS. WHOSE IDEA WAS IT?

BOTH OF US...I SUPPOSE, SIR.

PUZZLED, LARKIN LEFT THE PAIR.

I JUST THOUGHT OUT ON THE BEAM WOULD BE A GOOD PLACE. NEXT THING, THERE WE WERE.

SAME HERE. YOU NEVER SPOKE, NEITHER DID I. IT'S A BIT CREEPY...

IN HIGH SPIRITS THE SQUADRON, ESCORTED BY THREE SPITFIRES, FLEW TO THE SAME AREA THE FOLLOWING DAY, AND THERE MET THE FIGHTER PILOT'S DREAM — A PACK OF STUKAS.

THIS WILL BE A DUCK SHOOT. TALLY HO!

THE DEFIANTS SET ABOUT THE SLOW, UNGAINLY DIVE-BOMBERS, SCATTERING AND HUNTING THEM DOWN. BUT THEIR SPORT WAS INTERRUPTED BY A YELL FROM THE SPITFIRE LEADER.

IN A FLASH THE TABLES WERE TURNED. THE SLEEK Me 109s FELL ON THE DEFIANTS. THEIR EXPERIENCED PILOTS KNEW TO ATTACK FROM BELOW AND BEHIND WHERE THE DEFIANTS' GUNS COULDN'T BEAR.

BUT THE FASTER MESSERSCHMITT WAS UP WITH THEM IN SECONDS.

HERE HE COMES, AND I CAN'T DO A THING. BUT IF WE WERE UPSIDE DOWN... WHAT THE...?

THE DEFIANT WAS ALREADY ROLLING. ALAN'S HANDS FLEW TO THE TRIGGERS, AND THE LAST SIGHT THE FLABBERGASTED GERMAN SAW IN THIS WORLD WAS FOUR MUZZLES BELCHING FLAME AT HIM.

ALL SKITTLES AIRCRAFT. FORM ON ME AND GET DOWN TO SEA LEVEL.

THEIR BLIND SPOTS COVERED, AND CROSSING THEIR FIRE, THE SURVIVORS BEAT OFF THE MESSERSCHMITTS AND MADE GOOD THEIR ESCAPE.

BADLY SHAKEN, THE SURVIVORS LIMPED BACK TO BASE. THEY HAD RECEIVED A SHARP AND COSTLY LESSON.

THESE WORDS WERE ENOUGH TO START ANOTHER BARNEY WHICH ATTRACTED CRAIG.

WHAT DO YOU MEAN? I SAW THAT NAZI SLIDING IN UNDER OUR TAIL AND REACTED INSTINCTIVELY.

HOW COULD YOU SEE BEHIND AND BELOW? BUT FOR ME, WE'D BE DEAD DUCKS.

LARKIN LEFT THEM ARGUING AND WALKED OVER TO WARRANT OFFICER CRAIG.

THAT PAIR WRANGLING AGAIN! YOUNG BURNETT SEEMS TO HAVE THE IDEA HE'S SOME SORT OF THOUGHT READER. IT'S CO-OPERATION THAT'S DOING THE TRICK.

YET THEY REACTED IN SECONDS OUT THERE AND THERE WAS NO TIME FOR CHATTER. I ONLY WISH THEY'D CO-OPERATE MORE ON THE GROUND.

AND ALL THIS TIME THE GERMAN ADVANCE SWEPT ON, CARRYING ALL BEFORE IT. THE BRITISH FORCES RETREATED TO AWAIT EVACUATION.

EVERYTHING THAT WOULD FLOAT CROSSED THE CHANNEL TO TAKE THE WEARY BUT UNBEATEN SOLDIERS HOME. EVERYTHING THAT COULD FLY WAS PUT INTO THE AIR TO BEAT BACK THE LUFTWAFFE WHILE THE EVACUATION PROCEEDED.

THE DEFIANTS WERE IN THE THICK OF IT, AND ENJOYED A BRIEF MOMENT OF GLORY.

COLIN CLIMBED OUT OF THE TURMOIL. ALAN'S GUNS WERE NEARLY RED HOT, BUT THERE WAS NO RESPITE.

RED TWO TO LEADER. STUKAS COMING FROM INLAND!

ANOTHER BULLET-TORN MELEE ENSUED. BUT DESPITE EVERY EFFORT, A FEW OF THE VULTURE-LIKE DIVE BOMBERS BROKE THROUGH.

THAT ONE'S OURS. BLAZES, HE'S DIVING.

GO DOWN WITH HIM. WE'RE FASTER.

IN SECONDS THEY WERE ABREAST OF THE HURTLING DIVE-BOMBER. ALAN RAKED THE EVIL SHAPE FROM STEM TO STERN.

THAT'S HIM FINISHED. PULL OUT QUICK OR WE'LL CRASH.

SHE WON'T COME UP. THE CONTROLS HAVE LOCKED!

THE DEFIANT WAS NEVER INTENDED TO DIVE AT SPEED. COLIN TUGGED FRANTICALLY AT THE CONTROLS BUT THE THREE HUNDRED MILE AN HOUR SLIPSTREAM WAS STRONGER. THE GROUND RUSHED UP AT A TERRIFYING RATE.

AT THAT INSTANT THE FLAPS OPENED. THE DEFIANT JUDDERED HORRIBLY, BUT THE NOSE CAME UP. SOLDIERS WHO HAD WATCHED AND CHEERED THE VICTORY NOW SCATTERED FOR THEIR LIVES FROM THE WHIRLING PROPELLER.

ALAN AND COLIN WERE TOO SHAKEN AND THANKFUL TO BE ALIVE TO ARGUE OVER WHO THOUGHT OF OPENING THE FLAPS FIRST. NEXT DAY THEY FOUND, AS COLIN HAD PREDICTED, THAT THE GERMAN PILOTS HAD LEARNED HOW TO DEAL WITH THE DEFIANT.

IN TWO DAYS THE DEFIANT SQUADRONS WERE CUT TO PIECES. BUT THE JOB WAS DONE. THOUSANDS OF SOLDIERS HAD BEEN SNATCHED FROM UNDER THE ENEMY'S NOSE TO FIGHT AGAIN.

FRANCE HAD FALLEN. BRITAIN WAS NEXT ON THE LIST OF NAZI CONQUEST. GOERING BOASTED THAT HIS "INVINCIBLE LUFTWAFFE" WOULD BRING BRITAIN TO HER KNEES IN A FEW DAYS AS BOMBER FLEETS SWARMED ACROSS THE CHANNEL.

BUT THEY HAD RECKONED WITHOUT RADAR, AND THE SKILL, COURAGE AND DETERMINATION OF THE R.A.F. PILOTS AND GROUND CREWS.

THE DEFIANTS HAD THEIR PART TO PLAY. THE LESSONS LEARNED OVER HOLLAND AND FRANCE WERE PUT TO GOOD USE.

WE SHALL BE TEAMED UP WITH SPITFIRES AND HURRICANES. LEAVE THE FIGHTER ESCORTS TO THEM. OUR JOB IS TO GET BOMBERS.

THE DEFIANT PROVED AN IDEAL BOMBER DESTROYER. IN THE HANDS OF SKILLED CREWS, SCORES BEGAN TO PILE UP AGAIN.

AND ALL THE ACTION GAVE ALAN AND COLIN LITTLE TIME TO FIGHT BETWEEN THEMSELVES.

MORALE SOARED AS SCORES MOUNTED. THEN THE INEVITABLE HAPPENED. THE ENEMY INCREASED THE STRENGTH OF THE ESCORTS, WHICH BROKE THROUGH THE SINGLE-SEATER CORDON.

THAT WAS CLOSE. THE HURRICANE GOT HERE JUST IN TIME.

HERE WE GO FOR ANOTHER CARVE-UP.

BUT THIS TIME THE SLAUGHTER WAS AVOIDED. THE DEFIANTS WERE ORDERED NORTH.

WHY THE MOVE?

JERRY IS MAKING UNESCORTED RAIDS ON EAST COAST PORTS. WE CAN HANDLE THEM, AND RELEASE HURRI-CANES FOR HERE.

THE SQUADRON WAS CALLED TO READINESS ON ARRIVAL AT THE NEW BASE.

I'M BORED. WHY CAN'T WE GO AND FIND SOME NAZIS?

RELAX WHILE YOU CAN.

SECONDS AFTER COLIN SPOKE, BLACK-CROSSED DORNIERS THUNDERED OVER THE AIR-FIELD, BOMBS SPILLING FROM THEM.

HOW THE HECK DID THEY MANAGE TO JUMP US?

CAME IN LOW UNDER THE RADAR. LOOK OUT, HERE COMES THE SECOND WAVE.

THE SAFEST PLACE FOR MEN AND MACHINES WAS IN THE AIR. COLIN AND ALAN SPRINTED THROUGH THE DUST AND HUMMING SHRAPNEL TO THEIR DEFIANT.

ANOTHER FLIGHT COMING IN. GET GOING BEFORE THEY LAY THEIR EGGS!

WE'LL HAVE TO TAKE OFF CROSS-WIND. HANG ON.

THE RAIDERS VANISHED AS SUDDENLY AS THEY HAD COME. COLIN LANDED CAREFULLY ON THE CRATER-POCKED AIRFIELD. THEY HAD ADDED TO THEIR SCORE AND ALAN HAD A PERSONAL TROPHY – A FIRST-CLASS BLACK EYE.

HALF THE SQUADRON AIRCRAFT HAD BEEN DESTROYED OR DAMAGED IN THE LIGHTNING RAID, AND FIGHTER COMMAND WERE HAVING SECOND THOUGHTS ABOUT THE DEFIANT'S USEFULNESS AS A DAY FIGHTER.

NIGHT AFTER NIGHT THE ROOM WAS FESTOONED WITH WIRES, EVERY AVAILABLE SPACE CLUTTERED WITH SPARE PARTS.

I THOUGHT I'D HAVE A RUN THROUGH THE ULTRA LONG WAVE BAND. NEVER KNOW WHAT I MIGHT PICK UP.

BEST OF LUCK TO YOU. I'M GOING TO THE PICTURES. AT LEAST THERE'LL BE SOMEWHERE TO SIT DOWN.

BUT THEN SUDDENLY A STEADY HUMMING NOTE WAS HEARD.

A CONTINUOUS SIGNAL. WONDER WHAT IT IS?

A BIRD MAYBE?

OUTSIDE, DUSK HAD FALLEN. SOMETHING TANGLED IN ALAN'S FEET, SENDING HIM SPRAWLING.

WHAT ON EARTH? HUH, THREE GUESSES WHO PUT THAT THERE!

ALAN'S ANGRY ROAR BROUGHT COLIN TO THE WINDOW.

MUST YOU HAVE YOUR CLUTTER EVERYWHERE. I NEARLY BROKE MY NECK!

CAREFUL WITH THAT. IT'S MY DIRECTIONAL ANTENNA. WELL I'M BLOWED, THE SIGNAL'S CHANGED.

THE STEADY HUM HAD NOW BECOME A SERIES OF DASHES, BUT AS ALAN PUT THE AERIAL BACK IN POSITION THE HUM STARTED AGAIN.

I'M SURE IT'S A RADIO NAVIGATION BEAM...

WELL, I'M GOING. IF YOU DON'T MIND, I'D LIKE TO SEE THAT FILM!

BUT NO SOONER WAS ALAN IN THE CINEMA THAN AN AIR RAID WARNING WAS FLASHED ON THE SCREEN. HE MADE IT BACK TO CAMP JUST AS A SIZEABLE FORMATION OF ENEMY BOMBERS PASSED OVER.

IF THEY WERE GOING TO DROP BOMBS, THEY'D HAVE DONE IT BY NOW. THEY CAN'T BE HEADING FOR LONDON. THEY MUST BE LOST.

BY THE TIME THE ALL CLEAR SOUNDED, IT WAS TOO LATE TO GO BACK TO THE CINEMA. A VERY IRRITABLE ALAN RETURNED TO HIS ROOM TO FIND COLIN IN AN EXULTANT MOOD.

I WAS RIGHT. THAT WAS A RADIO BEAM AND THOSE NAZIS WERE FOLLOWING IT.

WHERE TO? THEY WERE LOST. AND I WISH SOME PEOPLE WOULD CLEAR UP THEIR MESS SO THAT OTHERS CAN GET TO BED!

THE AMPLIFIER BROKE AS IT FELL. COLIN LEAPT ANGRILY TO HIS FEET.

THE SHOUTING AND THUD OF BLOWS BROUGHT CRAIG RUNNING.

"BASHER" CRAIG SHOWED HIS NICKNAME WAS NOT LIGHTLY BESTOWED. HE STEPPED IN AND TWO DEFT, TELLING BLOWS SENT BOTH COMBATANTS SPRAWLING.

NEXT MORNING ALAN AND COLIN RECEIVED A THOROUGH DRESSING-DOWN FROM SQUADRON-LEADER LARKIN.

HE WAS MET BY A STONEY SILENCE.   DISLIKE EACH OTHER THEY MIGHT, BUT NEITHER ALAN NOR COLIN WOULD TELL TALES.

THANKFUL TO BE LET OFF, ALAN AND COLIN FOUND MORE TROUBLE WHEN CRAIG HAD HIS SAY.

BURNETT – GET IT INTO YOUR HEAD YOU DON'T KNOW EVERYTHING. OTHER PEOPLE CAN DO THINGS BETTER THAN YOU, LIKE FLYING AN AIR-CRAFT. HARVEY – I LIKE A MAN WITH A HOBBY, BUT NOT EVERYBODY SHARES YOUR ENTHUSIASM FOR RADIO.

CRAIG COULD SEE THAT HIS WORDS WERE STRIKING HOME.

AND IF YOU TWO SO MUCH AS BLINK AT EACH OTHER, I'LL HAVE YOU IN THE RING AND GIVE YOU THE PAST-ING OF YOUR LIVES. THAT'S A PROMISE, NOT A THREAT. NOW HOP IT!

THE TWO MADE THEIR ESCAPE TO THE SERGEANTS' MESS. THERE ALAN PICKED UP A NEWSPAPER WHICH TOLD OF A RAID ON A MIDLAND INDUSTRIAL TOWN THE PREVIOUS NIGHT.

THE COURSE THOSE NAZIS TOOK COULD HAVE LED THEM OVER THIS AIRFIELD. OH, HE'S SEEN IT TOO. WE'D BETTER LET THE SUBJECT DROP...

THEN THE GERMAN NIGHT OFFENSIVE GATHERED STRENGTH. BESIDES LONDON, SEAPORTS AND INDUSTRIAL TOWNS CAME UNDER THE LUFTWAFFE HAMMER. TO MEET THIS MENACE, THE DEFIANTS BECAME NIGHT FIGHTERS.

WE KNOW FROM EXPERIENCE THAT THE DEFIANT DOES BEST AGAINST BOMBERS. WE SHOULD HAVE SOME GOOD HUNTING.

FIRST WE HAVE TO LEARN TO SEE IN THE DARK.

AIRBORNE RADAR WAS IN ITS INFANCY, SO AFTER THE RAIDERS CROSSED THE COAST — "EYEBALLS, MARK ONE" WERE THE ORDER OF THE DAY.

BLACK AS THE PIT. A NAZI COULD PASS WITHIN YARDS OF US AND WE'D NEVER SEE HIM.

AND YET THEY FIND THEIR WAY TO THEIR TARGETS WITHOUT ANY TROUBLE. HOW DO THEY DO IT?

THE QUESTION WAS CAUSING GRAVE CONCERN IN HIGH PLACES. COLIN HAD SOMETHING ON HIS MIND TOO. HE ABANDONED HIS RECEIVER AND SPENT HIS SPARE TIME BUSILY BUILDING SOME OBSCURE DEVICE.

AS THEY WALKED OUT TO THEIR AIRCRAFT SEVERAL NIGHTS LATER, ALAN NOTICED THAT COLIN WAS CARRYING AN ODD CONTRAPTION.

COLIN STILL BELIEVED IN HIS RADIO BEAM BUT ALAN WAS SCEPTICAL.

WHEN THEY ARRIVED ON THEIR PATROL AREA –

NIGHTJAR TO SKITTLES THREE. BANDITS APPROACH-ING COURSE TWO EIGHT THREE.

NOW I'LL SWITCH ON MY BOX OF TRICKS.

LINING UP ON THE NAZIS' PREDICTED COURSE, COLIN PICKED UP THE HUM-MING SIGNAL WITH HIS GADGET. WHEN HE TURNED TO PORT HE GOT DOTS – TO STARBOARD, DASHES.

I WAS RIGHT, IT IS A RADIO BEAM.

BULLY FOR YOU, PROFESSOR, BUT WHERE'S JERRY?

THAT QUESTION WAS ANSWERED MINUTES LATER WHEN SHARP AND CLEAR AGAINST THE STARS LOOMED THE UNMISTAKABLE SILHOUETTES OF HEINKEL 111s. ALAN WASTED NO TIME.

NEVER KNEW WHAT HIT HIM.

THEY'LL SCATTER. PUT ME ON TO ANOTHER – QUICK, BEFORE WE LOSE THEM.

A SECOND HEINKEL WAS SENT SPINNING TO DESTRUCTION BEFORE THE REMAINDER VANISHED INTO THE GLOOM. AT ONCE COLIN PICKED UP THE RADIO BEAM AND RACED ALONG IT AT FULL THROTTLE.

SURE ENOUGH, THE SHAKEN GERMANS HAD HARDLY SETTLED BACK ON COURSE WHEN THEIR UNSEEN TORMENTOR PLUNGED OUT OF THE DARKNESS A SECOND TIME.

BACK AT BASE, COLIN WAS ALL FOR TELLING LARKIN OF HIS DISCOVERY, BUT ALAN WAS OF THE OPINION THAT SURELY THE BOFFINS, WITH THE FINEST BRAINS AND EQUIPMENT AT THEIR DISPOSAL, HAD LONG AGO FOUND OUT ABOUT THE RADIO BEAMS.

THE TERRIBLE TWINS' SCORE STEADILY MOUNTED, TO THE DELIGHT AND WONDER OF LARKIN.

PUZZLED, LARKIN SOUGHT OUT CRAIG.

A FEW NIGHTS LATER ALAN AND COLIN WERE ON PATROL, THEIR SECRET WEAPON HUMMING MERRILY. BUT NOTHING CAME THEIR WAY.

COLIN HEADED OUT TO SEA, FOLLOWING THE BEAM, BUT STILL THEY SAW NOTHING. SUDDENLY THE BEAM CUT OUT. COLIN AT ONCE REVERSED COURSE. THE SIGNAL RECOMMENCED AS THEY CROSSED THE FRENCH COAST.

ALAN RELUCTANTLY AGREED, FIRMLY CONVINCED THEY WERE WALKING INTO A LION'S DEN. THEY FOUND THE BEAM STATION EXPERTLY CAMOUFLAGED, AND HEAVILY GUARDED.

THERE'S THE ANTENNA. WISH WE COULD HAVE A LOOK INSIDE.

I THINK THOSE ARMED CHARACTERS WOULD OBJECT. YOU'VE HAD YOUR LOOK. LET'S GET AWAY FROM HERE.

SUDDENLY THERE WAS A SHOUT, A BURST OF FIRING, AND THE PEACEFUL SCENE EXPLODED INTO A HOWLING BEDLAM OF SHOTS AND EXPLOSIONS.

THEY'VE SEEN US. GET DOWN.

IT'S NOT US THEY'RE SHOOTING AT. I DON'T KNOW WHAT'S GOING ON, BUT THIS IS NO PLACE FOR US. RUN FOR IT!

THEY TOOK TO THEIR HEELS, CRASHING THROUGH THE UNDERGROWTH, THEN SKIDDING TO A HALT AS A FEARSOME FIGURE ROSE UP BEFORE THEM.

THE TERRIBLE TWINS HAD LANDED IN THE MIDDLE OF ONE OF THE FIRST COMMANDO RAIDS, WHICH HAD BEEN MOUNTED FOR SEVERAL REASONS, AS THE COMMANDO LEADER, LIEUTENANT MARK RUSHDEN, EXPLAINED.

RUSHDEN SNORTED IN DISGUST. A SCIENTIST HAD BEEN SENT WITH THEIR PARTY, BUT HAD BECOME SO SEASICK ON THE TRIP OVER THAT THEY HAD TO LEAVE HIM ON BOARD THE TORPEDO BOATS IN WHICH THEY HAD COME.

AND TO CAP IT ALL, YOU LOT NOSING AROUND MADE JERRY JUMPY. THAT'S WHY WE WERE SPOTTED. A PARTY HAS GONE ROUND TO CUT THEIR WAY THROUGH THE WIRE AND ATTACK FROM THE REAR.

SOUNDS LIKE THEY'VE DONE IT, SIR. COME ON, YOU TWO. CAN'T HAVE YOU HANGING ABOUT OUT HERE.

A FLURRY OF SHOTS CONFIRMED THE SERGEANT'S WORDS. YELLING LIKE FIENDS, THE COMMANDOS SWEPT IN. FIVE SAVAGE MINUTES LATER IT WAS OVER AND THEY STOOD IN THE MAIN TRANSMITTER ROOM.

ALL THIS CLUTTER MEANS NOTHING TO ME. I'M A FIGHTING SOLDIER, NOT A TECHNICIAN. GET THE CHARGES LAID, SERGEANT. HULLO, WHAT'S YOUR MATE UP TO?

HE KNOWS SOMETHING ABOUT RADIO, SIR.

WHILE THE COMMANDOS PLANTED EXPLOSIVES, ALAN EXAMINED THE EQUIPMENT, MAKING NOTES. THE LAST CHARGE WAS LAID, THE FUSES SET, AND THE RAIDERS MADE THEMSELVES SCARCE.

THANKS, CHUM. BETWEEN US WE'VE PUT PAID TO ANOTHER SECRET WEAPON.

SECRET WEAPON! CRIPES, I LEFT MY RECEIVER IN THE AIRCRAFT. IF THE GERMANS FIND IT THEY MIGHT GUESS WE'RE ON TO THEIR BEAM FREQUENCY AND CHANGE IT. THAT WOULD MAKE ALL YOUR WORK WORTHLESS.

LUCKILY THEY PASSED THE DEFIANT ON THE WAY BACK TO THE BOATS. RUSHDEN WAS SURPRISED AT ITS UNDAMAGED APPEARANCE.

IT'S THE ENGINE. IT JUST STOPPED DEAD.

LET ME LOOK. PITY TO WASTE A GOOD AEROPLANE IF IT CAN BE FIXED.

ALAN WATCHED DOUBTFULLY AS THE STOCKY SERGEANT PEERED INTO THE ENGINE. HE FOUND A PETROL LINE CUT BY A BULLET, AND PROCEEDED TO MEND IT, USING RAG, WIRE AND CHEWING GUM.

THERE WE ARE. IT'LL GET YOU TO ENGLAND.

A GENIUS!

THEY HAD JUST MANHANDLED THE DEFIANT TO FACE THE LENGTH OF THE FIELD WHEN A LORRY FULL OF GERMAN TROOPS CAME ROARING ONTO THE SCENE.

THEY WOULD CHOOSE THIS MOMENT TO COME ALONG. WE'RE OUT IN THE OPEN WITH NO COVER.

THE BANG WE MADE MUST HAVE BROUGHT THEM. I'LL SOON FLUSH THEM OUT.

ALAN VAULTED INTO THE TURRET AND SWUNG THE GUNS ROUND. A TORNADO OF WHITE-HOT STEEL LASHED THE HEDGE BEFORE THE GERMANS COULD FIRE MORE THAN A FEW SHOTS.

THAT'LL TEACH THEM TO BE NOSEY. ANY OF OUR LOT HURT?

COLIN WAS LIFTED GENTLY INTO THE TURRET. THOUGH IN GREAT PAIN, HE HAD THE INTERCOM CONNECTED.

HE'S GOT GUTS THAT ONE. HE'LL GIVE YOU INSTRUCTIONS. GOOD LUCK.

THANKS, I'M GOING TO NEED IT.

ALAN HAD A FAIR IDEA HOW THE DEFIANT BEHAVED, AND WITH COLIN'S ENCOURAGEMENT HE MANAGED TO STRUGGLE INTO THE AIR.

WELL, WE'RE FLYING. THAT'S A START.

MORE BY LUCK THAN MANAGEMENT!

ONCE AIRBORNE, ALAN FOUND CONTROL EASIER. HE LEVELLED OFF, SET COURSE OVER THE CHANNEL. DAWN WAS BREAKING AS THE COAST OF ENGLAND APPEARED.

SKITTLES THREE TO CONTROL. MAYDAY, MAYDAY. WOUNDED MAN ABOARD. HAVE AMBULANCE STANDING BY WHEN I LAND.

COLIN HAD PASSED OUT SECONDS AFTER TAKE-OFF AND WAS STILL UNCONSCIOUS.

AS THE AIRFIELD APPEARED BELOW, ALAN FELT THAT OLD TIGHTENING SENSATION. HE KNEW HE MUST CONQUER IT AND LAND BECAUSE COLIN'S LIFE DEPENDED ON HIM. THEN A CALM VOICE SPOKE —

STEADY, ALAN, STEADY. YOU KNOW WHERE THE UNDER-CARRIAGE CONTROL IS. NOW THE FLAPS...

COLIN! YOU'VE COME ROUND AGAIN!

THE VOICE KEPT UP A STEADY FLOW OF INSTRUCTIONS, WARNINGS, ENCOURAGEMENT. ALAN LISTENED AND OBEYED.

SHE WON'T GLIDE LIKE THE TIGER MOTH. KEEP THE POWER ON. NICELY...KEEP THE NOSE UP...THAT'S RIGHT.

DON'T PASS OUT NOW, COLIN. HOLD ON...

THE DEFIANT TOUCHED DOWN WITH HARDLY A BUMP. FEELING UTTERLY EXHAUSTED, ALAN SWITCHED OFF THE ENGINE. THEY WERE DOWN — HE HAD DONE IT.

I THINK YOU'VE GOT SOME EXPLAINING TO DO, SERGEANT BURNETT. WHERE THE DEVIL HAVE YOU BEEN?

IT'S QUITE A LONG STORY, SIR. SHALL WE GO TO YOUR OFFICE?

ALAN MADE A CLEAN BREAST OF THE WHOLE AFFAIR, ADDING NOTHING, LEAVING NOTHING OUT, MAKING NO EXCUSES. WHILE HE WAS TALKING, WARRANT OFFICER CRAIG BROUGHT IN THE SECRET WEAPON FROM THE DEFIANT.

I DON'T KNOW WHETHER TO RECOMMEND THE PAIR OF YOU FOR A MEDAL OR A COURT-MARTIAL. WHY ON EARTH DIDN'T HARVEY COME TO ME? THIS INFORMATION IS VITAL.

I'M AFRAID I TALKED HIM OUT OF IT, SIR.

CRAIG GLARED AT ALAN.

THEN WHY NOT COME TO ME? I WOULDN'T HAVE LAUGHED AT YOU, OR REPORTED YOU. YOU HELD BACK A MAJOR DISCOVERY OUT OF NOTHING MORE THAN STUPID PRIDE.

THEN THEY GET MIXED UP IN A COMMANDO RAID, AND BRING BACK EVEN MORE VITAL INFORMATION. WHAT A MUDDLE! GO AND GET SOME REST WHILE MISTER CRAIG AND I SORT THIS OUT.

ALAN HEADED STRAIGHT FOR THE HOSPITAL. HE WAITED IN AGONY UNTIL A WHITE-COATED DOCTOR APPROACHED.

IS HE GOING TO BE OK?

YOU GOT HIM HERE JUST IN TIME, BUT THAT BULLET SEVERED TENDONS. HE'LL BE PERMANENTLY LAME.

WITH THIS NAGGING AT HIM, ALAN COULDN'T SLEEP. HE WAS GLAD WHEN LARKIN SENT FOR HIM.

SUPPOSE I CAN KISS MY STRIPES GOODBYE. HULLO, THAT'S A USEFUL-LOOKING KITE.

WAITING WITH LARKIN   WAS A WING COMMANDER FROM INTELLIGENCE.   AND LARKIN HAD RECEIVED A PHONE CALL FROM RUSHDEN, FULL OF PRAISE FOR COLIN AND ALAN.

WE KNEW THERE WERE BEAMS, BUT THE FREQUENCY FOXED US. NOW WE CAN BEND THE BEAMS AND SEND THE JERRIES OFF COURSE.

THAT'S GOOD, SIR.   BUT WHAT'S TO HAPPEN TO HARVEY AND ME?

LARKIN'S EYEBROWS CAME DOWN, WHILE THE WING COMMANDER SMOTHERED A GRIN.

THE MATTER OF YOUR ASSORTED CAPERS IN FRANCE HAS BEEN DIS-CUSSED.   NO ACTION WILL BE TAKEN.   THERE'LL BE NO MEDALS, BUT NO COURT-MARTIAL EITHER.

PHEW, THAT'S A RELIEF. IN THAT CASE, CAN I RE-APPLY FOR PILOT TRAINING? NOW I'VE DONE A LANDING, ADMITTEDLY WITH HELP, I'M SURE I'LL HAVE NO MORE TROUBLE.

STRIKE WHILE THE IRON IS HOT AND THE ATMOSPHERE FRIENDLY, THOUGHT ALAN. LARKIN GLANCED QUESTIONINGLY AT THE WING COMMANDER, WHO NODDED.

WHAT ABOUT COLIN? WITH A GAMMY LEG HE'S FINISHED AS AN OPERATIONAL PILOT.

HE CAN BE VERY USEFUL. THAT NEW MACHINE OUTSIDE IS A BEAUFIGHTER. YOU'LL BE RE-EQUIPPING WITH THEM. THEY CARRY RADAR. WITH HIS KNOWLEDGE OF RADIO, YOUR FRIEND WILL BE A NATURAL OPERATOR.

ALAN TOLD COLIN ALL THIS WHEN HE VISITED THE PILOT IN HOSPITAL THAT EVENING. SOME GOOD HAD COME OF THEIR STORMY PARTNERSHIP.

PERHAPS WE CAN TEAM UP AGAIN LATER ON — IN OPPOSITE SEATS THIS TIME. THE TERRIBLE TWINS REUNITED.

ONLY TERRIBLE TO JERRY NOW. WE'VE LEARNED A BIT OF COMMON SENSE I HOPE. YOU'LL MAKE A GOOD PILOT, ALAN.

MESSERSCHMITT 109

Aircraft of the Second World War — No. 12

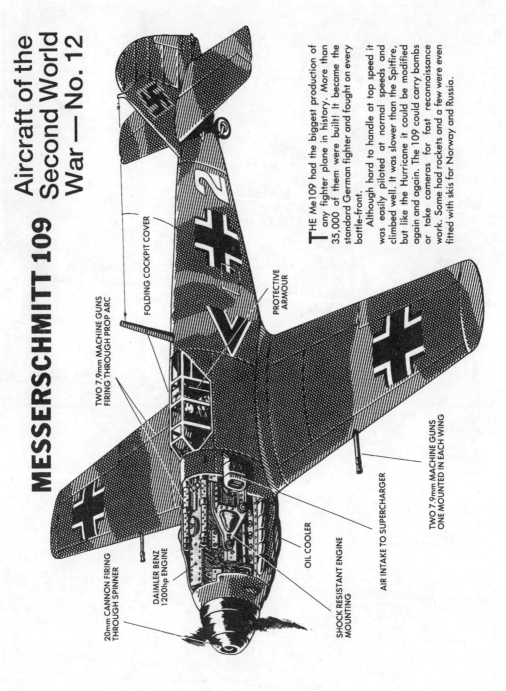

TWO 7.9mm MACHINE GUNS
FIRING THROUGH PROP ARC

FOLDING COCKPIT COVER

PROTECTIVE ARMOUR

20mm CANNON FIRING THROUGH SPINNER

DAIMLER BENZ 1200hp ENGINE

SHOCK RESISTANT ENGINE MOUNTING

OIL COOLER

AIR INTAKE TO SUPERCHARGER

TWO 7.9mm MACHINE GUNS
ONE MOUNTED IN EACH WING

THE Me109 had the biggest production of any fighter plane in history. More than 35,000 of them were built! It became the standard German fighter and fought on every battle-front.

Although hard to handle at top speed it was easily piloted at normal speeds and climbed well. It was slower than the Spitfire, but like the Hurricane it could be modified again and again. The 109 could carry bombs or take cameras for fast reconnaissance work. Some had rockets and a few were even fitted with skis for Norway and Russia.

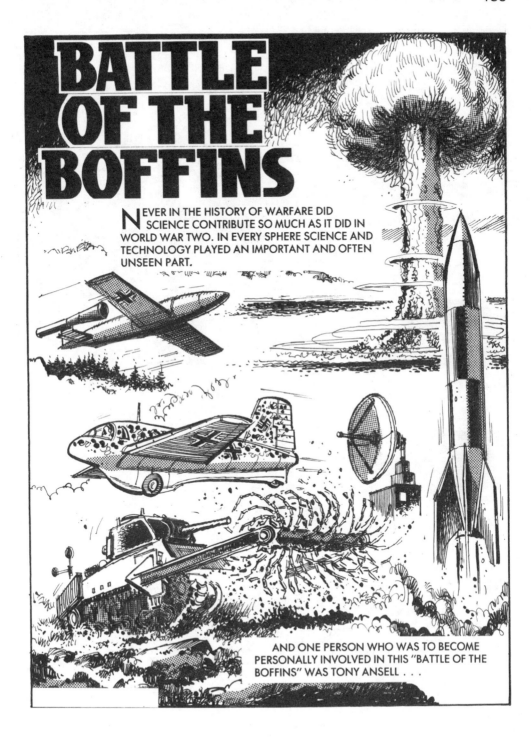

BATTLE OF THE BOFFINS

NEVER IN THE HISTORY OF WARFARE DID SCIENCE CONTRIBUTE SO MUCH AS IT DID IN WORLD WAR TWO. IN EVERY SPHERE SCIENCE AND TECHNOLOGY PLAYED AN IMPORTANT AND OFTEN UNSEEN PART.

AND ONE PERSON WHO WAS TO BECOME PERSONALLY INVOLVED IN THIS "BATTLE OF THE BOFFINS" WAS TONY ANSELL . . .

TONY WAS A "BRAINY SWOT" IN A SCHOOL WHERE THE BOYS RATED PROWESS AT GAMES MORE HIGHLY THAN ACADEMIC EXCELLENCE. AFTER THE MATCH HE CONGRATULATED HIS COUSIN ON HIS PERFORMANCE.

YOU'RE BOUND TO GET YOUR COLOURS. YOU VIRTUALLY WON THE MATCH YOURSELF.

I WAS LUCKY. EVERYTHING WENT MY WAY.

TONY AND DEREK USUALLY SPENT PART OF EACH HOLIDAY IN THE OTHER'S HOME. TONY CAME FROM A MILITARY FAMILY. A CRASHING FALL FROM A HORSE HAD FORCED HIS FATHER TO RETIRE AS A COLONEL.

YOU'VE FOUR WEEKS' HOLIDAY, SON. WHEN'S DEREK COMING TO STAY?

NEXT WEEK, IF THAT'S ALL RIGHT BY YOU.

THIS WAS SOMETHING THAT PARTICULARLY RANKLED WITH THE OLD WARRIOR, WHO REMEMBERED HOW HE HAD GIVEN TONY AN EXPENSIVE DOUBLE-BARRELLED SHOTGUN ON HIS FOURTEENTH BIRTHDAY.

IT'S A SUPER GUN. I DON'T KNOW HOW TO THANK YOU, GRANDAD.

JUST BECOME AS GOOD A SHOT AS YOUR FATHER AND YOUR OLD GRANDFATHER, TONY.

LATER THAT DAY TONY HAD HIS FIRST CHANCE TO TRY OUT HIS GUN.

CRIKEY, I HIT IT!

WELL DONE, SIR! YOU'RE A NATURAL SHOT, TONY.

BUT THAT ONE SHOT TAUGHT TONY THAT KILLING WAS REPUGNANT TO HIM.

WHAT A BEAUTIFUL CREATURE. WHY DID I KILL IT?

COME ON, SON. IT WAS A CLEAN SHOT. THE BIRD FELT NOTHING.

THERE AND THEN HE DECIDED NEVER AGAIN TO KILL ANIMALS FOR SPORT. HE KNEW THAT HE HAD OFFENDED THE GENERAL, AND TRIED TO MAKE AMENDS BY TAKING UP CLAY PIGEON SHOOTING.

NINE OUT OF TEN AGAIN. I GIVE UP.

BUT EVEN THOUGH HE SOON BECAME A FIRST CLASS CLAY PIGEON SHOT, HIS GRANDFATHER NEVER FORGAVE HIM.

THE YEARS PASSED AND AT LAST, WHILE TONY WAS STAYING WITH HIM, DEREK RECEIVED THE GOOD NEWS THAT HE'D BEEN ACCEPTED FOR PILOT TRAINING BY THE ROYAL AIR FORCE.

YOU LUCKY DOG. I'D GIVE ANYTHING TO BE A PILOT.

WITH YOUR BRAINS YOU'D BE WASTED. YOU'LL GET SOME FANTASTIC DEGREE AT UNIVERSITY.

DEREK'S FATHER, A LAWYER, CAME ACROSS TO JOIN THEM. ALTHOUGH HIS SON WAS JOINING THE AIR FORCE, MISTER HANSON HAD NO SPECIAL REGARD FOR THE MILITARY.

TONY SAYS HE'D LIKE TO BE A PILOT LIKE ME.

THEN YOU'RE AN ASS, TONY. YOU HAVE BRAINS AND IN WAR THAT'S JUST AS IMPORTANT AS BRAWN.

BY 1939, WHEN BRITAIN DECLARED WAR ON GERMANY, DEREK WAS A FULLY QUALIFIED PILOT OFFICER. HE FLEW TO FRANCE WITH HIS BLENHEIM SQUADRON.

WHAT A DUMP!

THE FACILITIES HE FOUND AT HIS AIRFIELD WERE NOT ENCOURAGING, HOWEVER.

THE SQUADRON'S ROLE WAS LONG RANGE RECONNAISSANCE FOR THE ARMY HIGH COMMAND. HOWEVER, THE FIRST WINTER OF THE WAR WAS PARTICULARLY SEVERE, SO THE BLENHEIMS DID LITTLE FLYING.

WHEN IS THIS WAR GOING TO TAKE OFF PROPERLY?

CERTAINLY NOT BEFORE THIS FILTHY WEATHER CLEARS.

BY THIS TIME TONY HAD BEEN AT UNIVERSITY AND GRADUATED WITH AN EXCELLENT SCIENCE DEGREE, TO BEGIN WORKING UNDER DOCTOR PETER SPENCE, AN EMINENT SCIENTIST AND INVENTOR. YET STILL HE LONGED TO BE A PILOT LIKE DEREK.

THE WORK WE'RE DOING IS OF THE UTMOST IMPORTANCE. YOU'RE FAR MORE VALUABLE HERE THAN IN UNIFORM.

IN THAT CASE I SUPPOSE I'LL HAVE TO LUMP IT, SIR.

SINCE TONY WAS IN A "RESERVED OCCUPATION", HE WAS EXEMPT FROM CALL UP FOR THE ARMED SERVICES.

TO FIGHT IN THE AIR HAD ALWAYS BEEN TONY'S ROMANTIC DREAM, UNATTAINABLE BECAUSE OF HIS POOR PHYSIQUE AND BAD EYESIGHT. HE IMAGINED HIS OLD SCHOOLFRIEND FIGHTING GLAMOROUS AERIAL BATTLES WHILE HE TOILED AT TRANSLATING THE SCIENTIST'S UNTIDY NOTES INTO COMPLICATED WIRING DIAGRAMS.

I WONDER WHAT DEREK'S DOING? PROBABLY WINNING A MEDAL.

TONY'S ENVY WAS MISPLACED, HOWEVER, FOR AT THAT MOMENT DEREK WAS FIGHTING FOR HIS LIFE AGAINST TWO OF THE LUFTWAFFE'S Me109s. HE WAS ON A SOLITARY RECCE MISSION, CROSSING THE GERMAN BORDER TO SEE IF THERE WAS ANY SIGN THAT THE ENEMY WAS ABOUT TO ADVANCE INTO FRANCE.

JERRY TURNING IN NOW, SKIPPER.

TELL ME WHEN HE'S IN RANGE.

THE BLENHEIM'S SINGLE REAR GUN WAS NO MATCH FOR THE Me109's HEAVY ARMAMENT, SO DEREK WORKED HIS WAY TOWARDS A FRIENDLY CLOUD IN A SERIES OF EVASIVE TURNS.

HOLD TIGHT. WE'RE NEARLY THERE.

A FEW PRECIOUS SECONDS WAS ALL HE NEEDED NOW.

THEY JUST MADE IT AS ONE OF THE Me109s OPENED FIRE.

IT'S A FRIENDLY CLOUD, EVEN IF A BUMPY ONE.

IT'S BETTER THAN CANNON SHELLS AND BULLETS.

WHEN THEY CAME OUT ON THE OTHER SIDE THEY'D SHAKEN OFF THE ENEMY FIGHTERS. ONCE SAFELY BACK AT BASE, DEREK SPOKE TO HIS C.O., A WING COMMANDER.

WE WERE BOUNCED AS SOON AS WE CROSSED THE BORDER, SIR.

OPS INT

YOU WERE LUCKY TO REACH CLOUD COVER.

IT WAS BECOMING CLEAR THAT DAYLIGHT RECCES BY SINGLE BLENHEIMS WERE IMPOSSIBLE UNLESS THERE WAS COMPLETE CLOUD COVER. A FEW DAYS LATER DEREK'S C.O. RECEIVED A VISIT FROM A SENIOR STAFF OFFICER AND A CIVILIAN EXPERT WHO HAD FOUND A POSSIBLE SOLUTION TO THE PROBLEM.

DAYLIGHT MISSIONS ARE TOO COSTLY IN CREWS AND AIRCRAFT, SO OUR SCIENTISTS HAVE COME UP WITH A NEW IDEA TO LET US FLY AT NIGHT.

WE'VE DEVELOPED A MAGNESIUM FLASH-LIGHT BOMB. IT WORKS LIKE A PHOTOFLASH.

THE EXPERT EXPLAINED TO THE WING COMMANDER HOW THE BOMB WAS TO BE USED. IT SOUNDED STRAIGHTFORWARD ENOUGH.

SO WE FLY OVER THE TARGET WITH THE CAMERA SHUTTER OPEN?

THAT'S RIGHT. THEN YOU RELEASE THE BOMB WHICH EXPLODES AT A PRE-SET HEIGHT IN A BLINDING FLASH.

NEXT MORNING THE C.O. BRIEFED HIS CREWS ABOUT THIS NEW DEVICE. A SUPPLY OF THESE NEW BOMBS WAS ALREADY ON ITS WAY.

AFTER THE FLASH, CLOSE THE CAMERA SHUTTER. WE'LL TRY IT OUT TONIGHT.

HE PICKED HIS MOST EXPERIENCED CREW TO TEST THE FLASHBOMB THAT EVENING, BUT THE AIRCRAFT MYSTERIOUSLY FAILED TO RETURN.

WE DON'T KNOW WHAT HAPPENED TO IT, SIR, BUT I'M HAVING A GO MYSELF TONIGHT.

THE C.O. THEN CARRIED OUT HIS OWN SUCCESFUL SORTIE WITH PROMISING RESULTS.

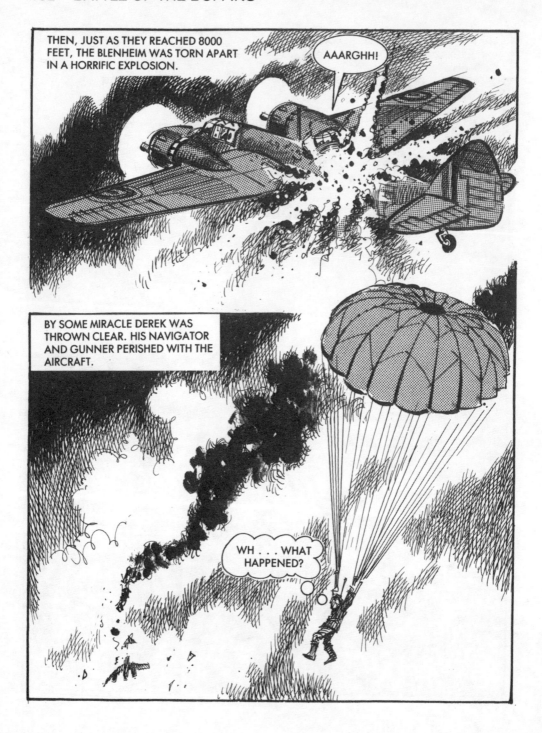

THOUGH BADLY BURNED HE SURVIVED. IN HOSPITAL HE WAS EXTENSIVELY QUESTIONED ABOUT THE INCIDENT.

THE AIRCRAFT EXPLODED AT EXACTLY EIGHT-THOUSAND FEET ON THE CLIMB. I REMEMBER THAT.

THE SAFETY DEVICE ON THE BAROMETRIC FUSE MUST HAVE FAILED.

BY NOW IT DIDN'T MATTER. THE GERMAN ARMY WAS RACING ACROSS FRANCE AND BELGIUM ON ITS WAY TO THE NORTH SEA COAST.

DEREK WAS IN HOSPITAL, AND LATER AT HOME CONVALESCING, FOR SEVERAL WEEKS. HE READ ABOUT THE DUNKIRK EVACUATION AND THE EARLY PART OF THE BATTLE OF BRITAIN IN THE NEWSPAPERS.

DURING THAT TIME TWO SEEMINGLY MINOR EVENTS TOOK PLACE WHICH WERE TO AFFECT HIS FUTURE AND THAT OF HIS COUSIN TONY.

THE MYSTERIOUS AERIAL AND THE WIRELESS SET CONNECTED TO IT WERE STRIPPED FROM THE HEINKEL AND SENT TO DOCTOR SPENCE'S LABORATORY. HE HAD ALREADY EXAMINED THIS RADIO DEVICE IN THE CRASHED AIRCRAFT, RECOGNISING IT AS AN ADVANCED VERSION OF AN EARLIER BLIND-LANDING DEVICE.

PUT IT HERE, PLEASE. GENTLY DOES IT.

WHAT DO YOU MAKE OF IT, SIR?

TECHNICAL EVIDENCE, SUPPORTED BY THE GERMAN AIRMAN'S CARELESS TALK, SUGGESTED THAT THIS WAS SOME KIND OF BLIND-BOMBING DEVICE.

I'M PRETTY SURE IT'S A RECEIVER FOR PICKING UP A DIRECTIONAL BEAM.

YOU MEAN A WIRELESS SIGNAL WHICH CAN GUIDE AN AIRCRAFT TO A TARGET.

THAT WAS EXACTLY WHAT SPENCE MEANT. NOW HE HAD BEEN GIVEN THE TASK OF PROBING THE DETAILS AND FINDING A COUNTER TO IT.

A POWERFUL TRANSMITTER SENDS OUT A DIRECTIONAL SIGNAL WHICH A PILOT CAN HEAR. IN THE MIDDLE OF THE BEAM HE HEARS A CONTINUOUS NOTE, TO THE LEFT MORSE DOTS, TO THE RIGHT MORSE DASHES.

FIRST THEY WOULD HAVE TO DISCOVER THE FREQUENCY ON WHICH THE DEVICE OPERATED. THIS COULD BE A LONG JOB.

YOU'D BETTER TAKE A FEW DAYS' LEAVE. ONCE WE START THERE'LL BE NO TIME OFF AT ALL.

THANK YOU, SIR.

THE NEXT DAY OSTERKAMP TOLD THE CREWS OF OTTO'S SQUADRON HOW THEY WOULD LEAD THE NIGHT ASSAULT ON BRITAIN. THEY WERE THE TARGET FINDERS.

BY FOLLOWING THIS BEAM YOU WILL FIND THE TARGET. THE CROSS BEAM WILL TELL YOU WHEN TO DROP YOUR MARKER BOMBS.

THEN THE TARGET WILL BE ANNIHILATED BY OUR COMRADES WHO FOLLOW.

OBLIVIOUS TO ALL THIS, DEREK HAD GONE TO VISIT TONY DURING HIS LEAVE.

YOU SAY YOU'RE FIT FOR FLYING BUT NOT FOR OPS. WHAT HAPPENS?

I SUPPOSE I'LL SIT BEHIND A DESK OR BECOME AN INSTRUCTOR.

NEITHER OPTION SEEMED TO APPEAL TO DEREK. THEN TONY REMEMBERED SOMETHING DOCTOR SPENCE HAD SAID.

I CAN'T SAY TOO MUCH, BUT MY BOSS NEEDS PILOTS FOR A SPECIAL HUSH-HUSH JOB.

SOUNDS INTERESTING. TELL ME MORE.

TONY SHOWED HIS COUSIN THE COMPLICATED RADIO EQUIPMENT WHICH NEARLY FILLED THE BACK OF THE SPECIALLY-ADAPTED ANSON.

EVERY NIGHT WE'LL PATROL THE SOUTH COAST WHILE I SEARCH FOR A BEAM SIGNAL WITH ALL THIS JUNK OF MINE.

AND I THOUGHT I WAS COMING HERE FOR A REST!

DEREK AND TONY USUALLY FLEW AT NIGHT, TONY SCANNING THE AIR WAVES FOR A TRANSMITTER WHICH MIGHT OR MIGHT NOT BE SENDING OUT A BEAM. FLYING TO AND FRO ALONG A PATROL LINE PARALLEL TO THE SOUTH COAST WAS BORING, BUT LIFE WAS NOT WITHOUT ITS DANGERS.

TIME TO TURN BACK, TONY. ANY LUCK?

SORRY, OLD SON, NOT A CHEEP.

THE TWO SET OUT EARLY THE NEXT MORNING SINCE ONE OF TONY'S GADGETS WAS GIVING TROUBLE WHICH HE WANTED CURED BEFORE THEIR USUAL NIGHT PATROL.

I SHOULDN'T TAKE LONG TO TEST THE SET. IT WAS PLAYING UP LAST NIGHT.

SUITS ME, TONY. I'LL BE ABLE TO SEE THE COUNTRSYIDE FOR A CHANGE.

AS DEREK FOLLOWED THE LINE OF THE SOUTH COAST HE SAW A PROWLING Me110 DIRECTLY IN FRONT OF HIM.

HOLD TIGHT, TONY. JERRY AHEAD.

THE ANSON WAS UNARMED, SO DEREK'S ONLY HOPE WAS TO DODGE THE HEAVILY ARMED FIGHTER-BOMBER AND HOPE THAT ITS PILOT WOULD MAKE A MISTAKE.

KEEP YOUR FINGERS CROSSED. I'LL TRY TO FOOL HIM.

FLYING AS LOW AND AS SLOWLY AS HE DARED, DEREK MANAGED TO KEEP OUT OF THE ENEMY PILOT'S SIGHTS.

I'LL SEE IF I CAN TEMPT HIM INTO TROUBLE.

MOMENTARILY STRAIGHTENING OUT, HE DIVED OVER THE SEA TO BELOW CLIFF LEVEL. THEN HE TEMPTED HIS OPPONENT INTO A STEEP TURN NEAR A CLIFF FACE.

I HOPE I DON'T OVERDO THE TURN AND STALL MYSELF.

THE GERMAN AIRCRAFT'S GREATER TURNING CIRCLE PROVED FATAL FOR ITS CREW, THE PILOT NOT SEEING THE TRAP TILL IT WAS TOO LATE. AS HE PULLED OUT OF HIS TURN HIS WING TIP HIT THE TOP OF THE CLIFF AND THE MESSERSCHMITT CART-WHEELED TO DESTRUCTION.

EEAARGHH!

TONY'S PRAISE WAS ECSTATIC. SECRETLY HE ENVIED HIS COUSIN'S GLAMOROUS ROLE OF A PILOT COMPARED TO HIS OWN AS A DULL SCIENTIST.

DESTROYING A FRONT LINE FIGHTER WITHOUT FIRING A SHOT — A WIZARD SHOW!

THANK YOUR LUCKY STARS. YOU DON'T KNOW HOW NEAR WE WERE TO A STICKY END.

HAVING BEEN SEARCHING FOR A BEAM WITHOUT SUCCESS FOR WEEKS, TONY WAS DELIGHTED WHEN AT LAST HE STRUCK LUCKY THAT NIGHT.

HIGH-PITCHED MORSE DASHES. I THINK I'VE GOT IT.

WILDLY EXCITED, HE TOLD DEREK THE NEWS. UNFORTUNATELY THE WEATHER WAS CLOSING IN.

I'M SWITCHING THE BEAM SIGNAL THROUGH TO YOU. SEE IF YOU CAN FIND THE MIDDLE OF THE BEAM.

WE'LL HAVE TO HURRY. THIS WEATHER'S PACKING IN FAST.

TONY PLEADED WITH DEREK TO CARRY ON FOR A FEW MORE MINUTES.

ONCE WE FIND THE DIRECTION OF THE BEAM I'VE FINISHED.

ALL RIGHT, BUT I DON'T LIKE IT.

A FEW SECONDS AFTER TONY HAD RETURNED TO HIS SEAT, DEREK HEARD THE HIGH-PITCHED MORSE DASHES IN HIS EARPHONES.

MORSE DASHES. I MUST FLY ON UNTIL I HEAR A CONTINUOUS NOTE IN THE BACKGROUND.

GUIDED ONLY BY SOUND, DEREK MANOEUVRED UNTIL THEY HEARD A CONTINUOUS HIGH-PITCHED NOTE. HE WAS IN THE MIDDLE OF THE BEAM.

THAT'S IT, TONY. WHAT'S OUR HEADING BY THE COMPASS?

ZERO-ONE-EIGHT DEGREES MAGNETIC.

HIGH ABOVE DEREK'S ANSON, OTTO HARTIG FLEW A HEINKEL BOMBER THROUGH THE CLOUDTOPS. HE WAS TESTING THE VERY SAME BEAM WHICH TONY HAD PICKED UP.

OBSERVER — HOW FAR ARE WE FROM THE TRANSMITTER?

BY MY RECKONING THREE-HUNDRED-AND-TEN KILOMETRES, HERR HAUPTMANN.

OTTO SENT A SIGNAL TO THE TRANSMITTING STATION AT ONCE.

HAUPTMANN HARTIG REPORTS PERFECT RECEPTION AT OVER THREE-HUNDRED KILOMETRES.

THIS IS GOOD NEWS, HERR MAJOR. NOW EVERYTHING IS READY FOR OUR FIRST BIG NIGHT RAID.

DEREK LOWERED HIS FLAPS AND BEGAN TO FEEL HIS WAY DOWN THROUGH THE DENSE RAIN CLOUD.

HEIGHT NINE-HUNDRED FEET.

THE SOUTH DOWNS ARE NEARLY THIS HIGH.

AT 500 FEET THEY WERE STILL IN THICK CLOUD.

I DON'T LIKE THIS. I HOPE WE ARE OVER THE SEA.

FOUR-HUNDRED — I THINK I CAN SEE WAVES.

DEREK LET OUT A SIGH OF RELIEF AND TURNED TO EDGE HIS WAY BACK TO THE COAST. THEY LANDED SAFELY BACK AT BASE BUT IT HAD BEEN THEIR SECOND NARROW SQUEAK THAT DAY AND DEREK FELT THE STRAIN. TONY THOUGHT IT ALL A JOKE.

CHEER UP, WE'RE DOWN IN ONE PIECE.

NO THANKS TO YOU, YOU SENSELESS BOFFIN. WE MIGHT HAVE FETCHED UP AS A BONFIRE ON THE SOUTH DOWNS.

DEREK LEFT HIS SEAT AND WENT TO THE DOOR. HE FELT THAT THIS WHOLE PROJECT WAS A WASTE OF TIME AND EFFORT.

NOW YOU'VE GOT YOUR INFORMATION WHAT ARE YOU GOING TO DO WITH IT?

HOLD ON, DEREK . . .

BUT THE PILOT WAS IN NO MOOD FOR AN ARGUMENT. HE JUMPED DOWN FROM THE AIRCRAFT AND STORMED OFF ALONE.

TONY FOLLOWED, DEEP IN THOUGHT —

WHEN HE RISKED HIS LIFE SEEKING INFORMATION HE WAS A HERO. WHEN I ASK HIM TO TAKE A CHANCE FOR VITAL INFORMATION I'M A SENSELESS BOFFIN!

IN GERMANY, OTTO HARTIG WOKE UP LATE THE NEXT MORNING, HAVING FLOWN UNTIL THE EARLY HOURS THE NIGHT BEFORE.

THE BIG ONE'S SCHEDULED FOR TONIGHT, HERR HAUPTMANN. GENERAL OSTERKAMP WILL BRIEF THE CREWS PERSONALLY.

GOOD, HEINI. WARN ALL PILOTS, OBSERVERS AND WIRELESS OPERATORS.

LATER THAT DAY, OSTERKAMP ADDRESSED OTTO'S CREWS, SPEAKING FOR SEVERAL MINUTES.

YOU HAVE THE HONOUR OF OPENING THE NIGHT OFFENSIVE TONIGHT. TWO WIRELESS BEAMS INTERSECT OVER THE TARGET. SUCCESS IS ASSURED.

OTTO PICKED UP THE BEAM AS PLANNED AND FLEW STEADILY ACROSS THE SEA TOWARDS THE ENGLISH COAST.

UPPER GUNNER — CAN YOU SEE ANYTHING OF THE OTHERS?

NUMBER TWO IS ABOUT ONE KILOMETRE BEHIND US, HERR HAUPTMANN.

MEANWHILE DEREK AND TONY WERE JUST TAKING OFF. THERE WAS TENSION BETWEEN THE COUSINS AND NONE OF THE USUAL BANTER AND JOKING.

WHAT NONSENSE ARE WE UP TO TONIGHT?

I WANT TO FIND LAST NIGHT'S BEAM AGAIN. IT SHOULD BE EASY NOW.

SCANNING THE FREQUENCY HE'D FOUND THE PREVIOUS NIGHT, TONY SOON PICKED UP THE TELL-TALE MORSE DASHES.

I'VE GOT IT. I'LL SWITCH THROUGH TO YOU AND SIGNAL BACK TO BASE.

OKAY, I'LL TRY TO GET ON TO THE BEAM.

GIVEN SOMETHING TO DO WHICH NEEDED SKILL AND CONCENTRATION, DEREK RECOVERED SOME OF HIS NORMAL GOOD HUMOUR. HE SOON PICKED UP THE BEAM AND FOLLOWED IT, UNAWARE THAT THOUSANDS OF FEET ABOVE HIM OTTO'S HEINKELS WERE ON THE SAME HEADING. HOWEVER, DOWN BELOW, AN ALERT OBSERVER CORPS POST HEARD THE GERMAN PATHFINDERS FLYING IN A NORTHERLY DIRECTION AND REPORTED THEM.

THEY'RE JERRIES ALL RIGHT. SOMEWHERE'S GOING TO COP IT.

THERE'S ANOTHER KITE LOWER DOWN. I THINK IT'S AN ANSON.

AS THEY APPROACHED THE TARGET OTTO'S OBSERVER BEGAN TO HEAR MORSE DOTS IN HIS EARPHONES. THEY WERE NEARING THE CROSS BEAM.

WE'RE NEARING THE TARGET, HERR HAUPTMANN. I'M HEARING DOTS MERGING WITH A STEADY NOTE.

BOMB DOORS OPEN. STAND BY TO RELEASE.

IT HAD BEEN A SUCCESSFUL NIGHT FOR BOTH THE GERMANS AND TONY BUT A DISASTROUS ONE FOR AN IMPORTANT INDUSTRIAL CENTRE.

TONY, I WANT TO APOLOGISE FOR WHAT I SAID LAST NIGHT. YOU'RE DOING SOMETHING FAR MORE IMPORTANT THAN A FOOL PILOT LIKE ME CAN DO.

THANKS, DEREK, BUT FORGET IT. WE'VE A LONG WAY TO GO STILL.

HE NOW REALISED THAT THESE BOFFINS, BY TAMPERING WITH THE BEAMS, MIGHT PREVENT UNTOLD DAMAGE AND SAVE THOUSANDS OF LIVES.

LET'S GO AND CELEBRATE YOUR SUCCESS IN FINDING THESE BEAMS.

NO, LET'S GO AND CELEBRATE MAKING UP A STUPID QUARREL.

IN A VERY SHORT TIME THE DOCTOR, HELPED BY R.A.F. SIGNALS EXPERTS, WAS SETTING UP DEVICES TO JAM THE GERMAN BEAMS.

AT FULL BLAST THIS SHOULD BLOT OUT THE BEAM FOR MANY MILES.

LET'S HOPE THEY'RE ON THE FREQUENCY WE KNOW.

THIS WAS THE BEGINNING OF A WIRELESS WAR AND OTTO'S TARGET FINDERS SOON RAN INTO DIFFICULTIES.

HIMMEL. I'VE LOST THE BEAM. ALL I CAN HEAR IS INTERFERENCE.

KEEP ON THIS COURSE, HERR HAUPTMANN. I MIGHT PICK UP THE CROSS BEAM.

FOR SEVERAL NIGHTS THE ENEMY DROPPED THEIR BOMBS ON OPEN SPACES. THEN ONCE MORE THEY BEGAN TO HIT IMPORTANT TARGETS.

THEY MUST BE USING DIFFERENT TRANSMITTING STATIONS AND NEW FREQUENCIES.

YOU WON LAST TIME, TONY. YOU CAN DO IT AGAIN.

THE BATTLE OF THE BOFFINS WENT ON, EACH SIDE GAINING A SHORT ADVANTAGE THEN LOSING IT TO THE OTHER.

AS TIME PASSED, NIGHT FIGHTERS, RADAR CONTROLLED ANTI-AIRCRAFT GUNS AND NEW FUSES DESTROYED AN INCREASING NUMBER OF ENEMY BOMBERS. THE NIGHT BLITZ WEAKENED AND WHEN HITLER INVADED RUSSIA IT STOPPED ALTOGETHER. DEREK WAS POSTED TO A WELLINGTON SQUADRON —

THANK YOU FOR ALL YOU'VE DONE TO HELP US, DEREK, AND THE BEST OF LUCK.

LOOK AFTER YOURSELF AND COME AND SEE US ONCE IN A WHILE.

NOW SPENCE AND HIS TEAM OF SCIENTISTS HAD A NEW PROJECT TO WORK ON.

BOMBER COMMAND'S SCREAMING FOR A BLIND BOMBING DEVICE. WE'LL USE RADAR.

WE'VE GONE FULL CYCLE FROM COUNTERING ONE SUCH SYSTEM TO DEVELOPING ONE OF OUR OWN.

OFF HAND THE AIR MARSHAL DIDN'T EVEN KNOW WHETHER HE WAS STILL ALIVE, THOUGH IN FACT DEREK AND HIS CREW WERE HALFWAY THROUGH THEIR TOUR OF OPERATIONS.

BOMBS GONE.

BOMB DOORS CLOSED. KEEP ALERT EVERYONE.

EXPERIENCE SHOWED THAT THE FLIGHT BACK FROM THE TARGET WAS THE MOST DANGEROUS PART OF ANY BOMBING MISSION.

FORTUNATELY THIS RETURN JOURNEY WAS WITHOUT INCIDENT. DEREK LANDED SAFELY AND TURNED OFF THE RUNWAY.

FLYING OFFICER HANSON TO REPORT TO THE STATION COMMANDER AS SOON AS POSSIBLE.

NOW WHAT HAVE I DONE?

THE STATION COMMANDER MET DEREK OUTSIDE THE CREWROOM.

BOMBER COMMAND HAVE BEEN ON THE BLOWER. A DOCTOR SPENCE NEEDS YOU FOR SOME SPECIAL JOB.

SPENCE! I WORKED FOR HIM BEFORE, SIR.

AFTER A CHAT WITH THE GROUP CAPTAIN IN HIS OFFICE, DEREK TOLD HIS CREW ABOUT DOCTOR SPENCE'S REQUEST.

YOU CAN PULL OUT IF YOU LIKE BUT THIS JOB WILL COUNT AS PART OF OUR TOUR.

I DON'T KNOW ABOUT YOU CHAPS BUT I'M ALL FOR STICKING TOGETHER.

THE WHOLE CREW AGREED, ANY DISAPPOINTMENT EVAPORATING WHEN THEY FOUND THEMSELVES OWNERS OF THE LATEST MODEL OF WELLINGTON THE NEXT MORNING.

LOOK, LADS, A FOUR GUN TURRET.

AND BRISTOL HERCULES ENGINES INSTEAD OF THE OLD PEGGIES.

HE SOON SETTLED DOWN WITH DEREK'S CREW WHO CALLED HIM "PROF". DAVE GREEN, THE REAR GUNNER, BECAME A SPECIAL FRIEND.

USE THE HANDLEBARS AS YOU DO ON A MOTORBIKE TO TURN THE TURRET. TWIST THE GRIPS TO RAISE OR LOWER THE GUNS.

IT SOUNDS EASY ENOUGH.

ONE DAY WHEN DEREK WAS GROUND TESTING HIS ENGINES HE LET TONY TRY OUT THE TURRET.

IT SWINGS MORE SMOOTHLY THAN I EXPECTED.

HE'S GOT THE HANG OF IT ALL RIGHT.

THEIR TARGETS FOR BLIND BOMBING TESTS WERE REMOTE WESTERN ISLANDS OR SOLITARY ROCKS MILES OUT IN THE ATLANTIC. TONY RELIED COMPLETELY ON HIS RADAR WIZARDRY TO FIND THEM. WHENEVER POSSIBLE THE BOMB AIMER CHECKED HIS RESULT VISUALLY.

COMING UP TO TARGET NOW. THREE . . . TWO . . . ONE . . . BOMBS GONE.

BANG ON, PROF. I CAN SEE WAVES BREAKING OVER THE ROCKS BELOW.

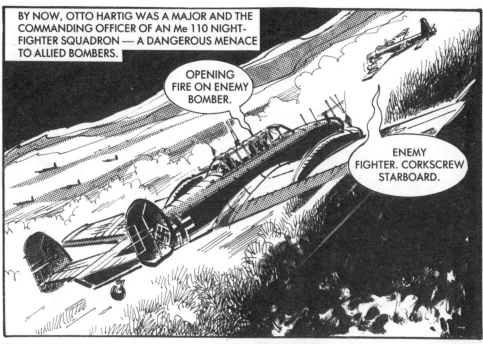

BY NOW, OTTO HARTIG WAS A MAJOR AND THE COMMANDING OFFICER OF AN Me 110 NIGHT-FIGHTER SQUADRON — A DANGEROUS MENACE TO ALLIED BOMBERS.

OPENING FIRE ON ENEMY BOMBER.

ENEMY FIGHTER. CORKSCREW STARBOARD.

MORE DANGEROUS STILL TO THE ALLIED CAUSE WERE THE U-BOATS WHICH WERE SINKING SHIPS AT AN ALARMING RATE.

LAST MONTH WE LOST OVER HALF A MILLION TONS OF SHIPPING. WE MUST DO SOMETHING.

THE U-BOAT PENS ARE COMPLETELY BOMBPROOF. WE'LL HAVE TO FIND SOME OTHER TARGET.

BOMBER COMMAND DECIDED THAT DEREK WOULD TEMPORARILY REJOIN HIS OLD SQUADRON FOR THIS SPECIAL OPERATION.

GLAD TO SEE YOU BACK. I UNDERSTAND THAT YOU'LL BE MARKING THE TARGET FOR THE MAIN FORCE.

PILOT OFFICER ANSELL AND HIS BLACK BOX WILL BE DOING THAT, SIR. I'M JUST THE CHAUFFEUR.

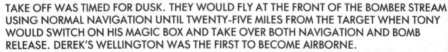

TAKE OFF WAS TIMED FOR DUSK. THEY WOULD FLY AT THE FRONT OF THE BOMBER STREAM USING NORMAL NAVIGATION UNTIL TWENTY-FIVE MILES FROM THE TARGET WHEN TONY WOULD SWITCH ON HIS MAGIC BOX AND TAKE OVER BOTH NAVIGATION AND BOMB RELEASE. DEREK'S WELLINGTON WAS THE FIRST TO BECOME AIRBORNE.

WHILE THE BOMBERS APPROACHED THEIR TARGET, OTTO WATCHED THEIR PROGRESS AS REPORTS CAME IN FROM FORWARD EARLY WARNING STATIONS. HE WANTED TO SEE HOW THE RAID DEVELOPED BEFORE TAKING OFF HIMSELF.

THEY'RE HEADING FOR OUR SECTOR BUT THEY'RE STILL FORTY MINUTES' FLYING TIME AWAY.

SEND OFF TWO AIRCRAFT TO PATROL OUR SECTOR BOUNDARY.

ONLY WHEN OTTO WAS SATISFIED THAT THE BOMBERS WERE HEADING FOR HIS AREA OF RESPONSIBILITY DID HE TAKE OFF HIMSELF.

THEY MIGHT BE HEADING FOR THE U-BOAT ENGINE WORKS, BUT IT COULD BE A BLUFF.

BOMBERS OFTEN FEINTED FOR ONE TARGET, ONLY TO ALTER COURSE UNEXPECTEDLY FOR ANOTHER, HOPING TO CATCH THE DEFENCES BY SURPRISE. SUCH A FEINT WAS JUST ABOUT TO HAPPEN — IN REVERSE.

TWENTY-FIVE MILES TO THE TARGET, SKIPPER.

OVER TO YOU, TONY. IT'S ALL YOURS NOW.

TONY SWITCHED ON HIS SET AND TOOK OVER FROM THE NAVIGATOR. AT THE SAME TIME A NUMBER OF THE LEADING BOMBERS ALTERED COURSE TO CREATE A DIVERSION AS DEREK FLEW STRAIGHT ON.

THAT INFORMATION WAS RELAYED TO OTTO.

THE BOMBER STREAM HAS TURNED SOUTH.

I CAN SEE SEARCHLIGHTS AND FLAK OVER THAT WAY.

DAVE HAD BARELY FINISHED SPEAKING WHEN HE SAW AN Me110 SNEAKING UP BEHIND. IT WAS NOT OTTO'S AIRCRAFT BUT JUST ANOTHER NIGHT-FIGHTER WHICH HAD COME ON THEM BY CHANCE.

NIGHT FIGHTER BEHIND AND BELOW, SKIP. OPENING FIRE.

TONY LISTENED ANXIOUSLY ON THE INTERCOM AS SHOTS WERE EXCHANGED.

GUNNER HERE, SKIP. I GOT HIM BUT HE HIT ME AND I CAN'T SEE PROPERLY.

HANG ON IF YOU CAN. WE'LL SOON BE BACK WITH THE OTHERS.

WHEN DAVE DIDN'T REPLY, DEREK ASKED TONY, WHOSE JOB WAS NOW FINISHED, TO GO BACK AND SEE HOW HE WAS.

HE'S UNCONSCIOUS!

TONY FIXED HIS GOGGLES THEN TESTED THE TURRET, PLEASED TO FIND IT WAS STILL IN WORKING ORDER.

GUNNER TO CAPTAIN. REAR GUNS MANNED AND READY.

TONY, WHAT THE DEVIL ARE YOU UP TO?

SOMEHOW DEREK HAD NEVER THOUGHT OF HIS COUSIN AS ONE OF THE CREW. THEN AGAIN, HE RECKONED THAT TONY WAS BETTER THAN NO REAR GUNNER. SOMEONE SHOOTING MIGHT DETER A FIGHTER.

I'M A FULL-BLOWN PILOT OFFICER, REMEMBER?

ALL RIGHT, TONY. PRETEND YOU'RE SHOOTING AT CLAY PIGEONS.

ACTING BY INSTINCT TONY LOOSED OFF A BURST WHICH FORCED OTTO TO DIVE AWAY.

THIS GUNNER'S WIDE AWAKE AND GOOD. BRING ME ROUND AGAIN, ERNST.

DEREK HAD FELT THE JUDDER AS TONY FIRED HIS FOUR BROWNINGS.

WHAT GOES ON, TONY?

THE BLIGHTER SHOT AT ME! IT'S THE FIRST TIME A CLAY PIGEON DID THAT.

INSIDE THE WELLINGTON'S FUSELAGE DAVE REGAINED CONSCIOUSNESS.

WHY AREN'T YOU IN MY TURRET?

IT'S ALL RIGHT, DAVE. THE PROF'S IN THERE SCARING THE DAYLIGHTS OUT OF JERRY.

BY DIVING AWAY OTTO HAD LOST VISUAL CONTACT OF THE WELLINGTON AND HAD TO BE GUIDED BY RADAR. IT TOOK HIM A FEW MINUTES TO PICK UP HIS TARGET AGAIN.

ENEMY FIGHTER COMING IN ON OUR PORT QUARTER.

ROGER, GUNNER.

IF THEY COULD HOLD OTTO OFF FOR ANOTHER MINUTE OR TWO THEY WOULD BE BACK IN THE COMPARATIVE SAFETY OF THE BOMBER STREAM.

FORTUNATELY TONY'S SKILL ON THE CLAY PIGEON RANGE STOOD HIM IN GOOD STEAD.

SWING THROUGH THE TARGET AND ALLOW FOR TARGET SPEED.

HIS FIRST BURST HIT OTTO'S WING TIP BUT DID LITTLE DAMAGE.

I'LL COME IN FROM BELOW.

STILL THINKING IN SHOTGUN TERMS TONY GAVE THE MESSERSCHMITT A LONG BURST WHICH SET IT ON FIRE.

GOT IT!

HE WAS RELIEVED TO SEE TWO PARACHUTES OPEN AS THE BURNING AIRCRAFT PLUNGED TOWARDS THE GROUND — THIS WAS THE FIRST TIME HE'D SHOT AT A LIVE TARGET SINCE HE KILLED THE PHEASANT WAY BACK ON HIS FOURTEENTH BIRTHDAY.

THEY LANDED SAFELY BACK AT BASE. WHILE THE CREW WAS BEING DEBRIEFED, TONY ACCOMPANIED DAVE TO SICK QUARTERS IN THE AMBULANCE. DEREK ASKED THE GROUP CAPTAIN TO RECOMMEND HIS COUSIN FOR A MEDAL.

DOCTOR SPENCE'S INVENTION HAD PROVED ITSELF AND WAS TO BE PUT INTO IMMEDIATE PRODUCTION.

I'M SORRY TO SEE YOU LEAVE US AGAIN, DEREK. PLEASE THANK YOUR CREW FOR ME.

WE'RE ALL HAVING LEAVE BEFORE GOING TO A NEW PATHFINDER OUTFIT, SIR.

TONY'S SPECIAL COMMISSION AS A PILOT OFFICER HAD BEEN ENDED. HE WAS BACK TO BEING A CIVILIAN BOFFIN, MUCH TO HIS REGRET. AS A CONSOLATION THE DOCTOR SENT HIM ON TEN DAYS' LEAVE.

HE AND DEREK STAYED AT TONY'S HOME—

YOU SHOULD BE PROUD OF HIM, SIR. NOT MANY SCIENTISTS HAVE SHOT DOWN A FRONT LINE FIGHTER.

I SUPPOSE NOT, BUT I FIND IT HARD TO BELIEVE.

AS DEREK FINISHED TELLING THE GENERAL ABOUT TONY'S Me110, THE PHONE RANG. IT WAS THE GROUP CAPTAIN FOR DEREK.

GOOD NEWS, HANSON. YOUR YOUNG BOFFIN FRIEND HAS BEEN AWARDED THE DISTINGUISHED FLYING CROSS.

SO IT'S ALL RIGHT IF I TELL HIM, SIR?

DEREK WAS DELIGHTED. HE'D NEVER THOUGHT THAT THE GROUP CAPTAIN WOULD BE ABLE TO WANGLE IT.

GREAT NEWS! TONY'S BEEN AWARDED THE D.F.C. — AND THAT'S OFFICIAL.

WELL DONE, TONY. THIS CALLS FOR A CELEBRATION.

WELL, THE LAD DESERVES IT, IF ONLY FOR SHOOTING AT LIVE GAME.

THE GENERAL'S LONG-STANDING DISAPPROVAL OF HIS GRANDSON WAS OVER AT LAST.

TONY'S TASTE OF ACTION MAY HAVE BEEN OVER BUT THE BATTLE OF THE BOFFINS MOST CERTAINLY WASN'T. FIRST ONE SIDE WOULD GAIN A TECHNICAL ADVANTAGE ONLY FOR THE ENEMY TO FIND A COUNTERMEASURE.

SCIENTISTS LIKE DOCTOR SPENCE AND TONY WERE LOCKED IN A CONTINUOUS STRUGGLE AGAINST THEIR GERMAN COUNTERPARTS RIGHT UP UNTIL THE LAST DAY OF THE WAR . . .

Commando
THE END

KNIGHTS OF THE AIR
the first warplanes

Sopwith Camel F1

Probably the most famous British single-seat fighter of the First World War. Camels entered service in mid-1917 and their twin Vickers guns had claimed 1,294 enemy aircraft by the Armistice in November 1918. Powered by a 130hp Clerget rotary engine, it had a 115mph top speed and also excellent manoeuvrability.

WINGED WOLVES

IT ALL BEGAN WITH A CLASH OF TWO AIRCRAFT ABOVE THE TRENCHES IN FRANCE DURING THE FIRST WORLD WAR. BUT THEN IT DEVELOPED INTO A BITTER DUEL WITH THE TWO PILOTS PUSHING THEMSELVES AND THEIR MACHINES TO THE LIMIT.

AND FROM THAT IT BECAME A SAVAGE VENDETTA WHICH LINKED TWO FAMILIES IN HATRED OVER A PERIOD OF BOTH WORLD WARS.

ONE OF THE LEADING ACES OF THE ROYAL FLYING CORPS WAS LIEUTENANT ROLAND PAGE. ENEMY AIRCRAFT FELL TO HIS GUNS ON ALMOST EVERY SORTIE HE FLEW AND FRIEND AND ENEMY ALIKE RESPECTED HIS SKILL AND COURAGE.

THE HUNS SEEM SHY LATELY. I THINK I'LL HAVE A LOOK AT THEIR PART OF THE WORLD.

HE SWUNG HIS AGILE SOPWITH CAMEL AROUND, THE 150 H.P. ENGINE RESPONDING WELL AS HE CONTINUED ON THIS LONE RECONNAISSANCE FLIGHT.

SOON HE WAS OVER THE GERMAN LINES, DIPPING LOW TO STRAFE A TRENCH SYSTEM IN SHEER HIGH SPIRITS. THE THRILL OF COMBAT NEVER LOST ITS EXCITEMENT FOR HIM.

JUST LET THEM KNOW WE'RE STILL IN BUSINESS. BETTER KEEP AN EYE OPEN FOR ANY OF THEIR KITES, THOUGH . . .

AT THAT MOMENT ON A GERMAN AIRFIELD JUST BEHIND THE LINES, HAUPTMANN FRANZ VON STELLEN WAS ABOUT TO MAKE A SIMILAR LONE RECONNAISSANCE FLIGHT. HE WAS ONE OF GERMANY'S GREATEST ACES, AND LET EVERYONE KNOW IT WITH HIS ARROGANT, OVER-BEARING WAYS.

STIFF – NECKED PRUSSIAN! STOPPED ME THREE WEEKS PAY YESTERDAY FOR NOT SHAVING.

A REAL SCHWEIN! BUT YOU HAVE TO ADMIT, HE'S MUSTARD WHEN IT COMES TO AIR FIGHTING.

BUT VON STELLEN WAS ALSO A CRUEL KILLER. HE RELISHED THE MOMENT WHEN SOME UNFORTUNATE ALLIED PILOT FELL BEFORE HIS GUNS.

I JUST HOPE THE ENEMY PROVIDE MORE SPORT TODAY THAN LAST WEEK.

THAT SAME DAY, AS FATE WOULD HAVE IT, VON STELLEN AND ROLAND PAGE WERE TO CLASH.

WHAT LUCK! AN ENGLANDER BEFORE BREAKFAST ADDS TO THE APPETITE.

VON STELLEN BROUGHT HIS FOKKER TRIPLANE INTO THE ATTACK IN THE USUAL WAY. HE HAD CLAIMED MANY A VICTIM BY HIS SAVAGE, ALL-OR-NOTHING FIRST MOVE.

FURIOUSLY VON STELLEN THREW THE TRIPLANE INTO THE ATTACK AGAIN—WITH NO MORE LUCK THAN HIS FIRST ATTEMPT AS ROLAND SKILFULLY PILOTED HIS SOPWITH CLEAR OF TROUBLE.

OOPS! TEMPER, TEMPER!

NOW, ENGLANDER, YOUR FLYING CAREER ENDS HERE!

TURN AND FIGHT!

NOT BAD. AH, IT'S VON STELLEN!

THE GERMAN'S AIRCRAFT WAS DISTINCTIVE AND WELL-KNOWN, BUT THIS WAS NO ORDINARY PILOT HE HAD ENCOUNTERED. ROLAND AVOIDED THE SLASHING ONSLAUGHT LIKE SOME TOREADOR WOULD AN ANGRY BULL.

ROLAND DID JUST THAT. A MASTERLY PIECE OF FLYING EARNED HIM SPACE TO ATTACK AND FOR THE FIRST TIME THE GERMAN FELT FEAR GRIP HIM AS HE TOO RECOGNISED HIS OPPONENT.

HE'S ON MY TAIL —LIKE A TERRIER, CURSE HIM!

IT TOOK ALL VON STELLEN'S CONSIDERABLE EXPERIENCE TO DODGE ROLAND'S CAMEL. EVEN THEN A LONG BURST FROM THE BRITISH AIRCRAFT ALMOST ENDED THE FIGHT.

'ERE, HE JUST ABOUT NAILED HIM THERE!

IT'S SOME SCRAP. KEEP AFTER HIM, LADDIE!

THE AIR DUEL HAD TAKEN THEM BACK OVER THE ALLIED LINES.

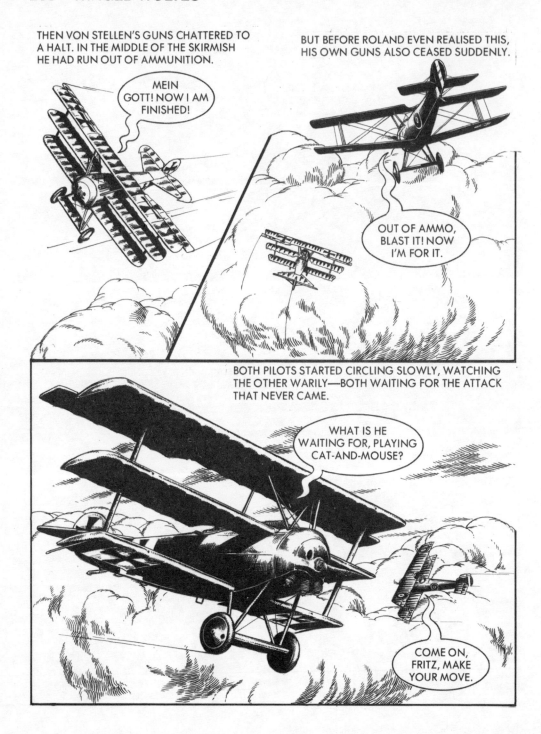

TOO LATE ROLAND SAW THE DANGER. HIS REFLEX ACTION SAVED THE IMPACT BEING COMPLETE, BUT BOTH MACHINES TOUCHED NEVERTHELESS WITH A TEARING OF CANVAS AND SPLINTERING OF STRUTS.

DIE, IMPUDENT FOOL!

HE'S A MANIAC!

THE TWO AIRCRAFT SPUN APART, BOTH PILOTS FIGHTING TO KEEP THEIR MACHINES FROM BEGINNING A DEATH DIVE. ROLAND NEEDED ALL HIS SKILL—

HECK, MUST GET HER UNDER CONTROL, OR I'LL BE FINISHED.

VON STELLEN WAS ALSO FIGHTING TO PULL HIS CRIPPLED MACHINE LEVEL AS HE HEADED BACK OVER HIS OWN LINES. IT WAS A LOSING BATTLE—

MUST GET MORE HEIGHT TO MISS THOSE TREES!

BY NOW ROLAND HAD NURSED HIS CAMEL BACK OVER THE LINES TO HIS OWN BASE. IT HAD TAKEN ALL HIS SKILL TO ACHIEVE WHAT TO MANY PILOTS WOULD HAVE BEEN ABSOLUTELY IMPOSSIBLE.

IT'S PAGE. HE'S BUMPED INTO TROUBLE BY THE LOOK OF IT, CHAPS.

EASY DOES IT, OLD THING, WE'RE HOME AND DRY NOW . . .

MEANWHILE VON STELLEN HAD BEEN RUSHED TO HOSPITAL. HE LOST A LEG AND THE USE OF ONE HAND AND NEVER AGAIN WOULD HE SEE ACTION. AND NOW THERE WERE SCARS THAT WOULD NEVER HEAL—IN HIS MIND.

HE HARDLY SPEAKS. JUST STARES INTO SPACE.

NEWS OF THAT ENGLISH PILOT STILL FIGHTING DIDN'T HELP.

VON STELLEN WAS A MAN WHO COULD HATE. AND NOW HE HATED THE BRITISH WITH A BURNING INTENSITY WHICH VERGED UPON MADNESS, FANNED TO THE FULL BY THE SUBSEQUENT NEWS OF THE BRILLIANT FLYING CAREER OF ROLAND WHO ENDED THE WAR AS A HIGHLY-DECORATED HERO.

IT WAS NOT UNTIL SOME YEARS AFTER THE WAR THAT VON STELLEN WAS JERKED OUT OF HIS BLACK MOOD BY INFLUENTIAL FRIENDS. THEY KNEW HE HAD MUCH TO OFFER FOR THE FUTURE AS GERMANY RE-BUILT AND THE NAZIS BEGAN TO COME TO THE FORE.

YOU SAVED MY NECK ONCE IN THE WAR, VON STELLEN. YOU CAN DO ME ANOTHER GREAT SERVICE BY TAKING AN INTEREST IN GERMANY'S FUTURE.

THE THOUGHT THAT WE SHALL AGAIN TAKE TO THE AIR AGAINST THE BRITISH IS GOOD. ONE DAY THE CLASH WILL COME!

AS THE YEARS ROLLED BY, VON STELLEN HAD TWO SONS—CARL AND ERICH. FROM THE DIFFERENCE IN THEIR NATURES, IT WAS HARD TO RECOGNISE THEY WERE BROTHERS.

CARL HAS THE MAKINGS OF A HUNTER. BUT ERICH I FEAR WILL BE TOO SOFT, TOO FORGIVING . . .

HARDLY A DAY PASSED BUT THE BROTHERS CAME TO BLOWS, THE ARGUMENTS USUALLY BROUGHT ABOUT BY THE BULLYING CARL TAKING OR BREAKING THE MODELS WHICH THE STUDIOUS ERICH PAINSTAKINGLY MADE.

IT WAS NOW IN CARL, THE ELDER SON, THAT VON STELLEN PUT HIS HOPES THAT THE BOY WOULD GROW UP TO HATE THE BRITISH—AND PERHAPS ONE DAY FLY AGAINST THEM.

ONE DAY A VON STELLEN WILL CLEAR THE SKIES OF THE CURSED BRITISH!

AND FOREVER ADDING FUEL TO VON STELLEN'S ANGER WAS THE FACT THAT ROLAND PAGE STILL FLEW AS A CIVILIAN PILOT, WINNING RACES, TESTING NEW AIRCRAFT. HE HAD BECOME A LEGEND IN HIS OWN TIME.

GERMANY IS RE-ARMING, AND THEIR LUFTWAFFE IS A FORCE TO BE RECKONED WITH EVEN NOW. I HOPE PETER NEVER HAS TO FLY IN COMBAT.

ROLAND HAD ONE SON—PETER. AND UNLIKE THE GERMAN, ROLAND HOPED HIS SON WOULD NEVER HAVE TO FIGHT IN ANY WAR.

AND AS THE THREAT OF WAR SPREAD OVER EUROPE, YOUNG MEN TOOK TO ARMS. NOW BOTH CARL AND ERICH WERE FIGHTER PILOTS—AND STILL FAR FROM FRIENDLY WHEN THEY CAME HOME ON LEAVE.

CARL HAD BECOME A FERVENT FOLLOWER OF THE NAZI CREED. SUCH TALK AS ERICH USED WAS ALMOST TREASONABLE TO HIS ANGRY BROTHER WHOSE FERVOUR MET WITH THEIR FATHER'S APPROVAL.

BUT FOR ERICH, VON STELLEN ONLY FELT CONTEMPT. HE KNEW HIS YOUNGER SON WAS NO NAZI, ALTHOUGH HE WOULD STILL DO HIS DUTY FOR HIS COUNTRY.

I TRUST YOU WILL NOT LET THE VON STELLEN NAME DOWN?

I SHALL FIGHT AS BEST AS I CAN, FATHER. BUT YOU CANNOT TEACH ME TO HATE MEN I HAVE NEVER MET.

AND WHEN THE INEVITABLE WAR CAME, IT WAS NOT LONG BEFORE CARL'S NATURAL APTITUDE AS A FLYER ASSERTED ITSELF. IN HIS FIRST SORTIE, A SPITFIRE FELL TO HIS GUNS.

HECK! BETTER GET CLEAR BEFORE SHE BLOWS UP!

AND LIKE HIS FATHER BEFORE HIM, CARL HAD THE KILLER INSTINCT. HE GAVE HIS VICTIM NO CHANCE TO SCRAMBLE CLEAR OF THE DOOMED AIRCRAFT.

ONE OF THE SCHWEIN LESS!

AAGH!

CARL ALSO INHERITED ALL HIS FATHER'S CRUEL ARROGANCE. AS HIS SCORE MOUNTED, HIS POPULARITY FELL WITH THE GROUND CREWS.

IMBECILE! I SAID I WANTED MY AIRCRAFT READY IN ONE HOUR.

I DID MY BEST, SIR . . .

NEITHER WAS CARL POPULAR WITH HIS FELLOW PILOTS.

A HECK OF A FLYER, BUT WHAT A PAIN IN THE NECK!

HE HAD FRITZ REPORTED FOR JOKING ABOUT GOERING.

PETER PAGE HAD MEANWHILE JOINED THE R.A.F. AND GOT OFF TO A SLOW START AS A
FIGHTER PILOT, A FACT HIS GREAT CHUM, DICK DALE, WOULD NOT LET HIM FORGET. DICK
HAD ALREADY BROUGHT TWO ENEMY MACHINES DOWN IN THEIR FLIGHTS FROM THE AIRFIELD
IN FRANCE WHERE THEIR HURRICANES WERE BASED.

GOING TO BAG ONE
TODAY, PETER? PERHAPS IF
YOU DIDN'T SHUT YOUR EYES
WHEN YOU FIRED,
IT WOULD HELP?

I'LL
SHOW YOU
YET! WE CAN'T ALL GET
A CLASSIC CASE OF
BEGINNER'S LUCK.

THE TWO PILOT OFFICERS RIBBED EACH
OTHER UNMERCIFULLY.

BUT PETER SOON NOTCHED UP
HIS FIRST KILL. A HEINKEL FELL TO
HIS GUNS THAT VERY SORTIE
WHEN THE SQUADRON
INTERCEPTED GERMAN RAIDERS.

GOT
HIM!

MEIN
GOTT, BALE
OUT!

THE HURRICANES CUT A SWATHE OF DESTRUCTION ACROSS FRANCE. THERE WERE MANY BITTER COMMENTS FROM SOME VICTIMS ABOUT THE ABILITY OF THE MUCH-VAUNTED LUFTWAFFE TO PROTECT THE WEHRMACHT.

OUR BRAVE PILOTS ARE CONSPICUOUS BY THEIR ABSENCE! PROBABLY BUSY GETTING READY FOR SOME PARTY TONIGHT.

BUT THE LUFTWAFFE WAS NOT ALWAYS CAUGHT NAPPING. ON THE NEXT SORTIE FLOWN BY PETER'S SQUADRON, CARL VON STELLEN LED HIS SQUADRON UP TO INTERCEPT.

MY FIRST ACTION LEADING A SQUADRON. FATHER'S INFLUENCE HELPED, BUT I WILL SHOW HIM I AM WORTHY OF THE HONOUR.

CARL WAS NOW A HAUPTMANN, IN CHARGE OF A NEWLY-FORMED SQUADRON.

HE HAD HIGH HOPES OF HIS UNIT. WITH IT HE HOPED TO GAIN EVEN MORE HONOURS AND PAINTED ON EACH NEW AIRCRAFT WAS THE INSIGNIA HE HAD CHOSEN TO STRIKE FEAR INTO ALL OPPONENTS—THE WOLF'S HEAD.

THE R.A.F. WILL LEARN THEIR MISTAKE IN FLYING OVER FRANCE. IT WILL BE A COSTLY LESSON FOR THEM.

AND AMONG THE RAIDING HURRICANES, PETER FELT A TINGLE OF NERVES GO THROUGH HIM AS HE SAW THE FAST-APPROACHING GERMAN FIGHERS. THE HURRICANES SWUNG TO MEET THE CHALLENGE.

TALLY HO! CUSTOMERS CLOSING FAST. GOOD LUCK, EVERYBODY.

THE TWO FORCES MET HEAD ON. THE SNARL OF CANNON FIRE AND THE RATTLE OF MACHINE GUNS COMBINED IN AN ORCHESTRA OF DEATH.

WHAT A SCRAP!

IN ALL THE CONFUSION, PETER LATCHED ON TO AN Me109, THE VERY ONE PILOTED BY CARL WHO WAS ANGRILY ALARMED THAT ANYONE HAD GOT ON TO HIS TAIL SO QUICKLY.

IMPUDENT SCHWEIN! HE WILL SOON LEARN JUST WHAT HE IS UP AGAINST!

A RUNNING FIGHT DEVELOPED, NEITHER PILOT REALISING THAT THEIR FATHERS HAD CLASHED LIKE THIS IN A PREVIOUS WAR.

ON CARL'S AIRFIELD FAR BELOW, IMPORTANT SPECTATORS WATCHED THE CLASH TAKING PLACE ABOVE THEIR HEADS. THESE V.I.P.s HAD BEEN ON A TOUR OF INSPECTION WHEN THE ALARM HAD BEEN SOUNDED.

BUT BY NOW CARL WAS FIGHTING FOR HIS LIFE. PETER WAS PROVING A VERY HARD OPPONENT.

FOR THE FIRST TIME IN HIS FLYING CAREER, CARL MADE A MISTAKE. PETER DID NOT MISS—

CARL'S NEXT MOVE WAS TO SNATCH OUT HIS LUGER AND FIRE AFTER THE HURRICANE. IT WAS ALMOST AS PATHETIC AS IT WAS FUTILE, AND HE KNEW IT.

WE SHALL MEET AGAIN. I HAVE YOUR MARKINGS . . . YOU WILL NOT LIVE TO BOAST OF YOUR LUCKY VICTORY!

NOW THERE'S WHAT I'D CALL A BAD LOSER.

THE FURIOUS NAZI LANDED ON HIS OWN RUNWAY, IN FULL SIGHT OF THE VISITING V.I.P. s. HE STALKED OFF ANGRILY.

OF ALL THE TIMES FOR THEM TO VISIT! AND OF ALL THE TIMES FOR ME TO GET SHOT DOWN.

ER — THAT IS CARL VON STELLEN, GENTLEMEN, OUR LEADING ACE.

AT THE BASE FROM WHICH PETER'S SQUADRON OPERATED, HIS FATHER WAS ON A VISIT AS A
REGULAR AND HONOURED GUEST OF THE R.A.F. THE FORMER ACE LOOKED WISTFULLY AT
THE HURRICANES.

WHAT I COULD HAVE DONE WITH ONE OF THESE BEAUTIES OVER FRANCE.

YOU DIDN'T DO SO BADLY WITH A CAMEL, DAD.

AT THAT MOMENT, THE LUFTWAFFE THREW ITS ATTACK
TOWARD THE AIRFIELD. A MASSED ARMADA DRONED NEARER,
CARL VON STELLEN LEADING HIS FIGHTERS WITH
VENGEANCE ON HIS MIND.

I AM BOUND TO RUN INTO THE ENGLISHMAN PAGE . . .

ALL THE OTHER GERMAN PILOTS HAD
STRICT INSTRUCTIONS TO LEAVE PETER
FOR CARL TO DEAL WITH.

MEANWHILE ROLAND PAGE HAD NOT HEEDED PETER'S URGING TO HEAD FOR COVER. HE LINGERED, HIS EYES LOOKING UP, WATCHING THE HURRICANES CLIMB TO BATTLE. THEN THE FIRST BOMBS WHISTLED DOWN, THE BLAST TOPPLING A LIGHT UTILITY CAR.

ROLAND COULD HAVE GOT TO SAFETY HIMSELF AND LEFT THE DRIVER OF THE UTILITY. BUT HE WAS NOT THAT TYPE OF MAN, AND DASHED BRAVELY FORWARD TO HELP.

BUT CRUEL, COLD EYES OF A MURDERER HAD SPOTTED THE RUNNING FIGURE AND A THUMB HOVERED OVER THE GUN BUTTON. CARL VON STELLEN DIVED IN FOR THE KILL—

THE FOOL WILL DIE FOR HIS COURAGE!

THE GERMAN FIGHTER'S GUNS HAMMERED BRIEFLY. ROLAND PAGE DIED JUST AS THE MAN HE WAS TRYING TO SAVE JUMPED CLEAR OF THE WRECKED VEHICLE.

MR PAGE! OH, NO —THE MURDERING DEVIL'S GOT HIM!

ROLAND PAGE HAD FALLEN VICTIM TO AIRCRAFT GUNS—BUT ON THE GROUND AND NOT IN THE AIR. AND IT WAS IRONIC THAT IT WAS THE CALLOUS SON OF HIS OLD ADVERSARY WHO WAS RESPONSIBLE.

THE UTILITY DRIVER HAD SEEN IT ALL, EVEN GOT A GLIMPSE OF THE AIRCRAFT'S REGISTRATION MARKINGS.

BY NOW THE HEINKELS HAD STRUCK HARD AT THE BASE. AND HAD CARL KNOWN WHAT HIS STRAFE HAD ACCOMPLISHED, HIS GRIN WOULD HAVE BEEN EVEN WIDER.

I'LL REMEMBER YOU . . .

WUNDERBAR! THE ENGLANDERS WILL REMEMBER US AFTER THIS DAY'S WORK!

BUT THE HEINKELS HAD NOT ALL GOT THROUGH THE HURRICANE SCREEN. PETER HIMSELF HAD DOWNED TWO, AND SEEN HIS CHUM DICK DALE NAIL ANOTHER.

THAT JERRY ESCORT WING SEEMED MORE INTERESTED IN SHOOTING UP THE FIELD THAN PROTECTING THESE HEAVY BOYS!

WHEN IT WAS ALL OVER, THE HURRICANES WERE DIVERTED TO OTHER FIGHTER FIELDS. PETER AND DICK, AS THEY LANDED, WERE IN HIGH SPIRITS, KNOWING NOTHING YET OF PETER'S FATHER'S TRAGIC DEATH.

GOOD OLD DICK. HE BAGGED THAT TAIL-ENDER WELL.

PETER CLOBBERED THREE. THAT LAD IS SOME ACE. I WISH I HAD HIS EYE.

IT WAS DARK BY THE TIME PETER AND DICK MANAGED TO GET A LIFT BACK TO THEIR AIRFIELD. THERE THEY SAW THE FULL EXTENT OF THE DAMAGE—AND HEARD THE GRIM NEWS.

DAD CAN'T BE DEAD . . . HE JUST CAN'T BE!

PETER'S TAKING IT VERY HARD. HE DOESN'T SEEM THE SAME CHAP.

ALL THAT NIGHT PETER PROWLED THE BASE, WATCHED ANXIOUSLY BY DICK WHO SAW JUST HOW BADLY PETER HAD BEEN AFFECTED BY THE INCIDENT.

IN THE WEEKS WHICH FOLLOWED, PETER GOT SOURER AND ANGRIER. HE HAD NEVER BEEN ONE TO HATE ALL GERMANS BLINDLY, BUT NOW THAT SEEMED TO BE THE CASE.

SOME OF THOSE LUFTWAFFE TYPES ARE JUST LIKE US. HAD ONE GIVE ME A THUMBS-UP WHEN I BALED OUT LAST MONTH.

DON'T TALK WET, BRADSHAW. THEY'RE NAZIS, FIGHTING TO KEEP HITLER IN POWER!

WORRIED AND UPSET BY HIS FRIEND'S ATTITUDE, DICK TRIED TO REASON WITH HIM, BUT HIS EFFORTS ONLY MADE PETER ANGRIER.

LOOK, PETER, IT WAS A BLOW TO LOSE YOUR FATHER LIKE THAT. BUT . . .

DON'T GIVE ME ANY OF THAT GUFF ABOUT THESE NAZIS BEING DECENT CHAPS. THEY'RE KILLERS. AND THE WOLF'S-HEAD SQUADRON ARE THE VERY WORST.

THE ACTUAL IDENTITY OF THE KILLER PILOT WAS WELL KNOWN NOW, THANKS TO THE UTILITY DRIVER NOTING THE AIRCRAFT'S INSIGNIA.

THAT SAME DAY PETER FLEW ON THE FIRST SORTIE SINCE HIS FATHER'S DEATH. HIS GRIM EXPRESSION MADE IT CLEAR HE WAS OUT FOR REVENGE.

WHEN CONTACT WAS MADE WITH A BUNCH OF UNESCORTED HEINKEL BOMBERS TRYING A SNEAK RAID, PETER WENT FOR THEM LIKE SOME BLOOD-THIRSTY TIGER.

RELIEF AT ESCAPING THE BURNING
BOMBER TURNED TO SUDDEN FEAR
AS THE GERMANS SAW THE
HURRICANE COMING IN AGAIN
MENACINGLY.

AHH, NO!
HE'S GOING
TO MACHINE-GUN
US. WE'VE NO
CHANCE . . .

HATE HAD FILLED PETER IN THE FIRST ATTACK,
BUT SUDDENLY THE SIGHT OF THE MEN
SWINGING HELPLESSLY AWAITING DEATH
CHANGED THINGS.

I CAN'T
DO IT! I JUST
CAN'T FIRE . . .

HE BANKED AWAY, LEAVING THEM TO LAND
SAFELY.

FUNNY
SENSE OF
HUMOUR!

AND THE GERMANS
THOUGHT PETER HAD
JUST BEEN TRYING TO
PUT A SCARE INTO
THEM. THEY LITTLE
KNEW.

ANOTHER GOOD PILOT WHO COULD NEVER KILL FOR THE LOVE OF IT WORE A DIFFERENT UNIFORM. ERICH VON STELLEN WAS AS GOOD A PILOT AS HIS BRUTAL BROTHER AND STILL A PERFECT GENTLEMAN.

NO SIGN OF THE ENGLANDERS TODAY. WE'D BEST JUST RETURN TO BASE.

HIS TOLERANT, CHIVALROUS POINT OF VIEW WAS NOT ONE HIS FATHER AND BROTHER SHARED, OR INDEED APPROVED OF.

SAY WHAT YOU LIKE, FATHER, YOU HAVE TO RESPECT SOME OF THESE ENGLANDERS. THEY'RE BRAVE MEN.

PAH! ERICH WOULD RATHER DROP LEAFLETS THAN BOMBS. I DO NOT RESPECT AN ENEMY OF THE REICH —I KILL HIM!

ERICH HIMSELF HAD FOUGHT WELL AND NOTCHED UP AN IMPRESSIVE SCORE AGAINST THE ENEMY, BUT HE LACKED THE HATE THEIR FATHER HAD INJECTED IN HIS OLDER BROTHER.

YOU'RE A MILKSOP, LIKE I THOUGHT YOU'D BE, ERICH!

LET HIM GO, FATHER. HE JUST HASN'T WHAT IT TAKES TO BE A TRUE VON STELLEN.

NOT THAT THAT TROUBLED ERICH. HE SOMETIMES WISHED HE DID NOT BEAR THE SAME NAME AS HIS FATHER AND BROTHER. HE JUST COULD NOT ACCEPT THEIR WAY OF THINKING.

CARL WAS STILL GLOATING OVER THE RAID ON PETER'S BASE AND THE NEWS OF ROLAND PAGE'S DEATH HAD ADDED TO THAT. BUT HE WAS TO BE EVEN MORE PLEASED WITH HIMSELF SOON. THE WOLF'S-HEAD SQUADRON WERE TO GET THE NEW FOCKE-WULF 190.

THIS MACHINE IS FAR BETTER THAN ANYTHING WE HAVE HAD YET, VON STELLEN. I EXPECT GREAT THINGS OF YOU WITH IT.

I SHALL NOT FAIL. WE WILL SWEEP THE R.A.F. FROM THE SKY.

HIS BLOOD TINGLED IN ANTICIPATION AT DEALING WITH PETER PAGE IN THE NEW AIRCRAFT.

AFTER WEEKS OF TRAINING, CARL'S PILOTS WERE READY TO TAKE THE NEW AIRCRAFT INTO ACTION. THEY PROVED TO BE A DEADLY WEAPON IN THE HANDS OF THE WOLF'S–HEAD SQUADRON.

HECK! THESE MUST BE NEW JOBS. THEY CAN OUT-TURN AND OUT-CLIMB US EASILY.

THE NEW GERMAN FIGHTER WAS A MENACE. ALLIED PRODUCTION COULD NOT MATCH THE LOSSES OF BRITISH FIGHTERS AND THE ONLY RAY OF HOPE WAS THAT THE SPITFIRE FIVE WAS ALMOST READY FOR USE.

THIS IS A GRAVE SITUATION, MATCHING THE THREAT THAT THE U-BOATS PRESENT.

I'M CONVINCED THE MARK FIVE IS THE ANSWER—BUT WE MUST WORK ROUND THE CLOCK TO GET THEM IN ACTION.

FLYING WITH HIS USUAL SKILL, PETER SOON FACED THE ENEMY PILOT WHO HAD BROUGHT HIS FRIEND'S AIRCRAFT TO DESTRUCTION.

GOT YOU! THEY CAN BE BROUGHT DOWN, BUT THEY'RE CERTAINLY A HANDFUL.

BUT AS PETER GLANCED ROUND TO WHERE HE HAD LAST SEEN DICK, HIS SIGH OF RELIEF TURNED TO A GASP OF HORROR.

DICK! THAT DEVIL IS MURDERING HIM . . .

IT WAS A GRIM SIGHT—A NAZI FIRING AT AND HITTING DICK WHO HUNG HELPLESS. AND THIS ACTION WAS ON CARL VON STELLEN'S PERSONAL ORDERS.

FACE TIGHT WITH ANGER, PETER HEADED FOR THE NAZI WHO HAD SO RUTHLESSLY KILLED HIS FRIEND.

PETER CLASHED WITH THE ABOVE-AVERAGE PILOT. WITH THE NEW FIGHTER, IT WAS A DEADLY COMBINATION.

YOU MIGHT GET ME AS WELL, BUT YOU WON'T LIVE TO BOAST ABOUT IT!

ACH! SO YOU WISH TO JOIN YOUR KAMERAD? IT WILL BE SO . . .

AS THEY DUELLED SAVAGELY, PETER THREW EVERY OUNCE OF SKILL INTO THE CONTEST. BUT EVEN SO, IT WAS NOT ENOUGH AND HIS AIRCRAFT WAS SOON HIT.

I'M HIT, BUT I'M NOT GETTING OUT YET!

ACH, SO! ANOTHER BURST SHOULD DO IT.

PETER THREW THE HURRICANE INTO A STEEP DIVE, FEIGNING DEATH.
IT WAS AN OLD TRICK HIS FATHER HAD TOLD HIM ABOUT, AND IT WORKED
NOW AS HE TURNED AND NAILED THE OVER-EAGER NAZI.

SHOULDN'T HAVE FOLLOWED ME DOWN. THE OLDEST MISTAKE IN THE BOOK, AND THE OLDEST TRICK!

COLD-FACED, PETER GAVE THE GERMAN PILOT AS MUCH CHANCE AS THE OTHER HAD
GIVEN HIS FRIEND—NONE. A WELL-AIMED BURST SMASHED INTO THE FOCKE-WULF.

ARGHHHHH!

THAT'S FOR DICK! NOT THAT IT WILL BRING HIM BACK . . .

BUT NOW HE CONCENTRATED ON SAVING HIS OWN LIFE.

UNSHAKEN BY HIS NARROW ESCAPE, PETER BITTERLY REALISED HE HAD DICK AS WELL AS HIS FATHER TO AVENGE NOW. HE CONTINUED TO FLY ALL THE SORTIES HE COULD—AS IF DRIVEN BY SOME INNER DEVIL WHICH WOULD NOT LET HIM REST ON THE GROUND.

PAGE IS OVER-DOING IT—HE CONSTANTLY REFUSES LEAVE.

I THINK IT'S TIME HE WAS MADE TO TAKE A BREAK FOR HIS OWN GOOD.

BUT ON THIS LATEST SORTIE, PETER WAS IN LUCK. HE SURPRISED A LONE FW190 ON AN INTRUDER SORTIE.

MUST BE NEW TO THE GAME. YOU'D THINK HE WAS TRAINING.

THE GERMAN WAS A NOVICE. ONLY THE FACT HIS FATHER WAS A HIGH-RANKING NAZI HAD GOT HIM POSTED TO FLY THE NEW AIRCRAFT. AND HE DIDN'T KNOW PETER WAS THERE UNTIL IT WAS TOO LATE—

HIMMEL! WHERE DID THE SCHWEIN COME FROM?

THE PILOT PANICKED. HIS AIRCRAFT WAS HARDLY DAMAGED, BUT HE CRASH-LANDED IN THE NEAREST FIELD, DECIDING A HERO'S DEATH WAS NOT FOR HIM.

I MUST SET FIRE TO THE MACHINE THOUGH . . .

ONE O' THEM DANGED NASTYS LANDING IN MY FIELD, EH?

THE LOCAL FARMER HAD WITNESSED THE DUEL AND WAS QUICK ON THE SCENE.

DESPERATELY THE NAZI TRIED TO SET THE AIRCRAFT ALIGHT, BUT THE RUNNING FARMER GUESSED HIS INTENTION.

IF HE SETS THAT ALIGHT, THE SPARKS COULD REACH MY HAY RICKS . . .

SO THE GERMAN'S ATTEMPT FAILED AS A WELL-FLUNG TURNIP STRUCK WITH A MIGHTY BLOW.

TAKE THAT!

AAGH!

THANKS TO THE ACTION OF THE QUICK-THINKING FARMER, THE FW190 HAD FALLEN INTACT INTO THE HANDS OF THE BRITISH. AND THE LOCAL HOME GUARD UNIT SOON COLLECTED THE PILOT.

WELL DONE, OLD CHAP. YOU THROW A MEAN TURNIP.

T'WEREN'T NUTHIN! COULDN'T RISK ME RICKS, COULD OI?

THE CAPTURED PLANE WAS TO BE TESTED AND EVALUATED, AND WHO WAS BETTER FITTED FOR THE JOB THAN PETER? HE DID NOT TAKE THE NEW POSTING WELL. HE WAS A MAN WHO HAD A LOT TO AVENGE AND KNEW THIS WAS YET ANOTHER ATTEMPT OF THE C.O. TO FORCE HIM TO TAKE A BREAK.

LIVES WILL BE SAVED IF WE CAN FIND OUT ABOUT THIS KITE, PETER. YOU ARE TO DO THE TEST FLIGHTS, AND THAT IS THAT.

IT'S NO USE ARGUING. THEY ARE DETERMINED TO KEEP ME OUT OF THE FIGHT.

ABOUT THIS SAME TIME THE NEW BRITISH SPITFIRE FIVE TOOK TO THE AIR. AS THE BOFFINS HAD PROMISED, THEY HAD WORKED ROUND THE CLOCK TO FINISH THIS PROJECT.

THERE SHE GOES. THE ANSWER, WE HOPE, TO THE LUFTWAFFE'S PET FIGHTER.

AND SHE IS EFFICIENT, MAKE NO MISTAKE.

THE NEW SPITFIRE WAS CERTAINLY ALL ITS DESIGNERS THOUGHT IT WOULD BE. IN ONE OF ITS FIRST ACTIONS, A FLIGHT OF THEM CARVED UP A STARTLED GERMAN FORMATION.

ACHTUNG! THESE ARE NEW AIRCRAFT TYPES. YOU MUST . . . AAGH!

IT'S ABOUT TIME WE HIT BACK LIKE THIS!

AND THOUGH THE PILOT SURVIVED WHEN HE CRASH-LANDED, HE HANDED THE BRAND NEW SPITFIRE TO THE GERMANS ON A PLATE. HE PASSED OUT BEFORE HE COULD DESTROY IT.

THE SPITFIRE— SCHNELL! BEFORE THE ENGLANDER CAN IGNITE IT.

THE JUBILANT NAZIS TOOK THE CAPTURED AIRCRAFT TO WHERE IT COULD BE EXAMINED AND FLIGHT TESTED, AND A NAME WAS PUT FORWARD FOR THE TASK OF FLIGHT TESTING— CARL VON STELLEN.

A PERFECT CHOICE. HIS FATHER HAS FOR SOME TIME BEEN ASKING FOR HIS SON TO BE TAKEN FROM COMBAT.

JA, IT WOULD BE BAD FOR MORALE IF ANYTHING HAPPENED TO CARL VON STELLEN. HE HAS DONE MORE THAN HIS SHARE ALREADY.

AND THAT WAS WHAT THE TOP BRASS AND FRANZ VON STELLEN THOUGHT AS THEY SECRETLY MADE PLANS TO KEEP CARL OUT OF DANGER AND TURN HIM INTO A PUBLIC HERO TO BOOST MORALE.

LIKE PETER PAGE, CARL VON STELLEN DID NOT TAKE THE FACT LIGHTLY THAT HE WAS TO COME OFF COMBAT FLYING. BUT HIS PROTESTS ALSO FELL ON DEAF EARS, AND HE HAD TO OBEY.

BUT AT A TIME LIKE THIS? MY WOLF'S-HEAD SQUADRON NEED ME.

THE REICH ALSO NEEDS YOU, VON STELLEN. AND BOTH YOUR FATHER AND GOERING HIMSELF WISH FOR YOU TO TEST THE SPITFIRE.

SO CARL HAD NO CHOICE BUT TO TEST FLY THE BRITISH MACHINE, MUCH TO THE GRATIFICATION OF HIS FATHER WHO WAS PROUDLY PRESENT AS A GUEST OF THE LUFTWAFFE AT THE TRIALS.

CARL HAS DONE ENOUGH FOR NOW. A REST WILL BE THE THING.

WE SHOULD LEARN MUCH FROM THE FIGHTER. IT IS A FORMIDABLE MACHINE.

AND FORMIDABLE IT PROVED TO BE AS CARL PUT IT THROUGH ITS PACES, THE EARLIER DAMAGE NOW REPAIRED AND THE AIRCRAFT SPORTING GERMAN MARKINGS.

BUT BACK IN ENGLAND, PETER PAGE STILL BROODED OVER THE LOSS OF HIS FATHER AND HIS FRIEND. HIS MIND RETURNED AGAIN AND AGAIN TO THE WOLF'S-HEAD SQUADRON AS HE RESTED FROM HIS TASK OF TESTING THE CAPTURED GERMAN FIGHTER.

I BET THEY THINK THEY'VE GOT AWAY WITH THAT RAID. IF ONLY WE COULD RETURN IT. ATTACK THE RATS IN THEIR NEST . . .

THE NEXT DAY THE FW190 WAS TO BE ARMED TO TEST THE FIRE-POWER, AND IT WAS THAT WHICH GAVE PETER HIS IDEA.

WHY NOT TEST IT ON THE NAZIS? THE TWO CHAPS ESCORTING ME KNEW DICK WELL. THEY WOULD AGREE . . .

THE TWO PILOTS WHO FLEW THEIR SPITFIRES IN COMPANY WITH THE FOCKE-WULF WELCOMED PETER'S SCHEME. BOTH HAD LOST GOOD FRIENDS TO THE WOLF'S-HEAD BUNCH.

TO HANG WITH THE CONSEQUENCES! COUNT ME IN.

SAME HERE!

BY NOW THE PILOTS ABOVE ALSO KNEW THERE WAS SOMETHING NOT QUITE RIGHT. AND THE FIRST BURST FROM ONE OF THE ESCORTING SPITFIRES SPARKED OFF THE BATTLE.

AAAGH!

GET INTO THEM, LADS!

AS EACH PILOT JOCKEYED FOR POSITION, THE TWO ACES DREW CLOSER TO EACH OTHER AND RECOGNITION WAS INSTANT AND DEFINITE ON BOTH SIDES.

HIM! NOW I CAN GET HIM . . .

SO, WE MEET AT LAST . . .

IT WAS IRONIC—THE LONG VENDETTA WAS ABOUT TO BE FOUGHT OUT WITH CARL IN A BRITISH KITE AND PETER FLYING A GERMAN ONE.

CARL CAME IN FIRST WITH A SAVAGE, ALL-OUT ATTACK. HE OPENED FIRE JUST A FRACTION TOO SOON, MISSING HIS TARGET.

TEUFEL! I ALMOST HAD HIM!

NOT GOOD ENOUGH, NAZI!

PETER JINKED ROUND, PRESSING HOME A DETERMINED ASSAULT.

NOW, IT'S MY TURN . . .

ON THE GROUND, THE SPECTATORS LOOKED ON ANXIOUSLY.

CARL WILL WIN, YOU WILL SEE . . .

MAYBE— THAT OTHER PILOT IS GOOD.

ALREADY THE OTHER TWO GERMAN PILOTS HAD BEEN DOWNED, AND PETER'S ESCORT HAD HAD TO TURN BACK FOR ENGLAND, BADLY DAMAGED BUT UNHURT. BUT IT HAD TAKEN BOTH MEN LEFT QUITE A WHILE TO REALLY MASTER THE UNFAMILIAR AIRCRAFT AND IT WAS PETER WHO GOT THE EDGE ON CARL. A NEAT TURN AND HE HAD HIM FULL IN HIS SIGHTS LONG ENOUGH TO AVENGE HIS FATHER AND DICK.

AAGH!

HIS KITE'S HAD IT!

IT WAS ALL OVER, BUT PETER FELT NO HATE. IT HAD EVAPORATED WITH THIS RECKONING, AND NOW HE FELT ALMOST CONCERNED.

WHY DOESN'T HE JUMP? HE COULD STILL GET OUT . . .

BUT IT WAS TOO LATE FOR THAT. CARL WAS ALREADY DEAD, KILLED WITH THAT PERFECT BURST FROM PETER.

THE DOOMED AIRCRAFT SLAPPED DOWN ON TO THE AIRFIELD, THE DULL EXPLOSION FOLLOWED BY A RISING COLUMN OF SMOKE AND FLAME. AND FRANZ VON STELLEN WATCHED, SNARLING HIS HATE FOR THE MAN WHO HAD BROUGHT ABOUT CARL'S DEATH.

CURSE THE ENGLANDERS! AGAIN THEY TRIUMPH AND CARL IS FINISHED.

THERE WAS MURDER IN FRANZ VON STELLEN'S EYES AS HE, ERICH AND THE OTHERS SAW PETER BRING HIS PLANE TO A CRASH-LANDING. IT TOO HAD BEEN HIT IN THE BATTLE.

DRIVER, TAKE US OVER THERE— SCHNELL!

WARILY PETER SCRAMBLED CLEAR OF THE WRECK AS THE GERMANS ARRIVED. AND THE ELDERLY VON STELLEN HAD MURDER ON HIS MIND, ESPECIALLY WHEN HE RECOGNISED PETER.

THERE STANDS THE MAN WHO SHOT YOUR BROTHER DOWN . . . KILL HIM!

WELL, IT WAS WORTH IT . . .

PETER ALSO KNEW JUST WHO THESE TWO MEN WERE. HE DIDN'T RATE HIS CHANCES OF SURVIVAL HIGHLY.

BUT ERICH VON STELLEN DID NOT DO WHAT HIS FATHER SO BADLY WANTED HIM TO DO. HIS TONE WAS FLAT AND COLD.

I AM A SOLDIER, NOT A MURDERER. CARL, TOO, WAS A SOLDIER, AND DIED LIKE ONE. IT IS FINISHED.

FOR THOUGH HE WAS SAD AT HIS BROTHER'S DEATH, ERICH SAW IT AS SOMETHING TO BE BLAMED ON THE WAR ITSELF AND NOT ONE MAN.

HIS FACE GREY, FRANZ VON STELLEN SEEMED TO COLLAPSE INWARDLY. THE OLD ARROGANCE WENT FOR EVER. HE WAS, WITH CARL'S DEATH, A BROKEN, OLD MAN.

POOR FATHER! HE SEEMS TO HAVE AGED IN MINUTES. BUT NO ONE CAN HATE FOR SO LONG WITHOUT PAYING THE PRICE.

HATE HAD BURNED HIM OUT TO A SHELL OF A MAN.

BUT PETER HAD LEARNED MUCH FROM MEETING ERICH VON STELLEN. HE KNEW NOW THE ENEMY WERE NOT ALL EVIL FANATICS, AND ANY REMNANTS OF HIS HATRED WERE GONE.

THE WAR IS OVER FOR YOU. I AM GLAD WE DID NOT MEET IN AN AIR DUEL.

THAT GOES FOR ME, TOO. WHEN THIS WAR IS OVER, PERHAPS WE MIGHT MEET AGAIN . . .

AND MEET AGAIN THEY DID WHEN THE WAR
FINISHED. RESPECT TURNED TO FRIENDSHIP AND
THE OLD ENMITIES WERE FORGOTTEN,
ESPECIALLY SINCE PETER HAD MANAGED TO
ESCAPE BACK TO ENGLAND AFTER HIS CAPTURE.

AND HE ALWAYS MAINTAINED THE
EXPLAINING HE HAD TO DO ABOUT HIS
UNOFFICIAL FLIGHT WAS THE TOUGHEST
TASK HE EVER HAD TO FACE—EVEN
ALTHOUGH HE DID ULTIMATELY WIN A
MEDAL FOR THE INCIDENT!

Commando
THE END

Commando FLY PAST

No. 4 — JUNKERS Ju 87B

Shown in the markings of Stukageschwader 51, Luftwaffe, in France, May, 1940.

DANGER BELOW

PETE PROBIN WAS A NATURAL PILOT, A MAN BORN TO FLY. HE COULD HANDLE ANY KITE, PUSH HIS SPITFIRE CLOSER TO THE LIMIT THAN ANY OTHER PILOTS DARED. HE HAD THE COURAGE TO MATCH HIS SKILL, AND A RISING TALLY OF KILLS THAT MARKED HIM AS AN ACE IN THE MAKING — A MAN FOR THE NAZIS TO STEER CLEAR OF.

YET THIS WAS THE VERY PILOT THAT THE TOP BRASS GROUNDED!

THE NAZI REGIME HAD BEGUN ITS BLITZKRIEG AGAINST FRANCE AND BELGIUM. SWEEPING ASIDE WHAT OPPOSITION THERE WAS, THE PANZERS ADVANCED TOWARDS THE CHANNEL.

THIS IS EASY. EXERCISES WERE MORE DANGEROUS.

WE HAVE NOT YET MET THE BRITISH. THAT MAY BE HARDER. AT LEAST WE CAN BE SURE THEY WILL FIGHT.

THE BRITISH DID FIGHT. BUT, WITH THE COLLAPSE OF THE FRENCH ARMY, THE BRITISH EXPEDITIONARY FORCE RETREATED TO DUNKIRK, AND THE R.A.F. DID ALL IT COULD TO HOLD UP THE PURSUING GERMANS.

THAT'S IT THEN, CHAPS. WE ARE TO KNOCK OUT THE BRIDGE BEFORE THE ENEMY GET THERE. THE BATTLES WILL GO AT A LOWER LEVEL AND THE THREE FORMATIONS OF HURRI- CANES GIVE THEM COVER.

BIG DEAL. THE BATTLES ARE USELESS AND HE KNOWS IT.

FLYING OFFICER PETE PROBIN WAS AN IMPETUOUS, COURAGEOUS PILOT, NOT FAMED FOR TACT.

FROM ABOVE, THE COPYBOOK FORMATION WAS BEING WATCHED BY ENEMY EYES...

DO THEY NEVER LEARN. THEY THINK THEY ARE AT A HENDON DISPLAY.

I WILL CALL THE REST OF THE SQUADRON. THERE ARE ENOUGH SIMPLE TARGETS FOR US ALL TO HAVE SOME. THE HURRICANES HAVEN'T EVEN SEEN US.

THE LUFTWAFFE VETERANS KNEW THE R.A.F. TACTICS WERE STUPID.. SO DID SOME OF THE HURRICANE PILOTS, BUT THEY WERE UNDER ORDERS.

LET'S BREAK IT UP A BIT, SIR. I'M SPENDING SO MUCH TIME KEEPING IN FORMATION, I HAVEN'T ANY LEFT TO WATCH FOR OTHER AIR-CRAFT.

NO. THIS IS THE WAY WE WERE TAUGHT. WHEN WE SEE THE ENEMY, WE WILL GO INTO FIGHT-ING AREA ATTACK, NUMBER ONE.

NEXT SECOND THE VERY AIR SEEMED TO EXPLODE –

BREAK UP – EVERY MAN FOR HIMSELF!

THE WARNING CAME TOO LATE FOR MANY. LIKE WOLVES THE Me109s TORE INTO THE ELDERLY BATTLES.

PETE HAD HIS KITE SHOT FROM UNDER HIM. ALTHOUGH BADLY WOUNDED, HE STRUGGLED CLEAR –

I HOPE WE'RE STILL ON OUR OWN SIDE OF THE FRONT LINES.

LUCKILY HE DID LAND NEAR BRITISH TROOPS.

HE'S HURT BAD... HOPE HE PULLS THROUGH.

DESPITE HIGH LOSSES, THE REMAINING BATTLES AND THEIR ESCORT STRUGGLED ON FOR THE BRIDGE — AND ATTACKED IT.

EASY. THEY CANNOT HIT THE BRIDGE AND OUR FIGHTERS ARE KNOCKING THEM DOWN LIKE CLAY PIGEONS.

BUT YOU CAN SEE THAT TO INVADE ENGLAND WILL NOT BE EASY. THEY FIGHT WELL AGAINST THE ODDS HERE. WHAT WILL THEY BE LIKE DEFENDING THEIR HOME-LAND?

VERY SOON AFTER THIS DEBACLE, PETE WAS IN A HOSPITAL IN ENGLAND WHERE HE HAD HIS LEFT EYE REMOVED, BUT CHEERFULLY HE DONNED A BLACK PATCH IN ITS PLACE.

WHEN YOU'RE DIS-CHARGED, YOU'RE GOING ON A RADAR CONTROLLING COURSE. WE NEED EX-PILOTS FOR CONTROLLERS.

EX-PILOT? I AM STILL A PILOT! I GOT TWO KILLS IN FRANCE, AND I GOT SHOT DOWN BECAUSE OF YOUR STUPID TACTICS.

THERE WAS ONE BRIGHT SPOT IN HIS TRANSFER — HE MET AN OLD FRIEND, TAFFY EVANS.

WE'RE MOVING UP IN THE WORLD, TAFFY. ME A FLIGHT LIEUTENANT, AND YOU A SQUADRON LEADER. BUT I'M STILL GROUNDED.

YOU THINK YOU CAN STILL FLY? I CAN FIX YOU WITH UN-OFFICIAL TRIPS IF GROUP CAPTAIN "TEXT-BOOK" TEMPLE DOESN'T FIND OUT.

PATCH JUMPED AT THE OFFER, AND THE TALK CONTINUED ON AIRCRAFT — AS USUAL.

WHY ARE YOUR KITES LINED UP LIKE THIS? THEY'RE SITTING DUCKS FOR STRAFING.

DON'T I KNOW IT. BUT NO-ONE'S CHANGED THE PEACETIME RULE BOOK YET, AND TEMPLE GOES BY THAT. LET'S HAVE A BEER.

THE OLD FRIENDS TALKED SHOP ON THE WAY TO THE MESS, AND PATCH WAS HORRIFIED TO LEARN THAT THE UNIT STILL FLEW IN V FORMATION, AND USED THE STANDARD FIGHTING AREA ATTACKS.

YOU'D THINK NO-ONE KNEW THERE WAS A WAR ON THE WAY THINGS ARE RUN.

AND TO CAP IT ALL, I'M LOSING PILOTS FOR NO APPARENT REASON. THEY JUST SEEM TO LOSE CONTROL...REALLY WEIRD. IT'S PLAYING HAVOC WITH THE MORALE TOO.

THEY TALKED OVER THE MYSTERY FOR QUITE A WHILE, BUT PATCH WAS SOON HITTING AT THE RULE BOOK AGAIN. PERHAPS HE SPOKE TOO LOUDLY, BUT HE CERTAINLY ATTRACTED GROUP CAPTAIN TEMPLE'S ATTENTION.

THE RULES HAVE BEEN DRAWN UP BY EXPERIENCED STAFF OFFICERS AND ARE TO BE AD-HERED TO UNTIL SUCH TIME AS THEY MAY BE CHANGED.

BUT, SIR, I SAW A LINE OF FRENCH PLANES DE-STROYED IN ONE STRAFING RUN BY A JERRY. THEY SHOULD BE DIS-PERSED...

NOBODY PAID MUCH ATTENTION TO FLYING OFFICER BROWN, THE UNIT'S SEEDY, UNPOPULAR INTELLIGENCE OFFICER.

ONCE OUT OF SIGHT, THE FOUR SPITS FORMED THE LOOSE PRACTICAL FORMATION DEVELOPED BY THE LUFTWAFFE IN SPAIN, AND PATCH CALLED THE SECTOR RADAR CONTROLLER.

BUTTERCUP, THIS IS GREEN SECTION. ANY TRADE FOR US?

ROGER. FIVE PLUS BANDITS ANGELS ONE-NINE-ZERO. STEER ONE SIX ZERO. I'LL BRING YOU IN OUT OF THE SUN, PATCH.

DAVID, A CHUM OF PATCH, WAS CONTROLLING AND RECOGNISED THE VOICE. PATCH KNEW HE WOULD KEEP THE SECRET, AND THE FOUR PLANES SWUNG GRACEFULLY ONTO THE HEADING.

DAVID WAS AN ACE CONTROLLER, AND LED THEM BEAUTIFULLY TO THE TARGET.

SPOT OF REVENGE FOR YOU, PATCH. TALLY HO. GET STUCK IN, CHAPS.

NOW TO SEE IF I CAN STILL FIGHT A PLANE AS WELL AS JUST FLY ONE.

HE SOON DISCOVERED THAT HE COULD.

THE SPITS KNOCKED DOWN SIX DORNIERS WITH NO LOSS TO THEMSELVES AND HEADED JUBILANTLY HOME.

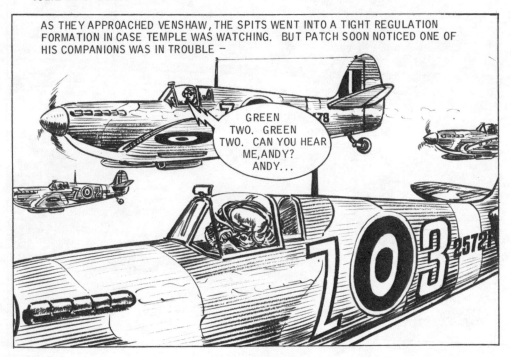

THE ENQUIRY PROVED NOTHING AND THINGS CONTINUED AS BEFORE. PATCH COULD ONLY FLY ON HIS DAYS OFF, AS HE WAS STILL A FULL TIME SECTOR CONTROLLER.

JUMPER SQUADRON, THIS IS BUTTERCUP. SECTOR TWO TWO FIVE. CLIMB ANGELS TWO FIVE ZERO.

EXCUSE ME, SIR. THE C.O. WANTS TO SEE YOU.

BUT PATCH WAS BUSY STEERING A SQUADRON AT THE ENEMY.

CAN'T YOU SEE I'M BUSY? THIS IS MORE IMPORTANT. TELL THE C.O. TO WAIT.

BANDITS AT TWO O'CLOCK, JUMPER. THREE THOUSAND FEET BELOW YOU.

THE OLD MAN WON'T LIKE THIS. HE WAS HOPPING MAD.

PATCH FORGOT THE INCIDENT UNTIL HIS SHIFT FINISHED AND HE WENT TO THE MESS.

HERE'S THE C.O. — LOOKS LIKE TROUBLE.

PROBIN — I SENT FOR YOU...

I WAS ENGAGED WITH A BATTLE, SIR. IT WAS IMPOSSIBLE TO LEAVE.

IT WASN'T A REQUEST, IT WAS AN ORDER.

TEMPLE KNEW HE COULDN'T ARGUE WITH THAT, AND HE COVERED HIS MISTAKE WITH A BLUSTER. HE HAD WANTED PATCH FOR ANOTHER MATTER.

I HAVE JUST HEARD YOU HAVE FLOWN. IT HAS TO STOP! RULES ARE RULES, AND YOU ARE GROUNDED. WE CAN'T AFFORD ONE-EYED PILOTS SMASHING UP VALUABLE PLANES.

PATCH FUMED, BUT TEMPLE WORE FOUR STRIPES AND PATCH TWO, SO HE COULD DO NOTHING. AND ACROSS THE CHANNEL OTHERS WERE ANGRY TOO —

BUT THIS HOPEFUL FORECAST WAS WRONG. THE LUFTWAFFE RADIO MEN HAD NO EASY ANSWER.

BUT THAT WAS EASIER SAID THAN DONE.

AFTER THAT FIRST ATTACK, PATCH RECKONED THE STATIONS DEFENCES WEREN'T GOOD, AND HE WORKED WITH THE SQUADRON ARMOURERS TO IMPROVE IT.

THESE VICKERS GUNS ON A GROUND MOUNTING WILL PACK QUITE A PUNCH.

I'VE A FEELING WE WILL NEED THEM SOON.

PATCH WAS RIGHT. THE GERMANS HAD REALISED THAT THE RAIDS ON THE AERIALS HAD FAILED AND WERE NOW TURNING THEIR ATTENTION TO AIRFIELDS.

I DON'T CARE WHAT THE C.O. TOLD YOU, SERGEANT. THOSE ARE MY SQUADRON'S KITES AND YOU'LL MOVE THEM.

ABOUT TIME TOO. I'VE A FEELING WE'RE IN FOR TROUBLE.

VERY WELL, SIR.

IT WAS ON THE VERY NEXT DAWN THAT THE NAZIS PREPARED THEIR NEXT ATTACK.

THE R.A.F. AIRFIELDS WILL REMEMBER IT WHEN OUR FLYERS PAY A VISIT.

JA, AND FLYING LOW WILL SURPRISE THE BRITISH.

THE WEAK LINK IN THE RADAR DEFENCE WAS AT LOW LEVELS.   THEN THE RADAR COULD ONLY GIVE VERY SHORT WARNING, AND AT VENSHAW THE AIR RAID SIRENS WENT ONLY MOMENTS BEFORE THE RAIDERS ARRIVED.

I JUST KNEW JERRY WOULD COME CALLING!

PATCH WATCHED HIS FRIENDS RUNNING FOR THEIR PLANES. THAT WAS WHERE HE SHOULD BE TOO INSTEAD OF GOING TO A MAKESHIFT GUN, AND HE SPOKE BLUNTLY, IGNORING TEMPLE'S ANGRY GLARE.

I HOPE THEY GET AIR-BORNE BEFORE THE JERRIES ARRIVE. IT'S A GOOD JOB TAFFY GOT HIS KITES DISPERSED.

THE JUNKERS ROARED IN ON AN ATTACK RUN, AND CAUGHT SOME OF THE SPITS BEFORE THEY WERE IN THE AIR.

NOW TO GET A COUPLE, AND EVEN THE ODDS A BIT.

WE HAVE CAUGHT THEM!

THE BOMBERS SOON FOUND THAT THE FIRE FROM THE GROUND, ALTHOUGH WEAK, WAS WELL-AIMED.

BY NOW THE SPITFIRES WERE HITTING BACK, DRIVING OFF THE INTRUDERS, ENCOURAGED BY THE BELLIGERENT TAFFY.

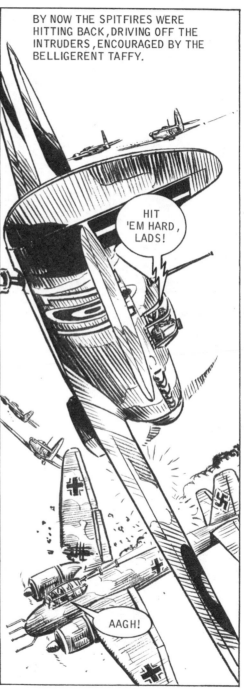

ONCE THEY HAD GOT OVER THE INITIAL SURPRISE, THE BRITISH PILOTS BEGAN TO TAKE A HEAVY TOLL ON THEIR INVADERS.

GOOD SHOW!

WISH I WAS UP THERE — I'D SHOW 'EM!

ONLY BROWN WAS UNENTHUSIASTIC, AND PATCH TOOK THE MATTER IN HAND —

CHEER UP, SQUIRE! ALL TOO NOISY AND NASTY FOR YOU, IS IT?

NO, IT'S JUST THAT I'M NOT FEELING TOO WELL.

PATCH PUSHED THE INCIDENT FROM HIS MIND AS HE AND THE OTHERS RUSHED TO CLEAR UP.

THE RAIDS ON THE AIRFIELD HURT THE R.A.F., NOT SO MUCH BECAUSE OF THE DAMAGE TO RUNWAYS OR HANGARS, BUT BECAUSE THE SECTOR CONTROL STATIONS WERE SOMETIMES HIT. YET SPITFIRES AND HURRICANES STILL ROSE TO MEET THE LUFTWAFFE ATTACKS.

THEY ARE STILL OPERATING. WE MUST DESTROY THE R.A.F. GUIDANCE SYSTEM.

JA, BUT HOW?

SO MORE AND MORE EXPERTS WERE CALLED IN TO DISCUSS MEASURES.

MEANWHILE PATCH HAD RECEIVED A LETTER FROM THE AIR MINISTRY.

CHEER UP, PATCH. EVEN IF THE CHAIRBORNE WARRIORS SAY YOU CAN'T FLY, YOU AND I KNOW DIFFERENTLY. LIKE A FERRY FLIGHT IN THE MORNING?

OK, AND TO HECK WITH TEMPLE!

THAT EVENING, IN THE CONTROL ROOM, PATCH NOTICED A CORPORAL LOOKING VERY WORRIED.

WHAT'S UP, SOMETHING THE MATTER?

HAVEN'T YOU MANAGED TO GET COMPASSIONATE LEAVE?

IT'S MY FATHER — HE'S SERIOUSLY ILL... I'VE JUST BEEN TOLD.

YES, BUT THERE ISN'T A TRAIN UNTIL LUNCH— TIME TOMORROW. THAT — THAT MIGHT BE TOO LATE.

THE STAFF WHO WORKED IN THE CONTROL ROOM WERE EFFICIENT, HARDWORKING AND HAD PROVED THEMSELVES BRAVE DURING THE BOMBING. NO ONE RESPECTED THEM MORE THAN THE PILOTS. PATCH DECIDED TO HELP...

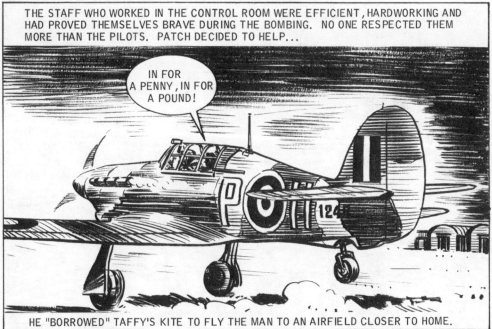

IN FOR A PENNY, IN FOR A POUND!

HE "BORROWED" TAFFY'S KITE TO FLY THE MAN TO AN AIRFIELD CLOSER TO HOME.

THE FLIGHT WAS UNEVENTFUL WITH NOT A SIGN OF THE LUFTWAFFE. THE LANDING HOWEVER WAS FULL OF INCIDENT. PATCH LANDED JUST WHEN THE C.O. WAS INSPECTING HIS PLANES.

THERE WAS NO WAY OUT. PATCH TOLD THE STORY.

PATCH WAS IN TROUBLE AND KNEW IT. HURRICANES WEREN'T SUPPOSED TO CARRY PASSENGERS! BUT HE COULD DO NOTHING BUT WAIT FOR TEMPLE TO GET THE REPORT. MEANWHILE HE JUST GOT ON WITH HIS JOB.

LUCKILY HE DID GET THE CHANCE OF MORE FLYING. THE PILOTS WERE GETTING SO WEARY THAT REGULATIONS HAD CEASED TO MATTER MUCH. THE STRAIN OF SEVERAL COMBAT FLIGHTS DAILY WAS TELLING.

ANOTHER FLIGHT FOR YOU TO-MORROW, BOYO, TO HECK WITH TEMPLE. MY BOYS ARE JUST TOO TIRED TO FLY KITES FOR REPAIR WHEN WE HAVE A READY-MADE TAXI SERVICE IN YOU.

YEAH, AND I HEAR YOU HAD ANOTHER MYSTER-IOUS CRASH YESTERDAY. THAT REALLY GETS THE LADS DOWN.

GLUMLY THEY DISCUSSED THE CRASHES THAT NIGHT, AND NEXT MORNING PATCH STROLLED TO THE DISPERSAL FOR A FLIGHT.

I HOPE TAFFY DOESN'T LAND HIMSELF IN BOTHER BECAUSE OF ME. BUT I DO WANT TO FLY AND ANY TRIP IS WELCOME. MIGHT EVEN MEET A JERRY ON THE WAY.

IT WAS THEN BROWN APPEARED AT HIS ELBOW —

I CAN SEE YOU ARE GOING TO FLY AGAIN. I WISH I COULD.

JUST DON'T TELL THE C.O., OR...

NO, I WOULDN'T DO THAT. I ADMIRE THE PILOTS — SAVE CHOCOLATE AND SWEETS FOR THEM SOMETIMES.

PATCH LIKED A BIT OF GUM OR A SWEET HIMSELF WHILE FLYING, AND THOUGHT THE SEEDY LITTLE INTELLIGENCE OFFICER PERHAPS WASN'T SUCH A BAD TYPE AT ALL.

ENJOY THEM — AND BRING DOWN A JERRY FOR ME.

THANKS VERY MUCH. I'LL TRY.

BUT TROUBLE WAS CLOSE FOR PATCH AND FOR TAFFY. TEMPLE HAD SUSPECTED PATCH WOULD FLY AGAIN AND WAS ON THE LOOK OUT.

THE DRIVER HAD NO ALTERNATIVE BUT TO TELL TEMPLE WHO THE PILOT WAS.

DELIBERATE DISOBEDIENCE OF ORDERS. REPORT TO MY OFFICE AT OH NINE HUNDRED HOURS TOMORROW.

YES, SIR.

PATCH RETURNED MISERABLY TO HIS ROOM. FIRST THE LETTER SAYING HE COULD NEVER FLY AGAIN, AND NOW THIS. HE FELT THE LUMP IN HIS POCKET AND PULLED OUT BROWN'S SWEETS —

MIGHT AS WELL EAT 'EM, EVEN THOUGH I'M NOT GOING TO BRING ONE DOWN FOR BROWN.

TAFFY HEARD ABOUT THE INCIDENT AND CALLED IN TO SEE HIS FRIEND, ONLY TO FIND HIM DOUBLED UP IN AGONY.

WHAT'S UP, PATCH? ARE YOU OK?

MY STOMACH, MATE... IT'S MY STOMACH.

PATCH WAS IMMEDIATELY RUSHED OFF TO HOSPITAL.

WILL HE BE OK, DOC?

WARD 2

CAN'T SAY YET. IT DEPENDS ON HOW LONG AGO HE ATE THE STUFF.

TEMPLE JOINED TAFFY IN THE WAITING ROOM AS PATCH UNDERWENT TREATMENT.

SEVERE FOOD POISONING, EH. HE LOOKED FIT ENOUGH THIS MORNING.

IT CAN'T BE FOOD POISONING. I HAD LUNCH AND TEA WITH HIM AND ATE THE SAME.

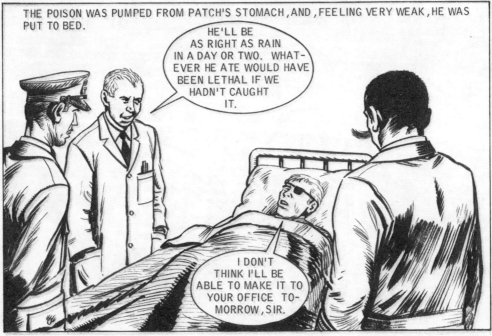

THE POISON WAS PUMPED FROM PATCH'S STOMACH, AND, FEELING VERY WEAK, HE WAS PUT TO BED.

HE'LL BE AS RIGHT AS RAIN IN A DAY OR TWO. WHATEVER HE ATE WOULD HAVE BEEN LETHAL IF WE HADN'T CAUGHT IT.

I DON'T THINK I'LL BE ABLE TO MAKE IT TO YOUR OFFICE TOMORROW, SIR.

MEANWHILE IN FRANCE, A TOUGH, EXPERIENCED GERMAN CAPTAIN CALLED KEIL WAS EXPOUNDING ON HIS OWN BRAINWAVE.

THE BRITISH ARE NOT ORGANISED FOR A GROUND RAID. WE COULD LAND, TAKE SOME PRISONERS, AND BLOW UP THOSE MASTS BEFORE THEY WOKE UP.

IT SOUNDS CRAZY.

BUT PRISONERS COULD TELL US WHERE THESE R.A.F. CONTROLLING STATIONS ARE. I AM SURE OUR FRIENDS IN THE GESTAPO WOULD HELP THEM. MAKE YOUR PLANS, HAUPTMAN KEIL.

KEIL DREW UP PLANS SIMILAR TO THOSE PUT INTO EFFECT A YEAR LATER BY BRITISH COMMANDOS.

THE U-BOAT WILL SURFACE AND FLY THE BRITISH FLAG. WE DIS-EMBARK AT VENSHAW IN BRITISH UNIFORM. WE WILL SPLIT INTO TWO GROUPS — ONE TO BLOW THE RADAR MASTS AND INSTALLATIONS. THE OTHER WILL TAKE PRISONERS.

THE GERMAN COMMANDO LEADER LEFT THE GENERAL'S OFFICE AND IN HIS USUAL BUSTLING WAY, HEADED STRAIGHT TO SUPERVISE THE ISSUE OF UNIFORM TO HIS SELECTED MEN.

LOOK AT HANS! HIS ENGLISH UNIFORM FITS AS WELL AS HIS PROPER ONE.

AFTER DUNKIRK WE HAVE A GOOD SELECTION. EVERYONE WILL BE FITTED PROPERLY.

NO. LET SOME OF THEM NOT FIT WELL. IT IS MORE AUTHEN-TIC.

WHILE ALL THESE PLANS WERE SET IN MOTION, PATCH LAY WEAKENED IN HIS HOSPITAL BED AND THOUGHT.

BROUGHT YOU SOME SWEETS, MATE. I KNOW YOU LIKE THEM.

THAT'S IT — THE SWEETS!

PATCH EXPLAINED ABOUT BROWN GIVING HIM THE SWEETS AND ABOUT THE INTELLIGENCE OFFICER NOT BEING JUBILANT WHEN THE NAZI BOMBERS WERE SHOT DOWN. TAFFY NODDED AND FETCHED TEMPLE TO HEAR.

ABSOLUTE NONSENSE. I HAVE HIS FILE IN MY OFFICE.

MY PILOTS HAVE BEEN CRASHING, AND IF HE'D BEEN GIVING THEM THE SWEETS, IT WOULD ALL FIT. I THINK WE SHOULD DO SOMETHING. WE MUST.

PATCH HAD GUESSED RIGHT. BROWN WAS IN HIS ROOM AT THAT MOMENT, EXAMINING A LETTER HE HAD RECEIVED FROM NEUTRAL PORTUGAL.

A RAID BY CRACK TROOPS ON VENSHAW. I WILL SINGLE OUT IMPORTANT PRISONERS FOR THEM, INCLUDING JONES AND PROBIN. THEY ARE BECOMING SUSPICIOUS OF ME.

EAGER TO RETURN TO HIS FATHERLAND, BROWN WAS LEAVING NOTHING TO CHANCE. HE DID NOT WANT TO BE EXPOSED BEFORE THE RAID, SO...

...ALL INCRIMINATING EVIDENCE WAS DESTROYED — THE POISONED SWEETS, MINIATURE CODE BOOKS, SECRET EQUIPMENT.

THAT'S THAT DONE. THEY CAN NEVER DISCOVER ME NOW. BY THIS TIME TOMORROW I COULD BE IN BERLIN.

TEMPLE STILL LISTENED TO PATCH WHO HAD WANGLED HIS WAY OUT OF THE SICK-BAY BUT HE STILL DIDN'T BELIEVE HIM.

NONSENSE, PROBIN. BROWN HAS BEEN IN THE R.A.F. SINCE BEFORE THE WAR.

MY PILOTS HAVE BEEN DYING — PATCH ALMOST DIED. YOU CAN'T IGNORE IT.

AND, OF COURSE, BROWN HAD COVERED HIS TRACKS WELL.

AS THE TWO PILOTS WONDERED HOW TO CATCH BROWN, CRACK TROOPS BOARDED A U-BOAT IN FRANCE.

THE SUBMARINE OPENLY SURFACED IN VENSHAW BAY NEXT MORNING AND THE SOLDIERS ROWED IN RUBBER DINGHIES TOWARDS THE CLIFF PATH.

WHAT'S GOING ON, HARRY?

SOME STUPID ARMY EXERCISE, I SUPPOSE. WHO DID YOU THINK THEY WERE — HITLER COME TO INSPECT YOU?

OTHER EYES WATCHED —

SOON I WILL BE IN GERMANY, AWAY FROM THESE STUPID ENGLISH.

BROWN SCURRIED DOWN THE PATH AND OPENLY WELCOMED KEIL.

HERR BRAUN, I ASSUME.

JAWOHL, HAUPTMANN. AT YOUR SERVICE.

THE SUBMARINE CAPTAIN WAS ANXIOUSLY WAITING FOR THE LAST SOLDIER TO DISEMBARK.

RIGHT! NOW TO DIVE AND GET AWAY UNTIL WE PICK THEM UP AGAIN. I DO NOT SHARE KEIL'S LOW OPINION OF THE BRITISH. I FOUGHT THEM IN THE LAST WAR ALSO.

KEIL AND HIS MEN WATCHED THE U-BOAT VANISH AND THEN SET ABOUT THEIR TASK.

I HOPE THEY DON'T FORGET TO PICK US UP AGAIN, WILHELM.

JA. I DO NOT WISH TO RE-MAIN IN ENGLAND UNTIL THE WAR IS OVER.

THE SHOTS FROM THE RADAR SITE WERE HEARD ALL OVER VENSHAW, BUT NO-ONE PAID MUCH ATTENTION. THERE WERE MANY EXPLANATIONS FOR SHOTS ON A WARTIME MILITARY CAMP.

WONDER WHAT THAT WAS?

SOME MOB AT THE RIFLE RANGE, I SUPPOSE.

BUT, WHEN THE MASTS WERE BLOWN UP, EVERYONE NOTICED, INCLUDING THE SHORT-TEMPERED, EXASPERATED TEMPLE.

I WONDER WHAT THAT WAS. BETTER GO AND SEE... SOME STUPID PRANK NO DOUBT.

A SNEERING VOICE MADE HIM SWING ROUND –

COME QUIETLY, TEMPLE. WE HAVE SOME FRIENDS IN FRANCE AND GERMANY WHO WOULD LIKE TO ASK YOU SOME QUESTIONS.

YOU DIRTY LITTLE SPY! SO PROBIN WAS RIGHT...

WRONG! HERR BRAUN IS A LOYAL GERMAN. NOW MOVE ...AND SCHNELL!

MEANWHILE THE PARTY DETAILED TO COLLECT PATCH AND TAFFY WERE APPROACHING THEIR OBJECTIVE –

SQUADRON LEADER EVANS AND FLIGHT LIEUTENANT PROBIN?

YES, WHAT CAN WE DO FOR YOU?

KEIL'S APPRAISAL OF THE STATE OF AIRFIELD DEFENCES WASN'T FAR WRONG, BUT HE HADN'T RECKONED ON THE STUBBORN RESISTANCE FROM THE R.A.F. MEN ONCE THEY REALISED WHAT WAS HAPPENING.

A SPITFIRE USED AS A MULTI-MACHINE GUN SOON DISCOURAGED ONE GERMAN CONTINGENT.

THE U-BOAT ARRIVED BACK AT THE RENDEZVOUS ON TIME, AND CAME UP TO PERISCOPE LEVEL.

THEY ARE COMING. TAKE HER UP, NUMBER ONE.

SMOOTHLY THE U-BOAT ROSE –

THEY'D BETTER GET A MOVE ON. I'M NOT GOING TO HANG ABOUT WAITING FOR THEM.

THE THREE PRISONERS WERE HERDED ABOARD THE SUB. THE CAPTAIN CHECKED HIS WATCH AND MADE READY TO SUBMERGE.

YOU CAN'T LEAVE. NOT ALL MY MEN HAVE RE-TURNED.

THEN THEY AREN'T RETURNING. I WON'T RISK MY BOAT ANY LONGER.

THE BRITISH ARMY HAD ARRIVED AT VENSHAW BY NOW, AND WERE MOPPING UP THE LAST OF THE GERMAN RESISTANCE.

DASHED ENTERPRISING OF JERRY. FACT IS, WE WEREN'T READY FOR HIM.

I WISH HE'D USE HIS ENTERPRISE SOMEWHERE ELSE. WE'VE HAD MORE DAMAGE THIS WAY THAN FROM AIR RAIDS.

BUT THE ARMY HAD ARRIVED TOO LATE TO STOP THE MAIN BODY OF KEIL'S MEN FROM MAKING THEIR ESCAPE, ALONG WITH THE TREACHEROUS BROWN.

DRAT – THEY'VE GOT AWAY!

SOON, RADIO MESSAGES WERE FLASHING THROUGH THE AIR, ALERTING THE BOMBER SQUADRONS AND THE NAVY.

AS THE U-BOAT MADE HEADWAY BACK TO BASE, THE THREE PRISONERS WERE UNDER GUARD, ALTHOUGH TAFFY WAS RECEIVING ATTENTION FOR HIS DAMAGED SHOULDER.

THEY HAD A READY-MADE DECOY IN TAFFY WHO COULD PUT ON A CONVINCING TURN WITH HIS DAMAGED SHOULDER.

HE'S IN AGONY. SEHR KRANK.

DOCTOR — GET A DOCTOR.

AAGH!

IT WORKED!

GOOD SHOW, PROBIN. NOW FOR STAGE TWO.

THE GUARD WAS TAKEN IN BY TAFFY'S ACT. HE WAS ONLY A SIMPLE SAILOR, AND NOT ONE OF THE PROFESSIONAL KILLERS THAT KEIL LED.

THE PRISONERS SET TO WORK RAPIDLY, COLLECTING ALL THE INFLAMMABLE MATERIAL THEY COULD FIND.

IF ONE CIGARETTE WORRIED THEM, THIS SHOULD CAUSE A PROBLEM.

THE SMOKE WAS NOTICED AS THE FIRE BURNT UP MUCH-NEEDED OXYGEN.

SMOKE... THERE IS A FIRE! WHERE IS IT COMING FROM?

THE PRISONER'S QUARTERS, SIR.

SAILORS RUSHED TO THE QUARTERS TO EXTINGUISH THE FIRE, BUT TEMPLE WAS READY FOR THEM WITH THE GUARD'S RIFLE.

HAVE THAT, MY GOOD MAN!

WE CAN EXPECT MORE OF THEM. IT DEPENDS WHETHER THEY HAVE TO SURFACE OR WHETHER WE ARE KILLED FIRST.

THE U-BOAT WAS FILLED WITH SMOKE AND THE CAPTAIN HAD NO CHOICE...

PREPARE TO SURFACE... WE HAVE NO CHOICE.

AND ALREADY THE BRITISH DESTROYER HAD AN ASDIC CONTACT.

BE READY FOR ANYTHING. THERE'S SOMETHING ODD GOING ON...

UP SHOT THE U-BOAT TO BE SPOTTED IMMEDIATELY BY A KEEN-EYED LOOK-OUT.

U-BOAT DEAD AHEAD, SIR!

OPEN FIRE!

THE U-BOAT SHOWED SIGNS OF DEFIANCE AND THE DESTROYER'S GUNS BLASTED OUT SAVAGELY.

THE ISSUE OF THE BATTLE WAS NEVER IN DOUBT.   BROWN DECIDED TO FLEE WHEN HE REALISED THAT THE OLD SEA DOG IN COMMAND OF THE U-BOAT WOULD NOT SURRENDER.

THE SMOKE CLEARED, AND THE GUARDS WERE DEAD. A PIECE OF LUCK HAD FINALLY COME THE PRISONERS' WAY...

GET OUT WHILE WE HAVE THE CHANCE. I RECKON THIS OLD TUB WON'T BE AROUND MUCH LONGER.

THEY STRUGGLED CLEAR WITH TAFFY AS SQUALLY RAIN SHOWERS STARTED.

YOU'LL NEVER MAKE IT HOLDING ME UP LIKE THIS. LET ME GO.

NONSENSE. YOU KEEP GOING, EVANS. THAT IS AN ORDER!

TEMPLE MIGHT BE A MARTINET AND AN OLD STICK-IN-THE-MUD, BUT PATCH RECOGNISED THAT HE HAD GUTS WHEN THE CHIPS WERE DOWN.

THE SUB CREW FOUGHT BACK BRAVELY...

...BUT THEY HAD NO REAL CHANCE.

THE DESTROYER SEARCHED BUT NO SURVIVORS WERE FOUND. THERE WERE VERY FEW AND THE WEATHER CONDITIONS SHIELDED THOSE FROM SEARCHING EYES. THE RADIO MESSAGES WENT OUT WITH THE NEWS, BUT THE AIRCRAFT ON THEIR HOMEWARD TRACK FROM THE SUB SEARCH DIDN'T AGREE...

THE WIMPEY DROPPED A DINGHY.

THAT SHOULD MAKE THEM A BIT MORE COMFORTABLE.

THE DOWNED FLIERS FELT A LITTLE BETTER AFTER THE RAIN STOPPED, AND WHEN THE DINGHY LANDED NEAR THEM.

THAT FEELS BETTER THAN SWIMMING.

YOU AREN'T JOKING.

ANOTHER SURVIVOR WAS ALSO FLOATING IN THE AREA. BROWN HAD GOT CLEAR AND WAS NOW WONDERING WHO THE OTHER SURVIVORS WERE.

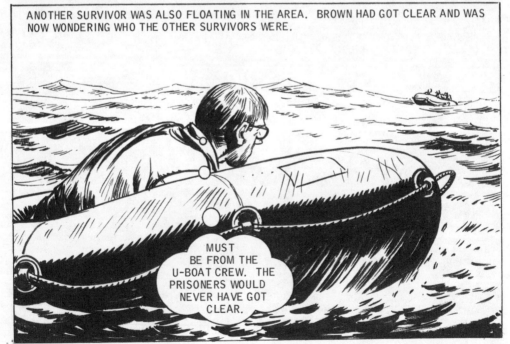

MUST BE FROM THE U-BOAT CREW. THE PRISONERS WOULD NEVER HAVE GOT CLEAR.

THE TWO DINGHIES CAME CLOSER — AND BROWN SUDDENLY CAME TO LIFE, HIS LUGER HELD ROCK STEADY AS HE PULLED THE TRIGGER.

BUT NO BULLET LEFT THE BARREL. SEA WATER HAD RENDERED THE GUN USELESS.

AND THE SPY DIDN'T GET A SECOND CHANCE AS PATCH LAUNCHED HIMSELF TOWARDS HIM.

IT WAS A SAVAGE DUEL, WATCHED BY TWO ANXIOUS EXCITED MEN.

STICK ONE ON HIM, BOYO!

OH, BE CAREFUL, PROBIN.

PATCH KNEW HE WAS FIGHTING FOR HIS LIFE AS HE SWEPT AWAY THE VICIOUS KNIFE THE NAZI HAD PULLED.

THEN, SECONDS LATER, IT WAS ALL OVER.   THE GERMAN'S LIFELESS BODY SANK TO THE DEPTHS.

EAGER HANDS HAULED THEM ABOARD AND THEY WERE SOON ON THEIR WAY TO SAFETY.

WELL, THAT'S THAT I SUPPOSE.

AND THEN YOU KNOW WHAT, BOYO. YOU GET GROUNDED.

AH, YES. I'VE BEEN MEANING TO TALK TO YOU ABOUT THAT. IT SEEMS I HAVE BEEN WRONG ABOUT MANY THINGS.

I THINK IF I TOLD H.Q. YOU HAD BEEN FLYING AND KNOCKING DOWN GERMANS, THEY WOULD ACCEPT THE INEVITABLE AND PUT YOU BACK ON FLYING. THE PROOF OF THE PUDDING IS IN THE EATING AFTER ALL, ISN'T IT?

FLY PAST

Commando

No. 100 — BOEING B-17G FORTRESS

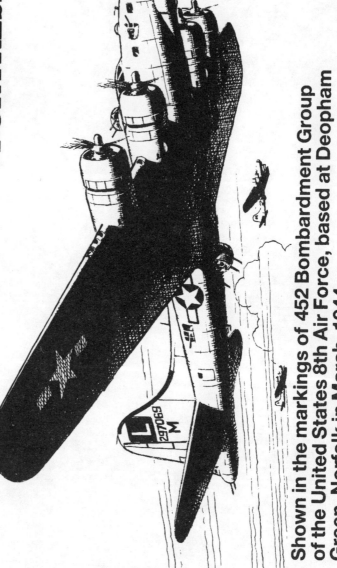

Kennedy

Shown in the markings of 452 Bombardment Group of the United States 8th Air Force, based at Deopham Green, Norfolk in March, 1944.

AS HE JUGGLED WITH THE THROTTLE AND CLOMPED HIS FLYING BOOTS INEPTLY ON THE RUDDER BAR, ANTON FELT COLD SWEAT TRICKLE BETWEEN HIS SHOULDERS.

DON'T LET ME FAIL! I DON'T WANT TO BE PUT OFF THE COURSE!

IT WAS NOT UNNATURAL THAT WITH A NAME LIKE RICHTHOFEN, ANTON HAD LONGED SINCE BOYHOOD TO BECOME A FAMOUS FIGHTER PILOT.

THAT RED BARON NAMESAKE OF MINE WAS AN ACE FLIER!

ANTON PASSED HIS INITIAL TESTS AND WAS SOON IN THE UNIFORM OF A CADET PILOT. BUT HAVING A NAME LIKE RICHTHOFEN WAS A GREAT CROSS TO BEAR IN A FLYING TRAINING ESTABLISHMENT. PERHAPS THAT AND A SHORT-TEMPERED INSTRUCTOR LED TO A LOSS OF CONFIDENCE.

ANTON'S NEW FRIEND, JOSEF BALBIN, WAS VERY SYMPATHETIC.

YOU'RE ONE OF THOSE TYPES WHO TAKES HIS OWN TIME BUT GETS THERE IN THE END, ANTON.

UNFORTUNATELY THEY DON'T GIVE US A LOT OF TIME, JOSEF.

ANOTHER CADET — BURLY, BARGING JAN JILMECK, LOVED TO TEASE ANTON.

YOU COULD TEACH A TORTOISE TO FLY EASIER THAN RICHTHOFEN. HE'S A WASTE OF STATE FUNDS.

LEAVE OFF, JILMECK. ANTON'S HAD A BAD DAY.

JAN WASN'T A BAD TYPE. HE WAS JUST A BIT INSENSITIVE AT TIMES.

BAD DAY, ALL RIGHT! HE NEARLY TAXIED INTO A PETROL BOWSER!

AND NOW ANTON WAS COMING IN FOR ANOTHER OF HIS UNPREDICTABLE LANDINGS, HIS CONFIDENCE RAPIDLY DRAINING AS THE RUNWAY HURTLED TOWARDS HIM.

TOO HIGH! NO . . . TOO LOW! MORE THROTTLE . . . DRIFTING . . . GOT TO STRAIGHTEN UP . . .

HE PULLED BACK THE STICK AND LET THE AIRCRAFT DROP — MUCH TOO FAST . . .

FORTUNATELY THE AIRCRAFT DIDN'T CATCH FIRE — PUPIL AND INSTRUCTOR WERE QUICKLY EXTRICATED. ANTON HAD HARDLY A SCRATCH.

ANTON'S HIGH HOPES OF BECOMING A DASHING FIGHTER PILOT ENDED THERE AND THEN. NEXT DAY HE WAS CALLED FOR AN INTERVIEW WITH THE CHIEF INSTRUCTOR AND TOLD THAT HE WAS BEING POSTED TO TRAIN AS AN OBSERVER GUNNER.

JAN'S INSENSITIVITY MADE JOSEF SEE RED.

YOU BUFFOON, JILMECK!

HEY . . . WHAT . . ?

ANTON GRABBED JOSEF'S ARM.

HOLD IT, OLD FRIEND. JILMECK'S PROBABLY RIGHT.

OF COURSE I AM. AT LEAST YOU SEE SENSE, RICHTHOFEN.

SADLY, ANTON BADE HIS FRIENDS GOODBYE AND BEGAN TRAINING AS AN OBSERVER. HE BECAME A PROFICIENT GUNNER AND CONSOLED HIMSELF WITH THE FACT THAT AT LEAST HE WAS FLYING.

IT'S BETTER THAN BEING ON THE GROUND IN SOME OFFICE JOB.

HE WAS A SERGEANT GUNNER IN OCTOBER 1938 WHEN THE GERMAN ARMY MARCHED INTO A PART OF CZECHOSLOVAKIA GIVEN TO THEM IN A PACT. LATER, WHEN THE COUNTRY WAS THREATENED BY TOTAL GERMAN DOMINATION, HE AND SOME COMRADES FROM HIS OWN SQUADRON DECIDED IT WAS TIME TO GET OUT.

WELCOMED INTO A POLISH ARMY CO-OPERATION SQUADRON, ANTON AND HIS COMRADES WENT INTO ACTION IN SEPTEMBER 1939 WHEN THE GERMANS INVADED POLAND.

ONE DAY, AS THEIR PZL MEWA AIRCRAFT FORMED UP AFTER A GROUND ATTACK, Me109s PEELED OUT OF THE SUN AND CAME DIVING DOWN ON THEM.

DEFENSIVE CIRCLE — GO!

IT'S LIKE IN WORLD WAR ONE, WHEN RICHTHOFEN ATTACKED!

BUT THE OLD FIRST WORLD WAR TACTIC OF FORMING A DEFENSIVE CIRCLE WAS NO USE AGAINST THE MARAUDING Me109s. THEY ROARED IN, GUNS BLAZING.

COME AND GET IT, NAZIS!

THE BLACK AND WHITE SPINNERS OF THE ENEMY SEEMED TO GLINT EVILLY AS THE ONE-OH-NINES DIVED.

THE GERMANS MADE MINCEMEAT OF THEM, KNOCKING DOWN TWO MEWAS IN THEIR FIRST PASS.

ANTON'S PILOT SHOVED THE STICK FORWARD AND DIVED STEEPLY FOR THE GROUND AS A THIRD MEWA BLEW UP BEHIND THEM.

BUT THEIR LUCK WAS IN. ONLY ONE ENEMY FIGHTER PURSUED THEM — AND ITS PILOT DECIDED VERY QUICKLY THAT DODGING BETWEEN HILLS AND TREES WAS NOT FOR HIM.

PHEW, HE'S TURNED BACK! PROBABLY THERE ARE EASIER TARGETS AROUND.

UNFORTUNATELY, WITHIN A FEW MORE DAYS, THEIR WHOLE SQUADRON WAS WIPED OUT. ANTON'S OWN PLANE WAS ATTACKED BY AN Me110 WHILE CLIMBING AWAY FROM THE AIRFIELD, ITS ENGINE BLOWING UP AND RIPPING OFF HALF OF A WING.

MUST GET OUT — FAST!

AGAIN ANTON WAS LUCKY. AS HE LOOSENED HIS STRAPS, THE AIRCRAFT ROLLED ONTO ITS BACK AND HE FELL CLEAR — OTHERWISE HE COULD HAVE BEEN PINNED IN THE COCKPIT AS THE AIRCRAFT FELL, SPINNING RAPIDLY.

THAT WAS ANTON'S LAST FLIGHT FOR THE POLISH AIR FORCE. AVOIDING THE ADVANCING GERMANS, HE MADE HIS WAY SOUTH TO THE MEDITERRANEAN AND BOARDED A SHIP FOR ENGLAND. UNFORTUNATELY, HIS PAPERS AND MONEY WERE STOLEN EN ROUTE.

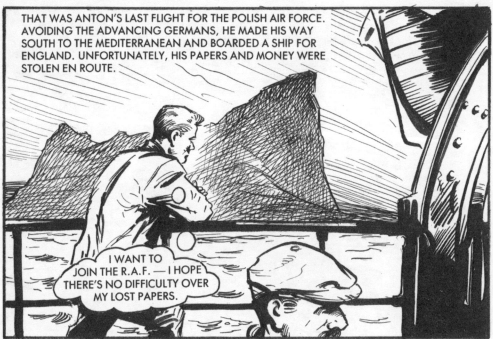

IN LONDON, HE WAS PROCESSED BY THE CZECH AUTHORITIES AND GIVEN NEW PAPERS.

RICHTHOFEN, ANTON . . . PILOT, NEWLY QUALIFIED. REPORT TO R.A.F. CALDIS HILL FOR TESTING. YOU SPEAK ENGLISH, SO YOU'LL HAVE NO PROBLEMS.

PILOT? BUT I . . .

THE SERGEANT WAVED AWAY HIS PROTESTS.

ALL YOU PILOTS THINK IT'S AN INSULT TO BE TESTED, BUT THE R.A.F. MUST FIND OUT WHAT TYPE OF PLANE YOU'RE MOST SUITED FOR.

YES, OF COURSE, SERGEANT. I'M SORRY.

ANTON ALMOST DANCED DOWN THE STEPS, HARDLY ABLE TO BELIEVE HIS LUCK. THERE HAD BEEN SOME COLOSSAL MISTAKE SOMEWHERE — NOT SURPRISING WITH ALL THE UPHEAVAL BACK HOME AND THE LACK OF RECORDS, BUT HE HAD NO INTENTION OF POINTING IT OUT.

A SECOND CHANCE TO BECOME A PILOT! IT'S MARVELLOUS!

BUT ANTON'S JOY QUICKLY EVAPORATED WHEN HE FOLLOWED HIS R.A.F. INSTRUCTOR FROM THE FLIGHT OFFICE AT CALDIS HILL AND SAW THE MILES MASTER TRAINER THAT WAS WAITING FOR HIM.

TRYING TO REMEMBER ALL THE INSTRUCTOR HAD TOLD HIM, ANTON CAREERED ALONG THE RUNWAY.

THE AIRCRAFT WAS MORE POWERFUL THAN ANYTHING ANTON HAD EVER HANDLED AND HE JUST COULDN'T COPE. AFTER A FEW HAIR-RAISING MANOEUVRES, THE INSTRUCTOR DECIDED HE'D HAD ENOUGH.

HANDS OFF! I'M TAKING OVER!

IT — IT'S ALL YOURS.

THE INSTRUCTOR MADE A PERFECT THREE POINT LANDING.

WHAT AN IDIOT I WAS TO BELIEVE I'D GET AWAY WITH IT. I DIDN'T LAST FIVE MINUTES UP THERE.

BUT ANTON'S LUCK WAS STILL IN.

COR, CHUM . . . DON'T KNOW HOW YOU EVER PASSED OUT. BUT IT'S BACK TO PILOT TRAINING FOR YOU.

THEY'RE NOT GOING TO THROW ME OUT! I'M GETTING ANOTHER CHANCE!

PROVIDED WITH AN R.A.F. UNIFORM, ANTON WAS PACKING TO LEAVE WHEN SOME OF HIS OLD COMRADES FROM PILOT TRAINING DAYS ARRIVED, JOSEF BALBIN AND JAN JILMECK AMONGST THEM — ALL SERGEANTS LIKE HIM.

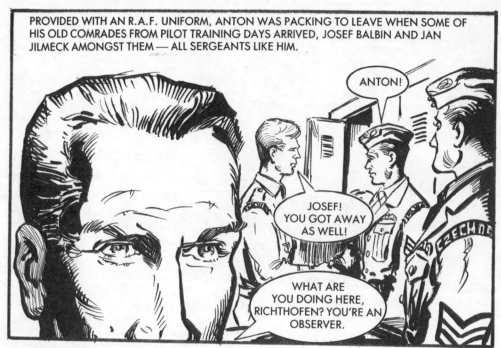

ANTON!

JOSEF! YOU GOT AWAY AS WELL!

WHAT ARE YOU DOING HERE, RICHTHOFEN? YOU'RE AN OBSERVER.

ANTON WAS QUICK WITH AN EXCUSE.

THE R.A.F. DON'T WANT OBSERVERS, THEY WANT PILOTS — SO I'VE TO RE-TRAIN.

HUH, THEY MUST BE HARD UP!

ANTON WAS POSTED TO R.A.F. HORNBY-UNDER-SWOLE FOR FLYING TRAINING. HIS INSTRUCTOR, FLIGHT LIEUTENANT NIGEL HERON, WAS A COOL, UNFLAPPABLE TYPE WHO NEVER BECAME TOO IRKED BY ANTON'S MISTAKES.

AS WE'RE COMING IN TO LAND, I THINK IT WOULD BE SENSIBLE IF WE LOWERED OUR FLAPS, OLD CHAP. ONE THIRD'LL DO FOR A START.

OH! ER . . . RIGHT, SIR.

THE CHIEF FLYING INSTRUCTOR, HOWEVER, WAS DOUBTFUL ABOUT CONTINUING ANTON'S TRAINING AFTER SEEING ONE OR TWO OF HIS LANDINGS.

WHAT'S HIS PROBLEM, HERON?

LACK OF CONFIDENCE, SIR. BUT I RECKON I CAN STRAIGHTEN HIM OUT.

ANTON WAS WAITING ANXIOUSLY FOR HERON'S RETURN.

HAVE THEY FAILED ME, SIR?

OF COURSE NOT, OLD BEAN. HOW COULD YOU FAIL WITH A NAME LIKE RICHTHOFEN?

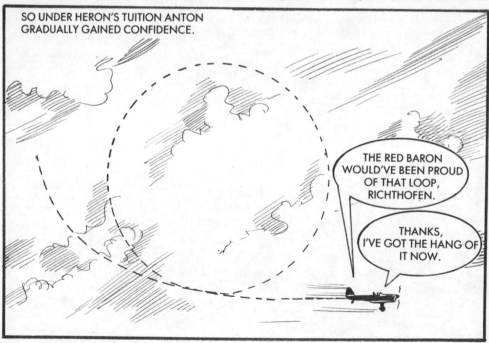

SO UNDER HERON'S TUITION ANTON GRADUALLY GAINED CONFIDENCE.

THE RED BARON WOULD'VE BEEN PROUD OF THAT LOOP, RICHTHOFEN.

THANKS, I'VE GOT THE HANG OF IT NOW.

DURING TRAINING, ANTON MADE FRIENDS WITH ANOTHER PUPIL, JIMMY MELROSE, A CHEERFUL, EASY-GOING TYPE FROM BRADFORD. JIMMY WAS FASCINATED BY ANTON'S EARLIER EXPERIENCE IN THE WAR.

YOU'RE A REAL VETERAN, ANTON! IT'S A PITY YOU DIDN'T SHOOT DOWN ANY OF THOSE LUFTWAFFE BUZZARDS, THOUGH.

THE MESSERSCHMITTS WERE VERY FAST, JIMMY.

THE BATTLE OF BRITAIN HAD JUST BEGUN AND ONE DAY ANTON AND HERON WERE ON A TRAINING FLIGHT WHEN A DARK-PAINTED AIRCRAFT DIVED OUT OF THE CLOUDS BEHIND THEM.

QUICKLY, GIVE ME THE CONTROLS, OLD BOY! IT'S A HUN!

YOU'VE GOT THEM, SIR!

PULLING OUT AT A THOUSAND FEET, ANTON EXPECTED THE JUNKERS TO HIT THE AIRCRAFT WITH ANOTHER BURST. BUT IT HAD RETURNED TO THE CLOUDS.

PROBABLY THE DIVE WAS TOO STEEP FOR THE PILOT TO FOLLOW. HE'LL FEEL SAFER IN THE CLOUDS, ANYWAY.

THE ENGINE KEPT SPLUTTERING AND BANGING, ITS TEMPERATURE RISING ALARMINGLY AS ANTON RACED BACK TOWARDS THE AIRFIELD, HOPING TO SAVE THE WOUNDED INSTRUCTOR'S LIFE.

AIRFIELD IN SIGHT NOW. CAN RISK SHUTTING OFF AND GLIDING IN.

KEEPING CALM, HE MADE THE BEST LANDING OF HIS LIFE.

MUSTN'T CAUSE NIGEL ANY UNNECESSARY PAIN.

THE C.O. AND THE CHIEF FLYING INSTRUCTOR WERE THERE TO CONGRATULATE HIM. BUT NIGEL DIED WHILE BEING LIFTED FROM THE AIRCRAFT.

TOO BAD, OLD CHAP. YOU DID YOUR BEST.

YES, PERFECT THREE POINTER. COULDN'T HAVE DONE BETTER MYSELF.

ELSEWHERE, FLYING IN A SPITFIRE SQUADRON OVER SOUTHERN ENGLAND, HIS OLD COMRADES JOSEF BALBIN AND JAN JILMECK WERE FIGHTING IN THE BATTLE OF BRITAIN.

BREAK, JOSEF, BREAK! HUN ON YOUR TAIL!

THE STORM OF TRACERS WHIPPING PAST JOSEF'S AIRCRAFT SUDDENLY CEASED WHEN THERE WAS A VIOLENT EXPLOSION BEHIND HIM.

YOU CAN RELAX, JOSEF. I GOT HIM!

THANKS, JAN! BUT — RELAX . . . ?

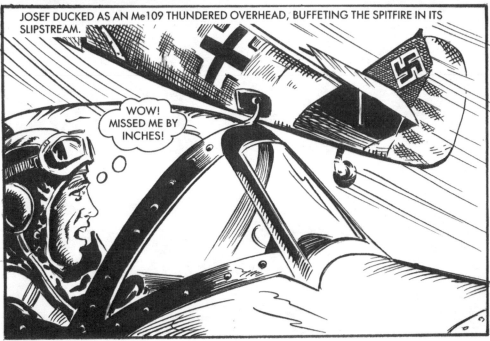

THE MESSERSCHMITT WENT INTO A DEATH DIVE, ITS PILOT TRAPPED IN THE COCKPIT.

RETURN TO BASE, CHICKWEED SQUADRON. WELL DONE, YOU CZECHS!

WELL DONE, INDEED! JAN AND I GOT OUR FIRST KILLS.

THAT SAME WEEK ANTON AND JIMMY WERE GIVEN WEEKEND PASSES TO LONDON. THEY WERE SITTING IN A CAFÉ WHEN THERE WAS A SHOUT FROM BEHIND THEM.

HEY, IT'S THE RED BARON!

THEY SEEM TO KNOW YOU.

JOSEF AND JAN — OLD COMRADES FROM CZECHOSLOVAKIA.

THE NEWCOMERS WERE STILL ELATED BY THEIR VICTORIES, WHICH THEY DESCRIBED IN VIVID DETAIL.

. . . BUT HEY, NO WINGS YET, RED BARON? I THOUGHT YOU'D HAVE YOUR OWN FLYING CIRCUS BY NOW.

HE'S GOING SOLO NEXT WEEK. NO PROBLEM.

IT WAS A LIE, OF COURSE, BUT JIMMY HAD BEEN ANGERED BY JAN'S BOISTEROUS TEASING.

GOOD LUCK THEN, ANTON!

HE'LL NEED IT. AND SO WILL ANYBODY ELSE IN THE VICINITY . . . BUT WE'D BETTER GO! TIME FOR OUR TRAIN.

ANTON AND JIMMY FOLLOWED THEM OUTSIDE AND CAUGHT A TAXI.

FOR TWO PINS I'D HAVE BOPPED THAT BUFFOON.

OH, JAN JILMECK'S OKAY REALLY. BUT I MUST SAY I ENVY THE PAIR OF THEM.

STRANGELY ENOUGH, ANTON DID GO SOLO A COUPLE OF WEEKS LATER — AND WITHOUT INCIDENT.

I WAS SO ENVIOUS OF THAT PAIR I WORKED HARDER THAN EVER — MUST'VE IMPRESSED MY INSTRUCTOR!

HIS CONFIDENCE INCREASED IN LEAPS AND BOUNDS AS HE GRADUATED TO ADVANCED TRAINING. SOON HE WAS NO LONGER THE LAST MAN ON HIS COURSE.

THIS IS FANTASTIC! THIS IS WHAT IT'S ALL ABOUT!

ANTON COULDN'T BELIEVE HIS EYES WHEN THE POSTINGS WENT UP.

WE'RE BOTH GOING TO FIGHTER TRAINING, ANTON!

REALLY? I MUST'VE MADE IT BY THE SKIN OF MY TEETH!

RECEIVING HIS WINGS HAD BEEN THE PROUDEST MOMENT OF ANTON'S LIFE. BUT TURNING UP AT HIS FIRST FIGHTER SQUADRON WAS ALMOST AS THRILLING.

RICHTHOFEN, EH? I'LL CERTAINLY EXPECT GREAT THINGS OF YOU!

GREAT THINGS, HOWEVER, WERE SLOW TO COME. ANTON'S FORMATION FLYING WASN'T EXACTLY IN THE TOP BRACKET FOR A START.

FOR PETE'S SAKE, RICHTHOFEN, GET YOUR WINGTIP OUT OF MY EARHOLE!

S-SORRY!

IN THE TWISTING DOG-FIGHTS, ANTON COULD NEVER KEEP A GERMAN IN HIS SIGHTS FOR ANY LENGTH OF TIME.

STAY STILL, YOU FOOL! I WANT TO HIT YOU!

AND OFTEN HE WAS TAKEN BY SURPRISE BY MORE EXPERIENCED ENEMY PILOTS.

BREAK, BLUE TWO! BREAK!

I DIDN'T SEE THAT MESSERSCHMITT ON MY TAIL . . .

ANTON CONGRATULATED HIS FRIEND ON HIS VICTORY BUT WAS SUNK IN GLOOM WHENEVER HE CONSIDERED HIS OWN PERFORMANCE.

GERMANS THREE . . . ME NIL. I'LL NEVER HAVE ANY SUCCESS AS A FIGHTER PILOT.

NONSENSE, ANTON. YOUR CHANCE WILL COME.

ONE DAY, SEPARATED AFTER A DOG-FIGHT, ANTON DROPPED THROUGH SOME CLOUD OVER SOUTHERN ENGLAND TO GET HIS BEARINGS.

THAT'S ASHFORD. I STEER NORTH EAST FROM THERE.

THE SPITFIRE SHUDDERED ON THE VERGE OF A HIGH SPEED STALL AS ANTON TIGHTENED AND TIGHTENED THE TURN.

HE'S TIGHTENING HIS TURN AS WELL! AND WHERE'S THE THIRD ONE? HE'LL BE LINING UP FOR A POT AT ME.

SUDDENLY, THE GERMAN FELL OUT OF THE TURN AND, SEIZING HIS CHANCE, ANTON SHOVED THE STICK FORWARD AND ZOOMED AFTER HIM.

HE'S HAD IT! THAT DAMAGED WING'S BREAKING OFF!

BUT ANTON'S BROWNINGS REMAINED SILENT — AND THE GERMAN ROLLED INTO A SPLIT-S AND DIVED OUT OF THE BATTLE.

THE SERGEANTS WERE INVITED INTO THE OFFICERS' MESS THAT NIGHT TO CELEBRATE ANTON'S TRIUMPHS . . . IT WAS ONE OF THE MOST POPULAR EVENTS IN THE SQUADRON FOR, IN A WAY, ANTON HAD BECOME A SQUADRON MASCOT.

THE C.O. ARRIVED IN THE MIDDLE OF IT ALL WITH NEWS THAT SET THE PILOTS CHEERING EVEN LOUDER.

INTELLIGENCE SAY THAT THE STRIPE-NOSED BLIGHTERS ANTON SHOT DOWN BELONG TO A CRACK SQUADRON. ALL TOP PILOTS!

FROM THAT DAY ON, ANTON'S CONFIDENCE GREW AND WITH IT HIS SUCCESS. FOUR MORE PLANES FELL TO HIS GUNS.

RED BARON SIX — GERMANS THREE!

BUT THE SQUADRON'S CASUALTIES MOUNTED STEADILY. "B" FLIGHT COMMANDER WAS KILLED AND MANY OTHER EXPERIENCED PILOTS DISAPPEARED.

TUBBY WALES WON'T PLAY THE PIANO WITH A PINT POT ON HIS HEAD ANY MORE!

THEY WERE SAD BUT EXCITING DAYS.

DUE TO A LACK OF EXPERIENCED OFFICERS, SERGEANT PILOTS OFTEN LED THEIR FLIGHTS INTO BATTLE, ANTON AND JIMMY GETTING THEIR CHANCE AS WELL.

TALLY HO, TALLY HO . . . BANDITS SIX O'CLOCK BELOW! FOLLOW ME!

FOLLOW THE RED BARON!

THE C.O. CALLED ANTON AND JIMMY INTO HIS OFFICE ONE DAY.

I'M RECOMMENDING YOU TWO FOR COMMISSIONS. YOU'VE BOTH SHOWN YOU CAN HANDLE A FLIGHT IN BATTLE EXTREMELY WELL.

THANK YOU, SIR.

SOON AFTERWARDS, THE SQUADRON WAS WITHDRAWN FROM THE LINE AND SENT TO YORKSHIRE FOR A HARD-EARNED REST. BUT ALL THE TIME, ANTON FRETTED TO GET BACK INTO BATTLE.

WE'VE BEEN HERE LONG ENOUGH COOLING OUR HEELS!

WHO DO YOU THINK YOU ARE, MATE? THE RED BARON? ENJOY THE BREAK WHILE YOU CAN.

COMING IN AGAIN, ANTON SENT A STREAM OF BULLETS SMASHING INTO THE LOCOMOTIVE CAB. CLOUDS OF STEAM SHOT INTO THE AIR FROM THE ENGINE BEFORE IT BLEW UP WITH A ROAR AND TUMBLED DOWN THE EMBANKMENT, THE WAGONS TRAILING BEHIND.

ANTON'S TALLY ROSE TO EIGHT AND HE FOUND HIMSELF PROMOTED TO FLIGHT LIEUTENANT AND "B" FLIGHT COMMANDER. THE NAME RICHTHOFEN HAD A NEW DEADLY RING TO IT NOW.

THE RED BARON'S GOT ANOTHER!

I WONDER HOW MANY TIMES THEY SAID THAT IN WORLD WAR ONE?

ONCE AGAIN THE SQUADRON WAS RESTED IN THE NORTH. WHILE THEY WERE THERE, SOME REPLACEMENTS ARRIVED.

BALBIN AND JILMECK, BOTH TO "B" FLIGHT UNDER FLIGHT LIEUTENANT RICHTHOFEN. COOPER TO "A" FLIGHT.

RICHTHOFEN? NOT . . . ANTON RICHTHOFEN!

JAN WAS INCENSED WHEN HE LEARNED THAT HIS NEW FLIGHT COMMANDER WAS HIS FELLOW PUPIL FROM EARLY FLYING SCHOOL.

I REFUSE TO FLY UNDER HIM! I DEMAND A SWOP WITH COOPER!

YOU'LL GO WHERE YOU'RE TOLD!

I DO AS YOU SAY. BUT THIS SQUADRON MUST BE REALLY HARD UP FOR FLIGHT COMMANDERS!

SHUT UP, JAN!

ANTON WAS PLEASED TO WELCOME THEM TO "B" FLIGHT, BUT EVEN AFTER LEARNING THAT HIS FLIGHT COMMANDER HAD SHOT DOWN EIGHT PLANES, JAN WAS VERY FAR FROM HAPPY. HE IMAGINED THERE HAD TO BE SOME SORT OF TRICKERY SOMEWHERE.

I KNOW YOU, RICHTHOFEN . . . YOU'RE NO RED BARON! JUST DON'T EXPECT ME TO PULL YOUR COALS OUT OF THE FIRE.

COALS, JAN? YOU FLY A STEAM ENGINE?

KNOWING JAN OF OLD, ANTON WAS GOOD-NATUREDLY TOLERANT.

WHEN THE SQUADRON RETURNED SOUTH AGAIN, ONE OF THEIR FIRST OPS WAS TO ESCORT FLYING FORTRESS BOMBERS OVER FRANCE. ON THIS OCCASION ANTON WAS IN CHARGE OF THE WHOLE SQUADRON. ANOTHER SPITFIRE SQUADRON, PART OF THE ESCORT, HAD ALREADY BEEN LURED INTO BATTLE FURTHER BACK.

HUNS, THREE O'CLOCK HIGH! SHOULD MAKE THEIR MOVE ANY MINUTE!

WE SHOULD GO FOR THEM!

THE VOICE ON THE R/T WAS JAN JILMECK'S.

ANTON IGNORED HIM AS THREE Me109s PEELED OFF —

THEY'RE TRYING TO SPLIT US UP! YELLOW SECTION — GO GET 'EM! EVERYBODY ELSE STAY PUT!

ROGER, BARON!

THEN THE REST OF THE GERMANS CAME SCREAMING DOWN ON THEM — FOCKE WULF Fw 190s AND Me 109s, THE LATTER WITH BLACK AND WHITE STRIPED SPINNERS.

GREEN, GO FOR THOSE FOCKE WULFS — YELLOW, LINK UP IF YOU CAN!

CANNON AND MACHINE GUNS THUNDERED AS, OUTNUMBERED BY TWO TO ONE, THE SPITFIRES HURTLED INTO THE GERMANS IN A TAIL-CHASING WHIRLING MELEE.

OUR STRIPE-NOSED FRIENDS AGAIN! BUT THAT'S ONE LESS!

MORE GERMANS JOINED THE FRAY AND THINGS BEGAN TO GO BADLY FOR THE SPITFIRE PILOTS FIGHTING VALIANTLY TO KEEP THEM AWAY FROM THE FORTS.

DIE, BRITISHER!

THE HEAVILY ARMED FORTRESSES HELD THEIR OWN.

LOUSY NAZI! GOTCHA!

ANTON'S SQUADRON LOST FIVE AIRCRAFT IN THE BATTLE. LATER JAN WAS MOROSE AND MOODY, BLAMING IT ALL ON ANTON.

THAT FOOL RICHTHOFEN HANDLED IT ALL WRONG.

NONSENSE, JAN! WHAT ELSE COULD HE DO . . . ONLY TWELVE OF US AGAINST THAT HORDE? AND THEY GOT REINFORCEMENTS.

THE FOLLOWING WEEK, WHILE ON A TWO PLANE SORTIE OVER FRANCE, ANTON AND JAN WERE BOUNCED BY FIVE FOCKE WULFS.

STAY CLOSE, JAN — AND KEEP CALM. WE'LL GET OUT OF THIS!

KEEP CALM, HE TELLS ME! HE FORGETS I USED TO WATCH THOSE PANICKY LANDINGS OF HIS!

WRENCHING HIS AIRCRAFT ALL OVER THE SKY, WITH JAN HARD PUT TO STAY WITH HIM, ANTON PROVED SUPERIOR TO THE GERMAN PILOTS AND SOON TURNED THE TABLES.

WHERE DID HE LEARN TO FLY LIKE THIS? THAT'S THE SECOND ONE HE'S SHOT DOWN!

THE BATTLE DROPPED LOWER AND LOWER, AND WHEN ANTON SHOT DOWN A THIRD GERMAN, THE REMAINDER DECIDED THEY'D HAD ENOUGH.

ACHTUNG! RETURN TO BASE!

JA! THESE SPITFIRE PILOTS ARE A HANDFUL!

AS THEY THUNDERED AT LOW LEVEL ACROSS THE ENGLISH CHANNEL, JAN WAS ALMOST — BUT NOT QUITE — SPEECHLESS. FOR THE FIRST TIME IN HIS LIFE HE REALISED THAT ANTON WAS A TOP CLASS PILOT, MUCH BETTER THAN HE'D EVER BE.

YOU TRULY ARE THE RED BARON, ANTON. WHERE DID YOU LEARN ALL THAT?

JUST CALL ME A LATE DEVELOPER, JAN.

FROM THAT DAY ON, JAN PUT ANTON UP ON A PEDESTAL.

TWO WEEKS LATER, ANTON WAS CALLED INTO THE STATION COMMANDER'S OFFICE AND TOLD HE HAD BEEN CHOSEN TO FORM A NEW SQUADRON.

. . . MANY OF THE PILOTS WILL BE FROM YOUR OWN PART OF THE WORLD.

THANK YOU, SIR. I'M HONOURED.

AS THEIR SCORE MOUNTED TO IMPRESSIVE HEIGHTS ANTON'S PILOTS ADOPTED A SWAGGER AND BEGAN CALLING THEMSELVES RICHTHOFEN'S FLYING CIRCUS — SOMETHING THE NEWSPAPERS PICKED UP ON.

THE RED BARON FLIES AGAIN—THIS TIME FOR BRITAIN

OH, NO . . . LOOK AT THIS!

WHAT'S WRONG WITH THAT, BARON? YOU'RE FAMOUS — AS YOU SHOULD BE!

ANNOYED AT FIRST, THE TOP BRASS AT FIGHTER COMMAND H.Q. SUDDENLY REALISED THE GREAT PROPAGANDA OPPORTUNITY AND BEGAN MILKING IT FOR ALL IT WAS WORTH. LUFTWAFFE HIGH COMMAND SOON GOT WIND OF IT.

GOERING IS FURIOUS ABOUT THIS ENGLISH PROPOGANDA. IT IS AN INSULT . . . HE WANTS THESE IMPOSTERS DESTROYED. RED BARON INDEED!

JAWOHL, HERR GENERAL. IT SHALL BE DONE!

THE GERMANS PUT THEIR PLAN INTO OPERATION. A SQUADRON OF BOMBERS WITH FIGHTER ESCORTS WOULD ATTACK ANTON'S AIRFIELD, LURING THE "CIRCUS" INTO THE SKY TO ATTACK THEM — BUT FOLLOWING CLOSE BEHIND AT LOW LEVEL TO EVADE THE BRITISH RADAR WOULD BE A CRACK FIGHTER SQUADRON WITH MORE THAN ITS REGULAR COMPLEMENT OF AIRCRAFT.

THE SO-CALLED RED BARON AND HIS MEN ARE IN FOR A NASTY SHOCK!

WHEN THE GERMAN BOMBERS WERE SPOTTED APPROACHING THE COAST, THE FLYING CIRCUS WAS SCRAMBLED TO INTERCEPT.

CONTROL TO BARON SQUADRON. TWELVE JUNKERS EIGHTY-EIGHT BOMBERS WITH TWELVE FOCKE-WULFS HEADING FOR YOUR FIELD.

ROGER! TAKING A BIG CHANCE IN DAYLIGHT, AREN'T THEY?

ANTON WAS UNEASY — AND WHEN THE ENEMY APPEARED IN THE DISTANCE HE DECIDED TO SPLIT HIS FORCE.

JOSEF . . . ATTACK WITH YOUR FLIGHT. I'M GOING TO KEEP CLIMBING.

ROGER, ANTON. LIKE YOU, I THINK THEY'RE UP TO SOMETHING.

IT HAD BEEN QUITE A TIME SINCE THE GERMANS HAD SENT OVER SUCH A FORCE IN DAYLIGHT.

JOSEF AND HIS PILOTS, TOP MEN ALL, THUNDERED AMONGST THE ATTACKERS, ONE HALF TAKING ON THE FIGHTERS, THE OTHERS SPLITTING UP THE BOMBERS.

TAKE THAT, NAZI DOGS!

FIVE GERMANS DISAPPEARED WITHIN SECONDS, THE GERMAN SQUADRON COMMANDER SHOUTING FRANTICALLY AS HIS FORCE WAS CHASED ALL OVER THE SKY . . .

STAY IN YOUR SECTIONS . . . STAY CLOSE! DON'T SPLIT UP!

. . . BUT HIS ORDERS WERE IN VAIN. THE GERMANS WERE TOO BADLY DISPERSED TO FORM A COHESIVE FORCE.

SUDDENLY HE SPOTTED A SPITFIRE BANKING TOWARDS HIM. UNKNOWN TO HIM IT WAS ANTON, THE MAN HE'D BRAGGED ABOUT DESTROYING IF THEY EVER CAME FACE TO FACE.

BRITISH SCHWEIN! IT'S A WOODEN BOX FOR YOU — IF THEY EVER FIND THE PIECES.

GUNS HAMMERING FURIOUSLY, THE TWO AIRCRAFT SCREAMED TOWARDS EACH OTHER, NEITHER PILOT GIVING WAY.

LET'S SEE WHOSE NERVE BREAKS FIRST, NAZI!

THE GERMAN BROKE FIRST — WHICH COST HIM DEARLY. A SLIGHT TOUCH ON THE RUDDER BAR AND STICK AND ANTON HAD THE GERMAN'S UNDERSIDE IN HIS SIGHTS.

HIT HIM . . . BUT NOWHERE VITAL PERHAPS. HE'S STILL FLYING!

THE GERMAN COMMANDER CAME ROUND AGAIN ON TO ANTON'S TAIL, BUT ANTON THREW HIM OFF EASILY.

. . . AGGRESSIVE TOO. BUT NOW IT'S MY TURN!

MESSERSCHMITT BF110

SPEED 550 km/h (342 mph)
CEILING 26,000 feet
RANGE 2100 km

ARMAMENT — TWO 30mm AND TWO 20mm CANNON IN NOSE,
TWO 7.9mm MACHINE GUNS IN REAR COCKPIT

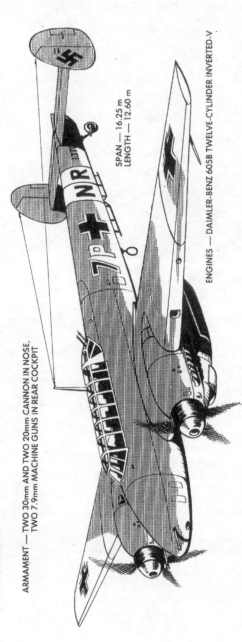

SPAN — 16.25 m
LENGTH — 12.60 m

ENGINES — DAIMLER-BENZ 605B TWELVE-CYLINDER INVERTED-V

THE Me110 was designed as a long-range escort fighter, but first went into action as a ground support plane during the invasion of Poland in 1939.

Not really meeting any opposition until the Battle of Britain, the Me110 then found itself hard pressed to protect itself, let alone the bomber formations which depended on it to keep the deadly Spitfires and Hurricanes at bay.

When the Me210 was withdrawn from production because of accidents, it was the Me110 which was flung in to bolster up Germany's fighter strength.

Used as a night-fighter, its numbers were again increased as the R.A.F built up their bomber offensive on Germany, and even the American day-bombers ran into opposition from this plane.

Although fast, it was sluggish in answering the controls and not easily manoeuvred. Thus it became rather easy meat for Allied single-seat fighters. As a long-range escort fighter it was a failure, soon just another shattered dream of Nazi Germany.

"SQUADRON- SCRAMBLE!"

IN EARLY 1940, DURING THE SO-CALLED "PHONEY WAR", R.A.F. PILOT OFFICERS LUKE FARMAN AND COLIN "MOOSE" BELL JOINED A HURRICANE FIGHTER SQUADRON BASED IN FRANCE, IN ANTICIPATION OF THE GERMAN BLITZKRIEG THEY ALL KNEW WOULD COME SOON.

LUKE AND MOOSE WERE CLOSE FRIENDS WHO HAD TRAINED TOGETHER. MOOSE, A FORMER CANADIAN LUMBERJACK, WOULD NEVER HAVE PASSED HIS WRITTEN EXAMS WITHOUT THE COACHING LUKE HAD GIVEN HIM EACH EVENING.

WOW, LUKE! FANCY THE C.O. LETTING US OFF THE LEASH, LIKE THIS.

YES. BEING A NEW BOY I'D EXPECT TO FLY A FEW TIMES WITH A SENIOR PILOT.

THE SQUADRON-LEADER, JOCK MATHESON, WAS A HARD TASK-MASTER WHO LED FROM THE FRONT. HE HAD A SURPRISE IN STORE FOR THE NEW PILOTS.

I MUST SHOCK THEM INTO LEARNING FAST WHAT WE LEARNT PAINFULLY IN COMBAT.

AS THE TWO HURRICANES CLIMBED OUT OF VIEW, JOCK CHANGED INTO FLYING GEAR THEN TOOK OFF IN HIS OWN PLANE.

THE CANADIAN WAS AS STRONG AS HIS NICKNAME IMPLIED,
BUT HIS REACTIONS WEREN'T AS SHARP AS LUKE'S.

LUKE'S SUDDEN MANOEUVRE BROUGHT HIM IN BEHIND HIS FRIEND.

AFTER THE FILM SHOWING, JOCK SPOKE TO THE NEWCOMERS OVER A DRINK.

WHEW! SO YOU STALKED US FOR TEN MINUTES AND WE NEVER SAW YOU?

RIGHT. ALL OUR CASUALTIES TO DATE WERE SURPRISED. THEY NEVER KNEW WHAT HIT THEM.

MOOSE FELT THAT THE C.O. HAD PLAYED UNFAIRLY BY NOT WARNING THEM BEFORE THE EXERCISE. LUKE DISAGREED.

NONSENSE, MOOSE! WE WERE SO ENGROSSED THAT WE FORGOT TO KEEP A LOOK OUT.

SO IT'S THE JERRY YOU DON'T SEE WHO KILLS YOU!

JOCK HAD TAUGHT THE YOUNG PILOTS A LESSON THEY WOULD NEVER FORGET.

THAT SAME EVENING, TWO-HUNDRED MILES AWAY IN GERMANY, HAUPTMANN KURT BAUER, C.O. OF A JUNKERS 87 DIVE-BOMBING SQUADRON, WAS BRIEFING HIS PILOTS.

REMEMBER, GENTLEMEN, WE STUKA PILOTS ARE THE ELITE OF THE LUFTWAFFE — TOMORROW WE ATTACK FRANCE.

HE'S RIGHT. IT WAS THE STUKAS AND PANZERS TOGETHER WHICH DEFEATED POLAND IN THREE WEEKS.

BAUER WAS ONE OF THE CONDOR LEGION VETERANS WHO HAD TESTED AND DEVELOPED THE DIVE-BOMBER IN ACTION DURING THE SPANISH CIVIL WAR.

TO THE GREATEST WEAPON OF MODERN WAR, GENTLEMEN — THE JUNKERS EIGHTY-SEVEN — AND VICTORY!

FRANZ, BOASTFUL BY NATURE, WAS SOON SHOWING OFF, DODGING BETWEEN THE AIRSTRIP BUILDINGS.

LOOK AT THAT, OTTO. FRANZ IS A GREAT PILOT.

I THINK HE'S A GREAT IDIOT!

OTTO AND FRANZ SHARED A TENT AT THE CAMP.

THAT STUNT-LANDING WON ME TEN MARKS IN BETS.

YOU'RE MAD TO SHOW OFF AND RISK YOUR NECK FOR THAT!

ON THE LAST DAY OF THEIR COURSE THEIR INSTRUCTOR TOLD THEM TO FLY A DUAL GLIDER AND SEE HOW HIGH THEY COULD CLIMB.

FLY HALF AN HOUR EACH AS PILOT.

TAILS — YOU FLY FIRST.

THE COURSE ENDED THE NEXT DAY, AND AS OTTO, FRANZ AND THE OTHERS DEPARTED,
THEY SAW THE SAME DUAL GLIDER COMING IN TO LAND, SHEDDING A WING.

ON 10th MAY, 1940, OTTO AND FRANZ TOOK OFF SHORTLY AFTER DAWN ON THEIR FIRST OPERATION, A SURPRISE ATTACK ON A DUTCH CITY.

A GLORIOUS SIGHT!

SOMEONE'S GOING TO HAVE A NASTY SHOCK!

STRONGLY ESCORTED BY Me109s AND Me110s, THE STUKAS BOMBED AN UNDEFENDED CITY WITHOUT A SHOT BEING FIRED AT THEM.

THIS ISN'T WAR, IT'S MURDER!

OTTO KEPT HIS THOUGHTS TO HIMSELF — JUST AS WELL IN THE FANATICAL NAZI CLIMATE OF THE DAY.

IN THE NEXT FEW DAYS LUKE AND MOOSE WERE CONSTANTLY ENGAGED IN FIERCE BATTLES AGAINST THE LUFTWAFFE'S FIGHTERS. THEY QUICKLY LEARNED THAT A HURRICANE COULD TURN INSIDE AN Me109, BUT COULDN'T MATCH IT FOR SPEED OR CLIMB.

THEY COULD EASILY OUT-MANOEUVRE THE CLUMSY Me110, BUT WOE BETIDE ANYONE CAUGHT IN ITS MASSIVE FIRE-POWER.

THE CRY OF "SQUADRON — SCRAMBLE!" BECAME A MONOTONOUS AND STOMACH-CHURNING SOUND TO THEM.

LUKE PROVED TO BE A NATURAL FIGHTER PILOT, SWIFT AND DEADLY IN ATTACK, QUICKSILVER ELUSIVE IN DEFENCE.

ALERT TO DANGER FROM BEHIND, LUKE SAW AN AVENGING Me109 IN HIS MIRROR. THROTTLING BACK, HE PULLED INTO A CLIMBING TURN.

LUKE LOST SPEED TO BRING HIMSELF IN CLOSE BEHIND HIS OPPONENT. A LETHAL BURST DENIED THE GERMAN PILOT THE CHANCE TO USE HIS SUPERIOR SPEED.

NO, YOU DON'T, JERRY.

THAT DAY'S SUCCESSES BROUGHT LUKE'S TOTAL TO SIX ENEMY AIRCRAFT DESTROYED.

THAT'S THREE YOU'VE SHOT OFF MOOSE'S TAIL. I RECKON YOU USE HIM AS BAIT.

NOT AT ALL. THE EASIEST NAZI TO KILL IS ONE WHO'S CONCENTRATING ON KILLING ONE OF US.

WITHOUT REALISING IT, LUKE HAD BEEN SHELTERING MOOSE.

LUKE'S GOT A POINT. A JERRY WHO'S AIMING IS NOT KEEPING A CAREFUL LOOKOUT.

AND LUKE SHOOTS DOWN ONE JERRY AND SAVES ONE OF US. CLEVER LAD!

AFTER A WEEK JOCK AND LUKE WERE JOINT TOP SCORERS WITH SIX VICTORIES EACH, BUT SEVERAL PILOTS HAD BEEN LOST.

SEVEN NEW PILOTS ARE DUE TONIGHT. TOMORROW WE LICK THEM INTO SHAPE.

THEN OPS AGAIN THE DAY AFTER?

BY THIS TIME THE GERMANS WERE ADVANCING RAPIDLY ACROSS FRANCE AND BELGIUM. HOLLAND HAD ALREADY SURRENDERED AND KURT BAUER'S Ju87s WERE SUPPORTING THE ARMY'S SPEARHEADING PANZERS.

SUCH OPERATIONS WERE VERY DANGEROUS FOR THE DIVE-BOMBER PILOTS, HOWEVER. HURRICANES OFTEN BROKE THROUGH THE ESCORTING FIGHTERS AND THE Ju87 WAS NO MATCH FOR THEM.

KEEP A GOOD LOOK OUT FOR FIGHTERS, MAX. THIS IS THE DANGEROUS TIME.

JAWOHL, HERR FECKLER.

MAX KLEIN, JUST TURNED EIGHTEEN, WAS OTTO'S REAR GUNNER.

HEADING FOR THE STUKAS WERE JOCK MATHESON'S HURRICANES, WITH LUKE NOW LEADING BLUE SECTION.

BLUE SECTION. TAKE ON THE STUKAS WHILE I OCCUPY THE ESCORTS.

WILCO. BLUE SECTION, FOLLOW ME.

LUKE'S SECTION COMPRISING OF HIMSELF, MOOSE AND A NEW PILOT, SERGEANT "BANDY" LEGGE, SPREAD OUT TO ATTACK.

TALLY-HO! CHOOSE YOUR TARGETS.

IN THE INITIAL ATTACK ALL THREE PILOTS CLAIMED A VICTIM. FOR MOOSE AND BANDY THIS WAS THEIR FIRST VICTORY.

NOW FOR NUMBER TWO.

AS THE ENGLISH WOULD SAY, I'VE BROKEN MY DUCK AT LAST!

OTTO WAS ON THE POINT OF STARTING HIS BOMBING
RUN WHEN LUKE BORED IN FROM ASTERN.

ENEMY FIGHTER COMING IN FAST FROM BEHIND.

HOLD TIGHT, MAX. ABOUT TO DIVE.

AS ALL THIS WAS UNFOLDING, A VOICE CRACKLED IN LUKE'S EAR AS ONE OF THE GUNNERS
HIT BANDY'S ENGINE.

LEADER FROM THREE. I'VE A BAD GLYCOL LEAK.

HEAD FOR HOME, NUMBER THREE. WATCH YOUR OIL TEMP!

OTTO, UNAWARE OF EVENTS BEHIND HIM, LINED UP ON A BATTERY OF BRITISH ARTILLERY BELOW.

BOMBS GONE, MAX. LET'S HEAD FOR HOME.

HIMMEL! HE MUST HAVE MISSED BY CENTIMETRES!

OTTO HEADED FOR HOME FLYING LOW, BUT AFTER SOME MINUTES THE AIRCRAFT STARTED TO JUDDER.

THIS ENGINE SOUNDS A BIT ROPEY, MAX.

MUST HAVE BEEN HIT BY THE FLAK.

SUDDENLY THE ENGINE SEIZED SOLID.

HOLD TIGHT, I'LL HAVE TO LAND STRAIGHT AHEAD.

THE BOMBER'S FIXED UNDERCARRIAGE CAUGHT IN A DITCH, FLINGING IT ON TO ITS BACK AND KNOCKING OTTO UNCONSCIOUS. MAX, UNHURT, DRAGGED HIM CLEAR.

HE'S ONLY KNOCKED HIMSELF OUT!

A NEW DANGER WAS EMERGING, THOUGH, IN THE SHAPE OF SOME ANGRY BELGIAN FARM-WORKERS WHO HAD SEEN THE STUKA CRASH LAND.

LET'S STRING THE BOCHES UP!

YES, COME ON! THEY KILLED MY SISTER AND ONE OF HER KIDS YESTERDAY.

A SHOT FROM OTTO THREW EARTH INTO ONE OF THE BELGIANS' EYES DISCOURAGING ANY FURTHER ADVANCE.

DO YOU THINK THEY'RE GIVING UP?

I DOUBT IT. MY GUESS IS HE'S GOING FOR HELP.

OTTO WAS RIGHT. SOME MINUTES LATER REINFORCEMENTS ARRIVED AND THE BELGIANS ADVANCED AGAIN.

I HAVE FIVE. LET'S HOLD FIRE UNTIL THEY'RE REALLY CLOSE.

I'M DOWN TO MY LAST THREE CARTRIDGES.

MUCH TO THEIR RELIEF, THE TIMELY ARRIVAL OF SOME GERMAN ARMOUR PUT AN END TO THE SIEGE.

THANKS, MAX. YOU SAVED MY LIFE.

DON'T THANK ME. I DIDN'T FANCY BEING HANGED ON A CONVENIENT TREE.

WHEN OTTO ARRIVED BACK AT HIS BASE THAT EVENING A GLOOMY KURT BAUER GREETED HIM.

THANK GOODNESS YOU'RE SAFE, OTTO. IT'S BEEN A BAD DAY.

WE LOST FOUR AIRCRAFT AND CREWS PLUS THE KITE YOU WROTE OFF.

THIS WAS THE FIRST TIME THE STUKA SQUADRON HAD SUFFERED HEAVY CASUALTIES. OPERATIONS OVER POLAND AND HOLLAND HAD BEEN A WALK-OVER IN COMPARISON.

THERE'S ONE BRIGHT SPOT, HERR HAUPTMANN. I UNDERSTAND FRANZ SHOT DOWN A HURRICANE.

HOT AIR! NO ONE SAW IT EXCEPT FRANZ, NOT EVEN HIS GUNNER!

THE MOOD WAS VERY DIFFERENT IN JOCK'S HURRICANE SQUADRON'S MESS. IT HAD BEEN A GOOD DAY WITH THE PILOTS CLAIMING FOUR Ju87s AND THREE Me109s.

IT'S A PITY THAT YOUNG LEGGE KILLED HIMSELF DOING A FORCED LANDING.

PARTICULARLY AFTER SHOOTING DOWN A STUKA ON HIS FIRST OP. MOOSE HAS SCORED A SINGLE AT LAST, THOUGH.

MOOSE CELEBRATED HIS FIRST VICTORY IN STYLE.

JUBILATION DIDN'T LAST LONG, THOUGH, AS THE NAZI ADVANCE CONTINUED UNABATED.

MY MOTTO'S "STICK TO LUKE AND STAY ALIVE!". YOU'VE GOT DANGER WHISKERS IN THE BACK OF YOUR HEAD.

LEAVE OFF, IT'S JUST DOWN TO CONSTANT VIGILANCE!

GERMAN ARMOUR WILL SOON OVERRUN OUR AIRFIELDS SO WE ARE FLYING BACK TO ENGLAND TODAY.

WE'LL CARRY ON THE FIGHT FROM THERE.

IN FACT JOCK'S SQUADRON FLEW STRAIGHT UP TO SCOTLAND TO REST AND TRAIN NEW PILOTS FOR THE BATTLES TO COME AS FRANCE FELL AND THE BRITISH EXPEDITIONARY FORCE WAS EVACUATED FROM DUNKIRK.

CLOSE UP! LET'S SHOW JERRY WE'RE FAR FROM BEATEN!

JOCK NOW HAD THE CHANCE TO REBUILD HIS SQUADRON AFTER THE LOSSES SUFFERED IN FRANCE. HIS FIRST MOVE WAS TO PROMOTE LUKE TO FLIGHT-LIEUTENANT.

YOU'LL TAKE OVER "A" FLIGHT WITH MOOSE AS BLUE SECTION LEADER.

THANK YOU, SIR. MOOSE DESERVES IT FOR HAVING KNOCKED DOWN FOUR STUKAS.

IN GERMAN-OCCUPIED FRANCE, KURT BAUER, NOW A MAJOR, ALSO HAD HIS PROBLEMS. HE HAD LOST MANY OF HIS EXPERIENCED CREWS.

OTTO, I'M MAKING YOU MY SECOND-IN-COMMAND TO HELP ME LICK OUR NEW LADS INTO SHAPE.

FRANZ WON'T LIKE THIS.

FRANZ IMPRESSED KURT ONLY WITH HIS STUPIDITY.

NEXT DAY THE STUKAS OPENED THE ASSAULT, THEIR TARGET THE COASTAL RADAR STATIONS.

ONCE WE OF THE LUFTWAFFE GAIN MASTERY OF THE AIR, THE SEABORNE ASSAULT CAN COMMENCE.

THE THREATENED RADAR STATIONS HAD ALREADY DETECTED THE Ju87s, AND THEIR FIGHTER ESCORT FORMING UP OVER FRANCE.

GINGER SQUADRON, SCRAMBLE! CLIMB TO ANGELS SIX.

JOCK'S SQUADRON, CODE-NAME GINGER, WAS NOW STATIONED IN SOUTHERN ENGLAND, IN THE FRONT LINE AGAIN, UP TO STRENGTH AND AT IMMEDIATE READINESS.

ANOTHER COASTAL CONVOY, I SUPPOSE.

BUT BEFORE JOCK'S HURRICANES COULD INTERCEPT, KURT'S Ju87s WERE DIVING ON THEIR TARGETS.

SMACK ON — WUNDERBAR!

GINGER SQUADRON CAUGHT THE STUKAS JUST AS THEY WERE REFORMING. MOOSE QUICKLY LATCHED ON TO FRANZ'S TAIL, STITCHING THE COCKPIT AND KILLING THE GUNNER.

HE'S BOUGHT IT, NOW FOR ANOTHER.

TEUFEL! I HOPE THIS PARACHUTE WORKS!

BUT BEFORE FRANZ HAD TIME TO THINK HE WAS CAPTURED BY THE HOME GUARD. TRUE TO FORM HE BLUSTERED IN HIS PASSABLE ENGLISH.

SOON YOU WILL ALL BE SHOT WHEN WE INVADE.

YOU'LL BE SHOT NOW IF YOU DON'T SHUT UP!

AFTER BEING INTERROGATED FRANZ WAS TAKEN TO A P.O.W. CAMP ALREADY HOUSING SEVERAL LUFTWAFFE AND KRIEGSMARINE PRISONERS.

WELCOME, KAMERAD. TELL US ALL THE LATEST NEWS.

THE INVASION WILL COME SOON AND WE WILL BE FREED. GENERALLEUTNANT BOHMBACH TOLD US SO YESTERDAY IN PERSON.

OVER THE NEXT FEW WEEKS THE Ju87s SUFFERED HEAVY LOSSES BUT OTTO AND MAX SURVIVED UNTIL THE DAY THEY ATTACKED DOVER.

FIGHTER COMING IN BEHIND, OTTO.

WHERE THE DEVIL ARE OUR ESCORTS?

THE HURRICANE WOUNDED MAX SERIOUSLY AND DAMAGED THE BOMBER'S
TAIL BEFORE ONE OF THE ESCORTING MESSERSCHMITTS DROVE IT OFF.

AAAGH . . .
I THINK I'M DONE FOR,
OTTO! I'M BLEEDING
PRETTY BADLY.

HOLD ON, MAX.
VERDAMMT . . . THERE'S
SOMETHING UP WITH
THE CONTROLS!

OTTO KNEW THEY HAD LITTLE CHANCE OF MAKING IT HOME
IN THE DAMAGED STUKA, AND IF THEY HAD TO DITCH MAX
WOULD CERTAINLY DIE. HE MADE A SNAP DECISION.

I'LL
LAND AT AN R.A.F.
AIRFIELD AND DESTROY THE
JUNKERS. MAX WILL GET HOSPITAL
TREATMENT AND I WON'T BE A
P.O.W. FOR LONG.

LUKE AND MOOSE ARRIVED ON THE SCENE JUST AS OTTO WAS ABOUT TO DESTROY HIS AIRCRAFT BY FIRING A FLARE INTO THE COCKPIT.

IN THE NICK OF TIME MOOSE KNOCKED OTTO TO THE GROUND, DISARMING HIM.

WITHIN A VERY SHORT TIME MAX WAS ON HIS WAY TO THE SICK-BAY.

DON'T WORRY. THEY'LL LOOK AFTER HIM.

THANK YOU. THAT'S WHAT I WANT MOST.

LUKE AND MOOSE TOOK OTTO TO THE GUARDROOM AND HANDED HIM OVER FOR SAFE KEEPING.

GIVE HIM SOME TEA, FLIGHT-SERGEANT, AND MAKE SURE YOU KEEP HIM SAFE.

DON'T YOU WORRY ABOUT THAT, SIR.

THE NEWSPAPERS HEARD THE STORY AND WERE ALLOWED TO PRINT IT AS BEING GOOD FOR MORALE.

GERMAN DIVE BOMBER CAPTURED INTACT

GERMAN DIVE

A STOLEN COPY OF ONE OF THE MORE SENSATIONAL PAPERS FOUND ITS WAY TO THE PRISON HUT WHERE FRANZ WAS HOUSED.

I KNOW OTTO FECKLER. HE WAS ALWAYS WET!

IT SAYS THAT THE JUNKERS WAS SCARCELY DAMAGED AND THAT THE R.A.F. HAVE REPAIRED IT.

FRANZ'S HATRED OF OTTO NOW VERGED ON MADNESS AND, SEEING A CHANCE TO GET EVEN WITH HIM, HE WENT TO SEE HAUPTMANN HORST WEISS, THE CAMP'S SENIOR GERMAN OFFICER.

WE WERE AT SCHOOL AND LATER TRAINED TOGETHER, HERR HAUPTMANN. HIS COURAGE WAS ALWAYS DOUBTFUL.

IT CERTAINLY LOOKS LIKE A CASE OF COWARDICE AND TREACHERY.

THE TWO OBERLEUTNANTS STILL FELT THAT OTTO SHOULD BE GIVEN A CHANCE TO EXONERATE HIMSELF, THOUGH.

IF HE DESTROYS THE CAPTURED AIRCRAFT I SAY WE SHOULD FORGET THE WHOLE THING.

WE'LL HELP HIM TO ESCAPE, THEN IT'S UP TO HIM.

RELUCTANTLY WEISS AGREED AND, WHEN THIS WAS KNOWN, OTTO FOUND SEVERAL HELPERS.

A MAN WORKING IN THE LATRINES LEFT THIS OLD JACKET SO I PINCHED IT.

ACCORDING TO THIS PAPER YOUR KITE IS STILL WHERE YOU LANDED.

THE CAMP COOKHOUSE WAS MANNED BY GERMAN OTHER RANK P.O.W.s SUPERVISED BY BRITISH ARMY COOKS. THIS GAVE OTTO AN IDEA.

THE LORRY PICKS UP PIG-SWILL FROM THE COOKHOUSE EVERY MORNING.

THAT CORPORAL'S NO BALL OF FIRE. I COULD HIDE IN THE WASHROOM, THEN CLIMB ABOARD UNSEEN.

NEXT MORNING OTTO WAITED IMPATIENTLY FOR THE PIG-SWILL LORRY TO ARRIVE.

IT'S LATE. I HOPE IT TURNS UP!

AT LAST THE TRUCK ARRIVED AND OTTO CLIMBED INTO THE BACK UNNOTICED.

THAT'S THE LOT NOW, BERT.

I'LL BE OFF THEN. SEE YOU TOMORROW.

SO FAR SO GOOD!

IT HAD BEEN EASY ENOUGH TO ESCAPE FROM THE CAMP, BUT WITHOUT MONEY OR PAPERS OTTO KNEW HE WAS UNLIKELY TO GET FAR. SURE ENOUGH HE SOON FOUND HIMSELF STUMBLING INTO AN IMPROVISED ROAD BLOCK MANNED BY THE HOME GUARD.

TOO LATE TO HIDE NOW. I'LL HAVE TO BLUFF IT OUT.

THE HOME GUARD, MANY OF THEM VETERANS FROM WORLD WAR ONE, WERE MUSTARD HOT AND ITCHING TO PROVE THEIR WORTH.

I'M A DUTCH SEAMAN. THIEVES ATTACKED ME AND STOLE MY MONEY AND PAPERS. MY SHIP LEFT WITHOUT ME.

A LIKELY STORY! I'M TAKING YOU IN FOR QUESTIONING.

REALISING THAT THE SERGEANT DIDN'T BELIEVE HIS STORY, OTTO MADE A RUN FOR IT.

THEY'RE ALL OLD MEN. THEY'RE PAST IT.

HALT OR WE FIRE!

BUT HE HAD UNDERESTIMATED THE VETERANS. THE SERGEANT SHOUTED A SECOND WARNING ONLY SECONDS BEFORE THE RIFLES FLAMED.

AAGH — MY LEG!

GOT HIM!

THE SERGEANT SENT FOR AN AMBULANCE AND OTTO WAS SOON IN HOSPITAL.

THIS MADE GOOD SENSE TO THE TWO PILOTS.

DON'T WORRY ABOUT THAT, JERRY. WE ALREADY HAD ONE STUKA FLYING BEFORE WE NABBED YOURS.

OTTO'S EXPLANATION SATISFIED THE I.O. WHO HAD ALREADY SUSPECTED THAT THE GERMAN PILOT MIGHT HAVE BEEN THE SUBJECT OF SOME UNOFFICIAL COURT.

AFTER OTTO'S ESCAPE THE PRISONERS' LOT BECAME A GREAT DEAL MORE AUSTERE. FRANZ COLLECTED MOST OF THE BLAME.

EVER SINCE OTTO ESCAPED IT'S BEEN NOTHING BUT ROLL-CALLS AND SEARCHES.

ALL THANKS TO THAT IDIOT STURM!

A FEW DAYS LATER MAJOR KURT BAUER, WHO HAD BEEN SHOT DOWN, ARRIVED AT THE CAMP AND REPLACED WEISS AS THE SENIOR GERMAN OFFICER.

YOU'LL WANT THIS ROOM, HERR MAJOR. I'LL CLEAR MY THINGS OUT AT ONCE.

JUST A MINUTE, WEISS. WHAT'S ALL THIS RUBBISH ABOUT OTTO FECKLER?

WHEN KURT HEARD THE WHOLE STORY HE WAS FURIOUS.

OTTO A COWARD? RIDICULOUS! YOU BELIEVED AN ARROGANT, BOASTFUL LIAR LIKE STURM? PARADE EVERYONE AT ONCE!

JAWOHL, HERR MAJOR.

KURT PUBLICLY REFUTED THE CHARGE THAT OTTO WAS A COWARD AND A TRAITOR. GERMAN INTELLIGENCE REPORTS CONFIRMED THAT HE WAS CAPTURED WHILE TRYING TO DESTROY HIS BADLY DAMAGED AIRCRAFT.

YOU HAVE BEEN MISLED BY AN UNRELIABLE LIAR AND BOASTER! LEUTNANT STURM, TAKE TWO PACES FORWARD.

KURT THEN SENTENCED FRANZ.

LEUTNANT FRANZ STURM IS TO BE UTTERLY IGNORED BY YOU ALL FOR FOUR WEEKS.

AFTER THE HUMILIATION OF THE PARADE, FRANZ SWITCHED HIS HATRED FROM OTTO ON TO KURT.

YOU CAN'T BELIEVE BAUER! HE'S ANOTHER TRAITOR!

GET IT INTO YOUR THICK SKULL. WE'RE NOT TALKING TO YOU!

FRANZ LISTENED OUTSIDE THE HUT. ALREADY AN IDEA WAS FORMING IN HIS DISARRANGED MIND.

I'LL LEAVE IT TO YOU THEN, CORPORAL.

THIS INJECTION WILL KNOCK HIM OUT UNTIL HE REACHES THE HOSPITAL.

FRANZ WAITED UNTIL THE CORPORAL WALKED ACROSS TO THE GUARDROOM TO PHONE FOR THE AMBULANCE. IT WAS THE P.O.W.s' LUNCHTIME. NO ONE WAS ABOUT

HURRIEDLY HE WRAPPED THE INJURED MAN'S BANDAGE ROUND HIS OWN HEAD AND BUNDLED HIS UNCONSCIOUS BODY UNDER THE BED.

I'LL SHOW THEM! I'LL ESCAPE AND FLY THE CAPTURED JUNKERS BACK TO FRANCE!

IT WAS A DESPICABLE ACT PULLED BY AN UNSCRUPULOUS RAT.

THE M.P. WARNED HIM THREE TIMES BEFORE FIRING.

SOON AFTER FRANZ'S DEATH THE BATTLE OF BRITAIN CAME TO AN END. THE LUFTWAFFE HAD BEEN FOILED AND NAZI HOPES OF INVADING ENGLAND HAD BEEN SHATTERED. JOCK, LUKE, AND MOOSE, WELL DECORATED ACES, SURVIVED TO FIGHT ON.

OTTO RETURNED TO THE PRISON CAMP AND HAD TO WAIT, LIKE THE OTHER LUFTWAFFE PRISONERS, NOT DAYS, NOT WEEKS, BUT FIVE MORE YEARS BEHIND BARBED WIRE BEFORE GERMANY'S FINAL DEFEAT RELEASED THEM.

Commando
THE END

HAWKER HURRICANE

Aircraft of the Second World War — No. 10

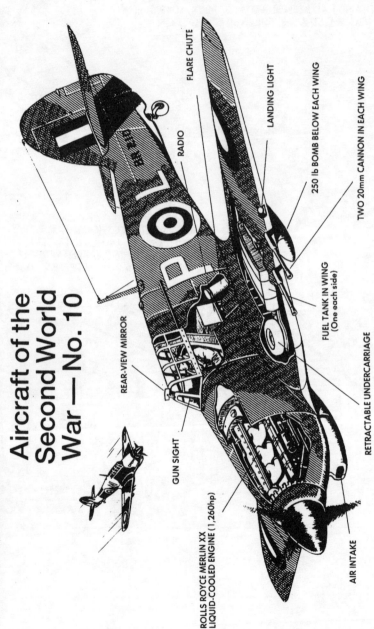

FLARE CHUTE

LANDING LIGHT

250 lb BOMB BELOW EACH WING

TWO 20mm CANNON IN EACH WING

RADIO

REAR-VIEW MIRROR

GUN SIGHT

ROLLS ROYCE MERLIN XX
LIQUID-COOLED ENGINE (1,260hp)

AIR INTAKE

RETRACTABLE UNDERCARRIAGE

FUEL TANK IN WING
(One each side)

THE famous "Hurri" was the first monoplane fighter used by the R.A.F. and the first British military aircraft capable of more than 300mph.

Together with the Spitfire it won the Battle Of Britain, then went on from there to serve in theatres of war all over the world. Many different versions were built. The Fleet Air Arm used it, one type had 40mm cannon below the wings for tank-busting, and it was also carried on a special catapult on merchant ships to protect convoys.

Total production of Hurricanes was 14,533.

A DEDICATED NAZI FROM A WELL-BORN FAMILY, HAUPTMANN OTTO MEITZEL PROWLED THE SKIES, EVER ALERT FOR A NEW TARGET. HE WAS AN AIR ACE, A BRILLIANT PILOT. HIS LUFTWAFFE COMRADES, ALTHOUGH ACKNOWLEDGING HIS SKILL AND COURAGE, DESPISED HIM FOR THE ARROGANT, COLD-EYED KILLER HE WAS. BUT MEITZEL CARED LITTLE FOR THEIR OPINION — ONLY ONE THING MATTERED TO HIM . . .

HIS DREAM WAS TO RECEIVE THE KNIGHT'S CROSS WITH OAK LEAVES AND SWORDS. HIS FATHER HAD WON THE COVETED AWARD IN THE FIRST WORLD WAR, AND HIS BROTHER HAD PAID FOR THE HONOUR IN THE NAZI'S FIRST SAVAGE ASSAULT ON POLAND WITH HIS LIFE.

NOW IT IS MY TURN. WHO CAN STOP ME? CERTAINLY NOT THESE ENGLANDERS.

ALREADY MANY R.A.F. PLANES HAD SHATTERED BEFORE THE STORMING FURY OF HIS GUNS.

HE RETURNED TO THE FIGHT, SELECTING A HURRICANE WHICH HAD BEEN CRIPPLED AND WAS SEEKING TO MOVE AWAY FROM THE ACTION. NOT FOR ONE MOMENT DID MEITZEL CONSIDER LETTING THE BRITISH PILOT ESCAPE.

THIS IS WAR. WITH HIS DEATH THERE WILL BE ONE LESS PILOT TO HARRY OUR BOMBERS.

IN HE BORED, POURING A DEADLY FIRE INTO THE HELPLESS HURRICANE.

UUURGH!

THE R.A.F. FLYER DIED IN THAT ONE SAVAGE ASSAULT.

DRAPED IN FLAMES, THE HURRI PLUNGED DOWN TO OBLIVION.

MEITZEL'S TALLY OF TWO FOR THE DAY SATISFIED HIM. HE FLEW HOME TO LAND AT HIS SQUADRON'S BASE IN FRANCE, FLUSHED WITH SUCCESS — YET AS SHARP-TONGUED AS EVER.

I WANT THE MAGNETOS CHECKED AND READY FOR ANOTHER TAKE-OFF WITHIN THE HOUR. I NEARLY MISSED AN ENGLANDER TODAY BECAUSE I LOST POWER!

WE SHALL DO OUR BEST . . .

THE CHIEF MECHANIC'S FACE TIGHTENED WITH ANGER, FOR HE AND HIS MEN HAD BEEN WORKING SINCE DAWN. THEY KNEW BETTER THOUGH THAN TO ARGUE WITH THE ARROGANT MEITZEL.

YOU WILL DO BETTER THAN THAT, OR I'LL HAVE YOUR HIDE! WE ARE FIGHTING A WAR UP THERE . . . YOU MERELY EAT AND DREAM OF HOME.

EYES GLINTED THEIR FURY AS THE NAZI STALKED OFF. ANGRY WORDS ESCAPED ONCE HE WAS OUT OF RANGE.

PUFFED-UP FOOL! HOW WOULD HE LIKE TO WRESTLE WITH AN ENGINE ON A FREEZING DAY?

EVEN SO, TAKE A LOOK AT HIS MAGNETO, FRITZ. THOUGH I BET THERE'S NOTHING WRONG WITH IT.

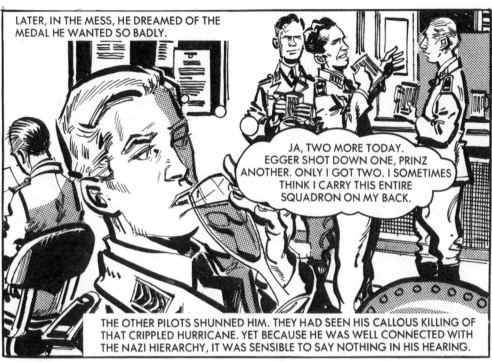

LATER, IN THE MESS, HE DREAMED OF THE MEDAL HE WANTED SO BADLY.

JA, TWO MORE TODAY. EGGER SHOT DOWN ONE, PRINZ ANOTHER. ONLY I GOT TWO. I SOMETIMES THINK I CARRY THIS ENTIRE SQUADRON ON MY BACK.

THE OTHER PILOTS SHUNNED HIM. THEY HAD SEEN HIS CALLOUS KILLING OF THAT CRIPPLED HURRICANE. YET BECAUSE HE WAS WELL CONNECTED WITH THE NAZI HIERARCHY, IT WAS SENSIBLE TO SAY NOTHING IN HIS HEARING.

NEXT DAY THE SQUADRON ESCORTED A CLOUD OF HEINKELS ON A DAYLIGHT RAID ON THE BRITISH PORTS. FOR MEITZEL IT MEANT A MARVELLOUS ELATION — THE ONLY TIME HE FELT REALLY ALIVE.

I SHALL STRIKE MORE ENGLANDERS FROM THE SKIES. THEN I WILL RECEIVE THE HONOUR I DESERVE.

MEANTIME, IN SOUTHERN ENGLAND, PILOT OFFICER ALBERT CRIBBEN WAITED AT DISPERSAL WITH THE OTHER PILOTS OF A SPITFIRE SQUADRON. TODAY WAS TO BE HIS FIRST OPERATIONAL SORTIE . . . HE FELT SCARED.

I DON'T KNOW HOW I'M GOING TO REACT WHEN SOME JERRY PLANE SQUIRTS HOT LEAD AT ME.

THEN, HEART THUMPING, HE HEARD THE ALARM KLAXON. HE RACED FOR HIS PLANE, THE DISTINCTIVE LION EMBLEM WHICH HAD BEEN HIS CHOICE OF MASCOT, GLEAMING ON IT.

LET'S GO TO IT, LADS! ALBERT, STAY CLOSE ON MY TAIL.

YOU BET, SIR!

THE CHEERY ENCOURAGEMENT FROM THE SQUADRON-LEADER, IAN GILCHRIST, HELPED CALM HIM AND ONCE IN HIS COCKPIT, SOME MORE OF HIS NERVES LEFT HIM.

ACTION FOLLOWED IN SECONDS. BLUE SECTION RIPPED INTO THE HEINKELS, GUNS FLAMING.

WOLF SECTION, DEFEND OUR BOMBERS. MEITZEL, TAKE FOX SECTION AND DEAL WITH THOSE SPITFIRES.

JA, THIS WILL TAKE BUT A FEW MINUTES.

THE NAZI ATTACK CAME IN AT WHAT SEEMED LIKE THE SPEED OF LIGHT TO ALBERT.

HERE THEY COME. HEY, BUT THEY'RE FAST!

THE CALM VOICE OF IAN GILCHRIST SOUNDED THROUGH HIS EARPHONES.

THE FIGHT'S BACK THIS WAY, ALBERT — WATCH MY TAIL.

OH, ER . . . SURE. SKIPPER!

HIS HEART THUDDED, HIS PALMS WERE GREASY WITH SWEAT.

HE SNARLED IN A TIGHT TURN TO STREAK BACK TO THE COMBAT. THOUGH STILL APPREHENSIVE, MUCH OF HIS NERVOUSNESS FADED AS HE FASTENED ON THE TAIL OF A NAZI PLANE, THUMB POISED OVER HIS FIRING BUTTON.

STAY LIKE THAT . . . JUST FOR A BIT LONGER . . .

THIS GERMAN WAS A WILY BIRD. SPOTTING ALBERT IN HIS MIRROR, HE SNARLED OFF IN A TIGHT, STOMACH-CLENCHING BANK.

I MESSED THAT UP! THESE CHAPS KNOW WHAT THEY'RE ABOUT.

FRANTICALLY HE SOUGHT IAN'S KITE. AFTER ALL, HIS MAIN ROLE WAS TO GUARD HIS SKIPPER'S TAIL.

MEANWHILE MEITZEL WAS ENJOYING HIMSELF. ALREADY HE HAD ADDED ANOTHER SCORE TO HIS TALLY.

TODAY I AM IN TOP FORM.

NO QUARTER WAS ASKED, NONE GIVEN IN THE WILD SKIRMISH IN THOSE HOSTILE SKIES.

AAARGH!

THAT WILL TEACH YOU TO TAKE US ON!

AS THE DOG-FIGHT DEVELOPED, ALBERT FOUND HE COULD NOT GET TO HIS BATTLE STATION FOR MEITZEL HAD FASTENED ON TO HIM LIKE A LEECH, POURING RED FIRE INTO HIS SPITFIRE.

ANOTHER EASY VICTORY FOR ME!

I'D BETTER GET MY KITE OUT OF HERE!

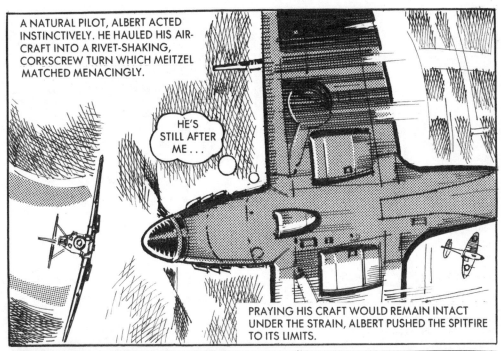

TRY AS HE MIGHT, MEITZEL COULD NOT SHAKE OFF THIS PERSISTENT ADVERSARY. AGAIN AND AGAIN, ALBERT'S GUNS RAKED THE MESSERSCHMITT.

HIMMEL, HE CAN FLY, THIS ONE!

MEITZEL HAD NO WAY OF KNOWING THIS WAS ALBERT'S FIRST ENGAGEMENT . . . THE FIRST TIME HE HAD FIRED HIS GUNS IN ANGER.

HEY, MY FIRST BANDIT!

HE HAS SHOT ME DOWN . . .

HEADY WITH EXCITEMENT, HE WATCHED THE NAZI PLANE SPIN TO EARTH, TRAILING FLAMES AND BLACK, GREASY SMOKE.

THEIR ACE'S PLUNGE TO DISASTER SHOOK THE REST OF THE GERMAN PILOTS. IF HE HAD BEEN BESTED IN THIS FIGHT, THEN THE SOONER THEY CALLED IT OFF THE BETTER. TO A MAN, THEY TURNED AND FLED.

WELL DONE, LADS!

SKIPPER, I GOT ONE! DID YOU SEE IT?

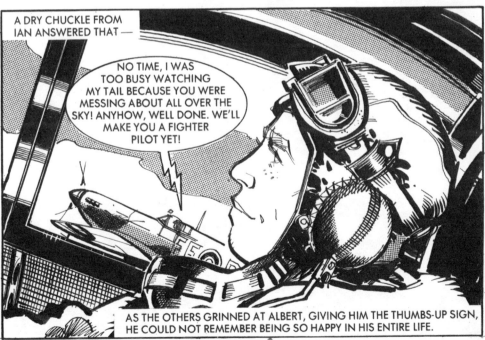

A DRY CHUCKLE FROM IAN ANSWERED THAT —

NO TIME, I WAS TOO BUSY WATCHING MY TAIL BECAUSE YOU WERE MESSING ABOUT ALL OVER THE SKY! ANYHOW, WELL DONE. WE'LL MAKE YOU A FIGHTER PILOT YET!

AS THE OTHERS GRINNED AT ALBERT, GIVING HIM THE THUMBS-UP SIGN, HE COULD NOT REMEMBER BEING SO HAPPY IN HIS ENTIRE LIFE.

MEANWHILE THE FURIOUS VICTIM, BADLY WOUNDED, HAD SOMEHOW REACHED FRENCH SOIL TO STAGGER IN FOR A CRASH LANDING. HE STILL COULD NOT BELIEVE THAT HE HAD BEEN BESTED.

IT MUST HAVE BEEN ONE OF THEIR ACES. OBVIOUSLY THOSE CURSED MECHANICS DIDN'T FIX MY MAGNETO . . . THAT'S WHY I LACKED THE POWER TO GET AWAY . . .

HE ALWAYS BLAMED OTHER PEOPLE FOR HIS OWN ERRORS — THE MEITZEL FAMILY JUST DID NOT MAKE MISTAKES. THEIR CODE WOULD NOT PERMIT IT. YET EVEN AS HE WAS TAKEN OFF BY AMBULANCE . . .

. . . TO BE RUSHED TO A HOSPITAL, THE LAST THING HE REMEMBERED AS HIS SENSES BLACKENED WAS THAT EMBLEM OF A LION ON ALBERT'S AIRCRAFT.

BACK AT THE SPITFIRE BASE, ALBERT THREW A PARTY. BECAUSE HE WAS A POPULAR SORT, THE MESS WAS CROWDED WITH CELEBRATING PILOTS WHEN IAN CAME IN WITH STAGGERING NEWS.

HEY, ALBERT, WE JUST HEARD FROM THE INTELLIGENCE OFFICER. KNOW WHO YOU SHOT DOWN TODAY?

PROBABLY SOMEBODY WHO WAS ON HIS FIRST MISSION LIKE ME?

GRINNING, THE SQUADRON-LEADER BROKE THE INCREDIBLE NEWS THAT IT WAS ONE OF THE TOP NAZI ACES WHO HAD BEEN DOWNED.

HE SAW THAT LION, ALBERT. HIS NERVES TURNED TO JELLY.

I DON'T BELIEVE IT! GOOD LORD, I'M SHAKING . . .

THE CELEBRATIONS WENT ON EVEN LONGER THAN PLANNED. ALBERT KNEW TOO THAT HE COULD CONTROL HIS NERVES WHEN IT CAME TO THE CRUNCH AGAIN.

ODDLY ENOUGH, OVER IN FRANCE, EVEN ALTHOUGH THEY HAD TAKEN A TERRIBLE BEATING THAT DAY, THE PILOTS OF MEITZEL'S SQUADRON WERE NOT TOO GLOOMY.

THINK OF IT, WE WON'T HAVE TO LISTEN TO HIS BOASTING, WATCH HIM CASTING A SHADOW OVER EVERYTHING.

JA, THE MESS WILL BE A BETTER PLACE. I WONDER WHO DOWNED HIM?

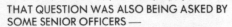

THAT QUESTION WAS ALSO BEING ASKED BY SOME SENIOR OFFICERS —

THE BRITISH WILL MAKE MUCH OF THIS, RUB SALT INTO MEITZEL'S WOUNDS.

WELL, I HOPE FOR OUR SAKE THAT HIS OPPONENT IS A WELL-KNOWN ACE, OR MEITZEL WILL BE IMPOSSIBLE TO LIVE WITH.

DRYLY ONE OF THE LUFTWAFFE OFFICERS REPLIED —

IT'S NOT OUR PROBLEM, MY FRIEND. OUR ACE WILL NEVER FLY AGAIN. HE IS BADLY BROKEN UP.

IN HOSPITAL THE NAZI HAD NOTHING TO LOOK FORWARD TO BUT A SERIES OF OPERATIONS. THE DOCTORS HAD TOLD HIM HE WOULD NEVER FLY AGAIN. SAVAGELY HE HEAPED THE ENTIRE BLAME ON HIS CONQUEROR.

ONE CARELESS MOMENT AND I MAY HAVE LOST ALL HOPE OF GETTING MY KNIGHT'S CROSS! HIMMEL, THAT ENGLANDER HAS A LOT TO ANSWER FOR.

IF HE COULD NOT FLY AGAIN, HE HAD LOST ALL CHANCE OF REVENGE. HATE BURNED THROUGH HIM.

WHATEVER ELSE HE WAS, MEITZEL WAS RESOURCEFUL — HE MEANT TO GET HIS MEDAL. SO IF HE COULD NOT FLY AGAIN, HE WOULD TRANSFER TO THE S.S. TO ACHIEVE HIS GOAL.

JA, MY FAMILY CONNECTIONS CAN MANAGE THAT. PERHAPS THERE I CAN DISTINGUISH MYSELF AS I HAVE DONE IN A FIGHTER. JA, NOTHING IS IMPOSSIBLE . . .

A MONTH LATER HE LEFT HOSPITAL, RETURNING TO HIS FORMER AIRFIELD ON GROUND DUTIES WHILE THE AUTHORITIES CONSIDERED HIS REQUEST FOR A TRANSFER. FIRST THOUGH HE LEARNED THE BITTER TRUTH —

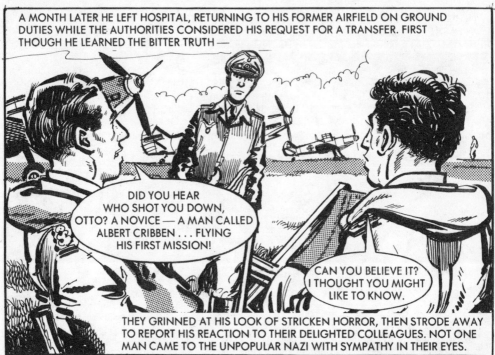

DID YOU HEAR WHO SHOT YOU DOWN, OTTO? A NOVICE — A MAN CALLED ALBERT CRIBBEN . . . FLYING HIS FIRST MISSION!

CAN YOU BELIEVE IT? I THOUGHT YOU MIGHT LIKE TO KNOW.

THEY GRINNED AT HIS LOOK OF STRICKEN HORROR, THEN STRODE AWAY TO REPORT HIS REACTION TO THEIR DELIGHTED COLLEAGUES. NOT ONE MAN CAME TO THE UNPOPULAR NAZI WITH SYMPATHY IN THEIR EYES.

AS THE WORDS ECHOED THROUGH MEITZEL'S HEAD, SHAME BURNED THROUGH HIM, THEN SCALED TO AN EVEN DEEPER HATE AS HE MEMORISED THE NAME OF THAT ONE R.A.F. PILOT.

WHEN WE MARCH INTO LONDON, I WILL SEND FOR HIM. HE WILL FEEL THE SHARP EDGE OF MY ANGER!

HE TURNED TO LIMP OFF TO HIS QUARTERS, AWAY FROM THE MOCKING EYES. YET SO LONG AS HE COULD BELIEVE THAT ONE DAY REVENGE WOULD BE HIS, HE COULD TOLERATE THE HUMILIATION.

ALL THIS TIME ALBERT WAS IN THE HEAT OF THE ACTION. NOW HE WAS ALMOST A VETERAN, WITH MORE SWASTIKAS PAINTED BENEATH THE LION ON HIS SPITFIRE.

HEAR YOU MADE FLIGHT-LIEUTENANT. CONGRATULATIONS, SIR!

THANKS, BUT YOU'RE A DAB HAND AT THAT ARTWORK. I'M GLAD I DECIDED TO KEEP THAT OLD LION ON. IT BRINGS ME LUCK, I RECKON.

NOW THAT THE BATTLE OF BRITAIN WAS OVER, THE R.A.F. WERE TAKING THE WAR TO OCCUPIED FRANCE, STRAFING NAZI GROUND TARGETS, KNOCKING THE LUFTWAFFE FROM THE AIR.

IT WAS ROUND-THE-CLOCK WORK. TODAY THEIR TARGET WAS AN AMMO TRAIN . . .

. . . REPORTED EN ROUTE TO THE CHANNEL PORTS.

IF THAT WENT WELL, THEIR SECOND OBJECTIVE WAS TO BE A NAZI AIRFIELD.

I ALWAYS LIKE HAMMERING THEIR PLANES ON THE GROUND . . . LOT EASIER THAN IN THE AIR!

THE TRAIN THEY SOUGHT SOON FELT THE CLAWS OF THE SLEEK INTRUDERS. THE R.A.F. FLYERS KNEW THE TRUCKS WERE PACKED WITH AMMO.

SAVE US A BIT TO DO, ALBERT!

YOU HAD FIRST GO LAST TIME, MIKE. HERE WE GO!

ALBERT'S TRACER LANCED INTO ONE OF THE TRUCKS, FINDING THE AMMO BOXES. THE RESULTING EXPLOSION WAS DRAMATIC.

I KNEW IT! ALBERT'S BEEN GREEDY FOR GLORY EVER SINCE HE KNOCKED MEITZEL OUT OF THE SKY!

THERE WAS STILL PLENTY EMPLOYMENT FOR EVERY SPITFIRE. IT WAS WORK THEY REVELLED IN.

MOMENTS LATER THE TRAIN WAS A WRECK, HEADING FOR TOTAL OBLIVION AS IT TOPPLED OFF A VIADUCT INTO THE RAVINE BENEATH.

ALL CHANGE!

THE FIGHTERS DID NOT LINGER. THEY ARROWED STRAIGHT FOR THE NAZI AIRFIELD THEY HAD BEEN ASSIGNED TO ATTACK.

BUT THE ALARM HAD BEEN RAISED NOW. AS THEY NEARED THEIR TARGET, A GAGGLE OF Me109s POUNCED ON THEM.

HIT THESE ARROGANT DEVILS!

VISITORS, LADS! LET'S HANDLE THEM FIRST!

WITHIN MINUTES THERE WERE DOG-FIGHTS ALL OVER THE SKY.

ALBERT TANGLED WITH ONE PILOT WHO SEEMED TO BEAR A CHARMED LIFE AS HE DODGED DEATH AGAIN AND AGAIN.

THIS BLOKE KNOWS A THING OR TWO!

THEN ALBERT'S PERSISTENCE TOLD. A WELL-AIMED BURST DID THE TRICK.

AH, BETTER!

HE TURNED AWAY — IT WAS OBVIOUS THE GERMAN HAD HAD IT.

BUT IN HIS TERROR THE NAZI BANKED IN THE SAME DIRECTION. AS THE Me109 BLEW UP, THE EXPLOSION ALL BUT ENGULFED ALBERT'S SPITFIRE, DOING UNTOLD DAMAGE. AT ONCE HE FELT THE CONTROLS GO SLACK —

CRIPES, WAS THE BLIGHTER TRYING TO TAKE ME WITH HIM?

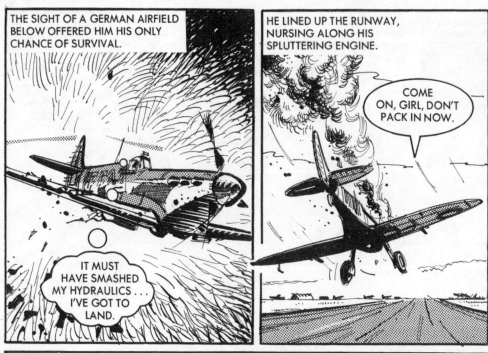

ALBERT DID NOT HAVE ANY DEGREE OF CONTROL LEFT TO HIM. HE COULD ONLY SIT HELPLESSLY WATCHING AS THE WING OF HIS CRAFT SMASHED INTO ONE OF THE Me109s.

YE GODS, THIS IS IT . . . I'VE HAD IT!

BUT THE SPITFIRE HAD OTHER IDEAS. IT SLEWED ROUND ON IMPACT, TO TRUNDLE AWAY FROM THE STATIONARY NAZI CRAFT.

THAT'S MY GIRL! BUT HOW THE HECK DO I GET OUT . . .

OBLIGINGLY THE KITE LURCHED TO A HALT. HE WAS FREE AS QUICKLY AS HE COULD UNFASTEN HIS HARNESS.

JUST THEN THE AIRCRAFT HE HAD HIT EXPLODED, SPILLING FLAMES ON TO THE OTHER NAZI CRAFT, ENGULFING THE FUEL BOWSER. IT TOO WENT UP.

HEY, I'M NOT GOING TO BE TOO POPULAR!

IN THAT ONE SECOND, THE NAZIS LOST TWO PLANES, A MASSIVE AMOUNT OF FUEL, COUNTLESS SERVICING TOOLS AND SEVERAL VEHICLES.

AS HIS HEAD CLEARED, ALBERT GLIMPSED A RECEPTION COMMITTEE OF AIRFIELD GUARDS.

I HOPE THEY'RE NOT THE SORT TO HOLD A GRUDGE!

LOCK THE MADMAN UP!

HE THOUGHT THEY MIGHT SHOOT HIM ON SIGHT. INSTEAD THEY TOOK HIM TO A SMALL BARRED ROOM AND LEFT HIM. FROM THERE HE COULD SEE THE DAMAGE WHICH HAD BEEN CAUSED.

WHAT A SHAMBLES . . .

AN HOUR LATER THE DOOR SWUNG OPEN TO ADMIT SOME ENEMY PILOTS WHO SPOKE FAIR ENGLISH.

YOU GOING TO FINISH ME IN HERE, THEN?

NEIN! YOU SHOT DOWN OTTO MEITZEL, JA? WE SAW THE LION ON YOUR SPITFIRE. SEVERAL OF US HAD THE MISFORTUNE TO SERVE WITH HIM. YOU DID US A FAVOUR THAT DAY!

WHEN THEY TOOK HIM TO THEIR MESS AS AN HONOURED GUEST, ALBERT WAS SURPRISED TO DISCOVER IT WAS MORE OR LESS A DUPLICATE OF HIS OWN SQUADRON'S.

I DON'T KNOW WHAT I THOUGHT IT WOULD BE LIKE OVER HERE . . . BUT CHEERS!

I AM KLAUS REGEN AND THIS IS MY FRIEND, WILHELM WEISS. WE BOTH SUFFERED AS JUNIOR PILOTS UNDER THE SHARP TONGUE OF MEITZEL.

AS IT DAWNED ON ALBERT THAT THESE GERMANS WERE NOT AT ALL BITTER, KLAUS DIVINED WHAT WAS ON HIS MIND.

YOU MUST UNDERSTAND — WE FIGHT, MAY EVEN DIE FOR GERMANY . . .BUT NOT HITLER. WE KNOW THIS WAR IS LOST, FOR OUR DEFEATS IN RUSSIA HAVE BEEN SAVAGE.

WITH THAT POINT CLEARED UP, THE PARTY REALLY GOT UNDER WAY.

SOON ALBERT WAS ENJOYING HIMSELF. AHEAD LAY CAPTIVITY, BUT HE KNEW HE WOULD ATTEMPT TO ESCAPE. WITH HIS LUCK, HE RECKONED HE COULD PULL IT OFF.

YET EVEN AS HE WAS THINKING THIS, MEITZEL ENTERED THE MESS UNANNOUNCED. HE ALWAYS KEPT AN EAR TO THE GROUND AND HAD RECEIVED A REPORT FROM A HIRELING AMONG THE GROUND CREWS THAT A SPITFIRE WITH A LION PAINTED ON ITS SIDE HAD CRASH-LANDED.

AT THE SOUND OF HIS HARSH VOICE, ALL FESTIVITIES SUDDENLY CEASED.

SO? MY LOYAL EX-COMRADES SPEND TIME WITH THE ENEMY, JA? IF YOU THINK THIS WAR IS A JOKE, YOU WILL SOON LEARN DIFFERENTLY. NOW, HERR CRIBBEN . . .

THE NAZI HAD BARKED HIS MESSAGE IN GERMAN. KLAUS, WHO HAD TOLD ALBERT OF THE MAN'S FURY AT HIS DISGRACE, QUIETLY TRANSLATED FOR THE BRITISH PILOT.

YOU MUST KNOW, MY FRIEND, THE S.S. RULE OUR LIVES. I AM DEEPLY SORRY TO HAVE BROUGHT THIS DANGER TO YOU.

NOT TO WORRY, CHUM. I'M A PRISONER-OF-WAR. ALL HE CAN DO IS TAKE ME TO A STALAG.

I HOPE SO, BUT WITH MEITZEL ONE CAN NEVER BE SURE.

SEEING THE S.S. MAN'S COLD HARD EYES, ALBERT FELT A TREMOR OF UNCERTAINTY. HE HID IT BENEATH A JOKE.

FOR ME THE WAR IS OVER, JA?

I HAVE WAITED A LONG TIME FOR THIS MOMENT. A LONG, HARD TIME . . .

MEITZEL SPOKE IN ENGLISH. SOMEHOW THAT LANGUAGE SWITCH INCREASED THE TENSION.

EVER SINCE THEN THE LION EMBLEM HAD HAUNTED HIS DREAMS. ALL THAT TIME HE HAD WAITED FOR THIS MOMENT.

NOW I AM IN A POSITION TO DESTROY YOU!

ONCE AT THE H.Q., ALBERT, WHO HAD PLENTY TO THINK ABOUT NOW, WAS FLUNG INTO A FILTHY CELL, LEFT ALONE.

HE'S CRAZY . . . ALL THAT STUFF WE HEARD ABOUT THE S.S. AND THEIR BRUTAL METHODS IS PROBABLY TRUE!

FOR MANY HOURS HE WONDERED WHAT LAY AHEAD. A QUICK SHOT IN SOME GREY, DAWN COURTYARD? TORTURE, PERHAPS? THEN THE DOOR CRASHED OPEN TO REVEAL MEITZEL WIELDING A DUELLING SABRE.

YOU THIRST? YOU HUNGER? NEVER MIND, SOON YOU WILL NOT BE FEELING SUCH TORMENTS. YOU WILL BE DEAD!

WITH THE S.S. MAJOR WAS A CAPTAIN WHO WAS HIS SECOND-IN-COMMAND, A BURLY THUG CALLED JURGEN.

WE FIGHT AT DAWN . . . IN AN HOUR. I AM LOOKING FORWARD TO IT. I INTEND TO CUT YOU TO PIECES! COME, JURGEN!

THEY LEFT ALBERT ALONE, THE COLD HATE IN THE GERMAN'S EYES BURNING IN HIS MIND.

ALREADY MEITZEL COULD FEEL HIMSELF TORMENTING THE ENGLANDER, SLICING INTO HIM . . .

. . . DEMONSTRATING ALL THE SKILLS LEARNED AT UNIVERSITY WHERE DUELLING HAD BEEN ALMOST A WAY OF LIFE.

JURGEN, ON THE OTHER HAND, CARED NOTHING FOR THIS SITUATION. HE HAD ONE GOAL IN MIND . . . THE TOTAL DISGRACE OF MEITZEL AND HIS OWN PROMOTION.

I HAVE SUFFERED TOO LONG UNDER HIS VICIOUS TONGUE. ONE DAY I WILL GET ENOUGH ON HIM TO FORCE BERLIN TO ACT.

THE SECOND-IN-COMMAND WAS ALWAYS SEARCHING FOR EVIDENCE TO BRING ABOUT MEITZEL'S DOWNFALL. SO FAR HE HAD BEEN UNLUCKY.

SOON DAWN CAME . . . THE DUEL WAS ABOUT TO BEGIN. THE SWORD PRESENTED TO HIM FELT STRANGE TO ALBERT'S HAND.

THERE'S NO WAY I CAN BEAT HIM AT THIS GAME . . .

THERE IS WATER AVAILABLE TO BATHE ANY WOUNDS. BUT LET ME ASSURE YOU, WOUNDS DO NOT MEAN AN END TO THIS DUEL.

SUDDENLY THE NAZI'S BLADE SNAKED TOWARDS ALBERT WHO STAGGERED CLUMSILY BACK.

COME, COME! ADOPT THE PROPER POSE AT LEAST!

YOU COME TO ME, MATE!

TRUTH WAS, ALBERT DID NOT HAVE A CLUE. ANYWAY, HIS ATTENTION WAS ON THOSE BUCKETS OF WATER . . . AND ON THE FACT THAT MEITZEL, IN HIS ARROGANCE, HAD NOT BOTHERED TO LOCK THE DOOR.

WHILE THE CURSING MEITZEL RETREATED A FEW PACES, PARRYING AWAY THE THROWN BLADE, ALBERT SPUN ROUND TO SLAM A HARD PUNCH INTO JURGEN'S FACE.

SNATCHING UP ONE OF THE WATER BUCKETS THEN, HE TURNED IT INTO A DEADLY WEAPON WHICH CAUGHT MEITZEL HARD IN THE CHEST.

THAT WAS ALL HE HAD TIME TO SAY BEFORE ALBERT BORED IN, FISTS COCKED FOR ACTION.

GRABBING UP A SWORD, ALBERT HARED FOR THE DOOR.

I DON'T KNOW WHERE TO HEAD FOR, BUT ANYTHING'S BETTER THAN STAYING HERE!

FORTUNATELY THE BUILDING WAS ALMOST DESERTED, ONLY A SKELETON STAFF ON DUTY.

THE FEW SLEEPY GUARDS WERE EASILY DODGED BY A MAN AS DESPERATE AS ALBERT.

NOT A HAND WAS RAISED TO STOP HIM. SOON HE RACED OUT BY A BACK DOOR, HEADING ACROSS OPEN FIELDS TOWARDS THE COVER OF A WOOD.

LUCK'S WITH ME SO FAR . . .

IN THE ROOM WHERE THE STRANGE DUEL HAD TAKEN PLACE, THE TWO GERMAN OFFICERS WERE JUST COMING ROUND.

HIMMEL, MY HEAD . . .

DON'T JUST STAND THERE — GET MEN, CHASE HIM! IF HE IS NOT RECAPTURED, YOU WILL PAY!

TRYING HARD TO PULL HIS SPINNING SENSES TOGETHER, JURGEN CALLED FOR SOME TROOPERS TO SET OUT ON FOOT AFTER THE FUGITIVE.

ALTHOUGH THE TRACKS WERE CLEARLY VISIBLE IN THE DEW-BRIGHT GRASS, THE SCHEMING SECOND-IN-COMMAND WAS NOT TOO DILIGENT. HE SAW THIS AS A HEAVEN-SENT OPPORTUNITY.

WE WILL SEARCH BUT NOT TOO HARD. I WANT THE ENGLANDER TO ESCAPE. MEITZEL WILL BE FURIOUS, BUT I WILL THEN SEND A REPORT TO BERLIN . . .

IN IT WOULD BE AN EXACT DESCRIPTION OF WHAT HAD HAPPENED — A REPORT WHICH WOULD SEE HIS C.O. DISGRACED.

...HE HAS PUT HIS OWN THIRST FOR VENGEANCE ABOVE HIS DUTY TO THE REICH. JA, OUR SUPERIORS WILL NOT LIKE THAT.

SO, SPENDING ENOUGH TIME AND EFFORT TO AVOID AROUSING SUSPICION, JURGEN AT LAST CALLED OFF THE HUNT.

ENOUGH! THERE'S NO SENSE IN TIRING OURSELVES OUT IN FRUITLESS WALKING. H.Q. IS SIGNALLING ALL STATIONS IN THE AREA — HE WILL RUN INTO OUR NET.

THE MEN OBEYED WITH RELIEF. A CHASE WAS NOT THE BEST WAY TO START A DAY.

UNAWARE OF ALL THESE GOINGS-ON, ALBERT HAD CHANGED DIRECTION TWICE TO THROW OFF THE PURSUIT WHICH HE WAS SURPRISED HAD NOT COME CLOSER.

I CAN'T HEAR A THING . . .

WITHOUT ANY TRUE IDEA OF HIS POSITION, HE BLUNDERED ON IN AN ATTEMPT TO FIND A GOOD PLACE TO HIDE.

BY NOW JURGEN HAD REPORTED BACK TO MEITZEL THAT THE PRISONER COULD NOT BE FOUND.

TIRED, THIRSTY, HUNGRY? YET HE OUT-PACED YOU ALL?

FEAR LENDS WINGS . . .

A BRUTAL ANSWER STOPPED THAT EXPLANATION. AS JURGEN, SECRETLY GLOATING, LEFT TO SIGNAL HIS REPORT TO BERLIN, HIS C.O. SNATCHED UP THE TELEPHONE.

HAVE MY CAR BROUGHT TO THE FRONT DOOR. IMMEDIATELY!

THE NAZI SAW IT AS A POSSIBILITY THAT THE BRITISH PILOT WOULD MAKE FOR THE AIRFIELD ONCE HE HAD GOT HIS BEARINGS, IN THE HOPE OF GRABBING A PLANE TO TAKE HIM TO ENGLAND.

IN FACT, ALREADY CLOSE TO THE AIRFIELD WHICH HE HAD INDEED HEADED FOR AFTER MONITORING AIRCRAFT MOVEMENTS, ALBERT TOOK COVER IN THE LONG GRASS AS HE HEARD SOMEONE APPROACHING.

HE'S BOUND TO SEE ME... I'VE GOT TO ACT FAST...

AS THE MAN CAME CLOSER, SUDDENLY ALBERT ROSE LIKE SOME VIKING BERSERKER.

HIMMEL!

DON'T YOU MOVE...

THE THREAT DIED IN HIS THROAT WHEN HE SAW IT WAS KLAUS — ONE OF THE FRIENDLY GERMAN PILOTS WHO HAD DONE SO MUCH FOR HIM — TOGGED OUT IN CIVILIAN CLOTHES.

MEIN GOTT, YOU GAVE ME A SHOCK. I'M OUT BIRD-WATCHING . . . MY HOBBY. USUALLY IT IS A PEACEFUL THING TO DO.

SORRY, KLAUS, I DIDN'T KNOW IT WAS YOU.

AS HE TOOK A WELCOME SWIG OF THE COFFEE KLAUS OFFERED, HE BROUGHT HIS GERMAN FRIEND UP TO DATE WITH EVENTS.

KLAUS HAD SOME NEWS TOO —

WE SIGNALLED OUR H.Q. TELLING THEM WHAT MEITZEL HAD DONE, BUT WE HEARD NOTHING. ALL MEN WALK IN FEAR OF THE S.S.

WELL, I BEAT HIM AGAIN, BUT WHAT DO I DO NOW?

AS A LOYAL GERMAN, IT WENT AGAINST THE GRAIN FOR KLAUS TO HELP AN ENEMY.

BUT WE CANNOT LET THEM MURDER YOU. EVEN IN A STALAG, HE WOULD GET YOU.

YES, I MUST MOVE ON. COULD YOU FETCH ME GRUB, A WATER-BOTTLE AND A MAP?

IMMEDIATELY KLAUS SENT FOR WILHELM WHO FELT EXACTLY THE SAME AS REGARDS THE SITUATION.

OF COURSE WE WILL HELP. YOU MIGHT EVEN COME ACROSS SOME FRENCH PARTISANS.

THEY ARE CERTAINLY ACTIVE ALL OVER THE AREA. MY FEAR IS THAT MEITZEL WILL FIND YOU FIRST. HE COULD EASILY GUESS THAT YOU WILL COME HERE.

ALREADY MEITZEL HAD ARRIVED AT THE AIRFIELD. HE GAVE AN AIDE INSTRUCTIONS TO PASS ON TO JURGEN TO ENSURE THAT PATROLS CONTINUED TO COMB THE AREA.

AND SEE THAT THE ORDER I ISSUED, WARNING ANY FRENCH PARTISAN AGAINST HELPING THIS ESCAPED SPY, IS PROPERLY DISPLAYED. UNDERSTOOD?

THE CAR LEFT AND THE ARROGANT S.S. MAN STRUTTED IN TO SEE THE STATION COMMANDER. MINUTES LATER, HEAVY DETAILS WERE GUARDING THE PLANES CLOSELY. THIS ESCAPE ROUTE WAS NOW BLOCKED.

THEN HE HEARD THE ROAR OF APPROACHING ENGINES. SIMULTANEOUSLY A WARNING VOICE BARKED THROUGH THE STATION'S LOUDSPEAKERS.

GO TO YOUR POSTS AT ONCE — MOSQUITOES ARE APPROACHING!

HIMMEL, CAN THESE DOGS COME AND GO AS THEY PLEASE? WHY ARE THERE NO GERMAN PLANES IN THE SKY TO HAMMER THEM DOWN?

IN FACT MOSSIES HAD ALREADY EVADED THE Me109s SENT TO REPULSE THEM. THE AIRFIELD WAS THEIR INTENDED TARGET.

AAGH!

EVEN MEITZEL FORGOT HIS DIGNITY AS HE SPRINTED FOR COVER.

IN THE ROOM HE HAD COME TO FOR SAFETY, ALBERT HUGGED THE FLOOR WITH WILHELM AND KLAUS, CURSING THE FATES THAT HAD PUT HIM IN THE POSITION WHERE HE COULD WELL BE SLAUGHTERED BY HIS OWN SIDE.

BLIMEY, WHAT A TURN-UP FOR THE BOOKS!

IN THE INTRUDERS ROARED FOR ANOTHER ATTACK, DESTROYING EVERYTHING IN SIGHT.

LIKE SHOOTING FISH IN A BARREL!

MAKE THE MOST OF IT. JERRY IS BOUND TO SEND FIGHTERS AFTER US.

MINUTES LATER, AS THEY TURNED TO CLIMB AWAY, THE AIRFIELD WAS A SHAMBLES. NOT A SINGLE PLANE SURVIVED. MANY PILOTS AND GROUNDCREW HAD DIED. THE ADMINISTRATIVE BUILDINGS HAD CEASED TO EXIST.

AT THE HUT WHERE ALBERT WAS SHELTERING WITH HIS TWO FRIENDS, ANOTHER GERMAN PILOT PUT IN AN APPEARANCE —

WE'RE LEAVING FOR ANOTHER STATION IMMEDIATELY. TRUCKS ARE CALLING FOR US IN FIVE MINUTES!

TO THE MESSENGER, ALREADY DODGING OUT OF THE ROOM, ALBERT WAS JUST ANOTHER DUST-COVERED, UNRECOGNISABLE FIGURE.

WHILE ALBERT LOOKED ON, HIS TWO GERMAN FRIENDS STARTED TO THROW WHAT WAS LEFT OF THEIR POSSESSIONS INTO CASES.

ALBERT, LET US GET AWAY, THEN HEAD OFF ON YOUR OWN.

YES, SURE, THAT'S FINE. GOOD LUCK TO YOU BLOKES.

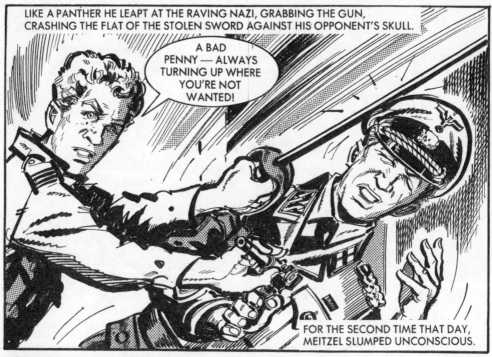

LIKE A PANTHER HE LEAPT AT THE RAVING NAZI, GRABBING THE GUN, CRASHING THE FLAT OF THE STOLEN SWORD AGAINST HIS OPPONENT'S SKULL.

A BAD PENNY — ALWAYS TURNING UP WHERE YOU'RE NOT WANTED!

FOR THE SECOND TIME THAT DAY, MEITZEL SLUMPED UNCONSCIOUS.

AS HE SNATCHED UP THE GUN DROPPED BY THE UNCONSCIOUS MAN, ALBERT SAW THE FEAR IN HIS FRIENDS' EYES.

YOU BLOKES GO — LEAVE HIM TO ME. HE'LL NEVER GET THE CHANCE TO TELL ANY-ONE ABOUT THIS.

THEY GRIMLY REALISED THEIR FRIEND WOULD HAVE TO KILL TO KEEP HIS WORD. SILENTLY THEY SHOOK HANDS BEFORE TURNING TO DEPART.

GRIMLY ALBERT HEARD THE SURVIVORS DRIVE OFF. SOON THE SHATTERED AIRFIELD WAS SILENT . . . A TIME TO THINK.

I CAN'T SHOOT A BLOKE, EVEN HIM, IN COLD BLOOD. BUT IF I DON'T, KLAUS AND WILHELM WILL SUFFER.

MINUTES TICKED PAST AS HE AGONISED OVER HIS PROBLEM.

HE PAID THE PRICE FOR NOT KEEPING A CAREFUL WATCH WHEN TWO BURLY FRENCH PARTISANS SLIPPED IN MENACINGLY.

AH, TWO BOCHES!

I WONDER WHY THE OTHERS LEFT THEM BEHIND?

OBVIOUSLY THEY HAD COME TO SALVAGE ANY WEAPONS FROM THE DEBRIS.

WITH HARDLY A WORD OF FRENCH AND PRAYING THE TWO PARTISANS UNDERSTOOD ENGLISH, ALBERT TOLD THEM HIS STORY, INDICATING WHO HIS PRISONER WAS.

THIS IS OTTO MEITZEL. HE'S BEEN TRYING TO KILL ME.

OUI, IT IS HIM, YOU HAVE IDENTIFICATION, ANGLAIS?

THE NEWCOMERS TOOK SOME CONVINCING BEFORE ALBERT'S CLAIM WAS BELIEVED. THE NAZI'S HANDS WERE FIRMLY SECURED.

WE WILL SENTENCE AND HANG HIM. THE PEOPLE WILL BE GLAD. TOO MANY HAVE SUFFERED AT HIS ORDERS.

FAIR ENOUGH, BUT CAN YOU GET ME BACK TO ENGLAND?

OF COURSE, WE HAVE HELPED MANY LIKE YOU.

ONLY MEITZEL'S EYES BETRAYED HIS SEETHING EMOTIONS. GLITTERING AND BRIGHT, THEY SPOKE OF HIS BURNING HATRED FOR ALBERT, FOR THE TWO PARTISANS.

FREE NOW OF THE NECESSITY TO KILL THE S.S. OFFICER HIMSELF, A RELIEVED ALBERT WAS LED AWAY AFTER HE HAD FLUNG THE HEAVY DUELLING SWORD FAR INTO THE DEBRIS.

IT'S A GOOD JOB YOU BLOKES TURNED UP. I DIDN'T FANCY SHOOTING HIM MYSELF.

WE WELCOME THE CHANCE. MY ELDEST SON DIED IN HIS PRISON.

OUI, MY BROTHERS ALSO . . . THIS FIEND USED THEM FOR SWORD PRACTICE.

ONCE IN GOOD COVER, THE PARTY SPLIT UP. ONE FRENCHMAN PREPARED TO GUIDE ALBERT TO A SAFE PLACE FROM WHERE HE WOULD BE FERRIED TO ENGLAND. THE OTHER TOOK MEITZEL TOWARDS THEIR HIDE-OUT TO AWAIT EXECUTION.

THE EMBITTERED NAZI WAS FORCED ON FOR SOME MILES BEFORE HIS LUCK AT LAST CHANGED AS HIS PATH CROSSED THAT OF ONE OF THE PATROLS STILL LOOKING FOR ALBERT.

SEEING THE GAME WAS UP, THE PARTISAN TURNED TO FLEE. HE GOT NO DISTANCE AT ALL BEFORE HE WAS CUT DOWN.

UUURGH!

GOOD. UNTIE ME, MAN!

SO THE KILLER ESCAPED THE WRATH OF HIS FRENCH CAPTORS. NOW HE WAS DRIVEN FAST TO HIS H.Q.

WHEN HE WALKED INTO HIS OFFICE, JURGEN WAS LAZING AT EASE AT THE DESK. MEITZEL ALMOST EXPLODED —

WHAT ARE YOU DOING? HIMMEL, I'LL HAVE YOUR SKIN FOR THIS IMPERTINENCE!

READ THIS SIGNAL. THEN I MIGHT DECIDE TO OVERLOOK YOUR INSUBORDINATION.

THE MESSAGE CAME FROM THOSE VERY CLOSE TO THE TOP IN BERLIN. THEY WERE NOT AT ALL PLEASED WITH MEITZEL'S RECENT BEHAVIOUR.

YOU SEE, YOU ARE DISMISSED YOUR COMMAND. I AM TO TAKE OVER. YOU MAY GO TO YOUR QUARTERS UNTIL BERLIN DECIDES YOUR FATE.

AS THE DERANGED MAN STARED INTO THE GLOATING FACE OF JURGEN, HE FELT HIS MIND SPIN, SAW HIS CAREFUL PLANS CRUMBLE INTO DUST.

HE SCREAMED HIS FRUSTRATION AS HE GRABBED UP JURGEN'S PISTOL WHICH LAY ON THE DESK . . . FIRING IT AT POINT-BLANK RANGE INTO HIS FORMER SECOND-IN-COMMAND'S BODY.

UURGH!

DOG — YOU BETRAYED ME! PAY NOW!

MEITZEL TURNED TO PUSH PAST THE BADLY-SHAKEN GUARD WHO HAD SEEN IT ALL. ONLY ONE IMAGE WAS CLEAR IN HIS FEVERED BRAIN . . . THE MEDAL HE COVETED SO.

SEIZING A PARKED MOTOR-CYCLE, HE
ROARED OFF FOR THE NEAREST AIRFIELD.
THE ONE TO WHICH THE SQUADRON
CONTAINING KLAUS AND WILHELM HAD MOVED.

I AM NOT YET
BEATEN. I SET OUT TO
WIN MY KNIGHT'S CROSS IN
THE AIR AND THAT I
WILL DO — I SWEAR!

HIS MIND, LONG UNBALANCED, TIPPED OVER NOW INTO
INSANITY. HE KNEW HE WAS DOOMED — THE WITNESS TO THE
SHOOTING OF JURGEN WOULD SEE TO THAT. WHATEVER
JOURNEY HE NOW UNDERTOOK WOULD HAVE TO BE ONE-WAY.

AT THE AIRFIELD, AS HE STRODE WITH ALL HIS OLD ARROGANCE TOWARDS THE PILOTS
LOUNGING BY THEIR MACHINES, KLAUS AND WILHELM THOUGHT HE HAD COME FOR
THEM. BUT —

I AM TAKING A
MACHINE! TODAY, I WILL
PERSONALLY DESTROY MOST OF THE
BRITISH AIR FORCE. YOU MAY
COME WITH ME OR NOT.

ALL THE OTHERS GAPED, REALISING THIS MAN WAS CRAZY.
BUT THE GUN AIMED IN THEIR DIRECTION WAS STEADY
ENOUGH, SO NOBODY WAS ABOUT TO STOP HIM.

IT WAS DOUBTFUL THAT MEITZEL EVEN SAW KLAUS AND WILHELM. THEY STOOD WITH THEIR COLLEAGUES, BREATHING THEIR RELIEF, AS THE UNBALANCED NAZI HEADED FOR TAKE-OFF.

WHAT HAPPENED TO ALBERT, I WONDER?

FORTUNATELY FOR US, KLAUS, WE WILL PROBABLY LIVE LONG ENOUGH TO FIND OUT THE ANSWER. BUT MEITZEL WILL DIE TODAY. HE IS MAD!

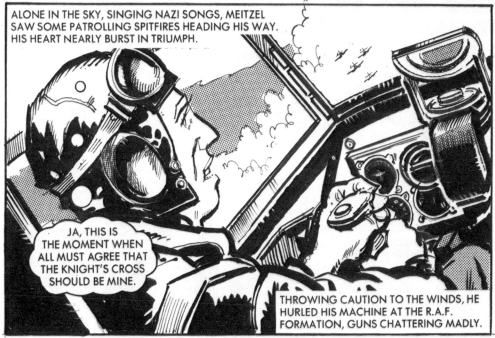

ALONE IN THE SKY, SINGING NAZI SONGS, MEITZEL SAW SOME PATROLLING SPITFIRES HEADING HIS WAY. HIS HEART NEARLY BURST IN TRIUMPH.

JA, THIS IS THE MOMENT WHEN ALL MUST AGREE THAT THE KNIGHT'S CROSS SHOULD BE MINE.

THROWING CAUTION TO THE WINDS, HE HURLED HIS MACHINE AT THE R.A.F. FORMATION, GUNS CHATTERING MADLY.

THE BRITISH PILOTS COULD HARDLY BELIEVE THEIR EYES AT THIS SUICIDAL, FOOLHARDY TACTIC.

IS THIS BLOKE BARMY?

MAYBE THE NAZIS HAVE GONE IN FOR THIS SUICIDE LARK!

ONE SPITFIRE BANKED, LATCHING ON TO THE Me109's TAIL.

PASSING RIGHT THROUGH THE SCATTERED BRITISH KITES, MEITZEL LAUGHED ALOUD IN HIS JOY, UNAWARE HE HAD MISSED THEM ALL.

THEY ARE GONE — SWEPT AWAY! THEY FELL BEFORE MY GUNS, ONE BY ONE.

HE DID NOT EVEN BOTHER TO GLANCE INTO HIS MIRROR. HAD HE DONE SO, HE WOULD HAVE SEEN IT FILLED BY A SPITFIRE, GUNS FLICKERING RED ALONG ITS WINGS.

HE PERISHED IN THAT SAVAGE ASSAULT, IN WHAT HE TRULY THOUGHT WAS A MOMENT OF GLORY.

AAARGH!

WITH HIM DIED HIS GRAND DREAMS OF A MEDAL TO WIN HIM LEGENDARY FAME.

STILL AMAZED, THE BRITISH PILOTS REFORMED TO HEAD FOR THEIR ORIGINAL TARGET.

HOW ABOUT THAT? MY FIRST OP AND I DOWN A JERRY. HOW ABOUT A FEW CHEERS?

YOU RECKON THAT COUNTS? THE BLOKE WAS COMMITTING SUICIDE.

THE FINAL IRONY WAS THAT FOR THE SECOND TIME OTTO MEITZEL HAD BEEN THE VICTIM OF A NOVICE PILOT.

IN BERLIN, DETAILS OF THE ESCAPADE REACHED A VERY HIGH LEVEL. ACUTELY EMBARRASSED, THESE MEN SAW TO IT THAT NO OTHER MEMBER OF THE MEITZEL FAMILY WOULD CAUSE THEM PROBLEMS.

ARREST THE FATHER AND SEE HE STAYS IN A CELL. BAD BLOOD LIKE THIS MUST BE STAMPED OUT. ERASE ALL HONOURS WON BY THE FAMILY, CONFISCATE THEIR ESTATES.

NO MEDALS, NO HONOURS. ONLY DISGRACE AND LASTING SHAME.

NOT LONG AFTER THIS, ALBERT GOT BACK HOME IN ONE PIECE, THANKS TO THE FRENCH RESISTANCE. WITHIN A FEW DAYS HE WAS FLYING AGAIN IN A GLEAMING NEW SPITFIRE WITH A LION EMBLEM TO MATCH.

THAT'S EVEN BETTER THAN THE OLD ONE, THANKS.

I'LL PUT ALL THE SWASTIKAS ON WHEN YOU GET BACK FROM THIS SORTIE, SIR. MAYBE YOU CAN ADD TO 'EM TODAY.

YET ON THAT AND EVERY OTHER SORTIE, ALTHOUGH ALBERT FOUGHT TO THE BEST OF HIS ABILITY, HE NEVER FORGOT THAT THE MAJORITY OF THE MEN HE WAS UP AGAINST WERE BASICALLY JUST THE SAME AS HIM.

AFTER THE WAR, HE SOUGHT OUT KLAUS AND WILHELM, RELIEVED TO FIND THEY HAD SURVIVED. ONLY THEN DID HE LEARN OF MEITZEL'S LAST MAD SORTIE . . . AND BEGAN A FRIENDSHIP WHICH ENDURES TO THIS DAY.

Commando
THE END

KEY TO THE COCKPITS

No. 2 HEINKEL 111

ORIGINALLY a civil aircraft, the Heinkel 111 was to become the standard medium bomber used by Germany during the Second World War. It was extremely successful in the early stages when opposition was slight, but it had its limitations and these were exaggerated by the increasing effectiveness of air defences. It soon became obsolete and should have been scrapped with its reputation intact, but Germany failed to find a replacement, so the Heinkel 111 was forced to soldier on till the end.

1. Emergency bomb jettison lever
2. Fuel gauge, starboard
3. Fuel gauge, port
4. Pilot's auxiliary windscreen
5. Repeater compass (magnetic)
6. Airspeed indicator
7. Altimeter
8. Rate-of-climb indicator
9. Artificial horizon
10. Control column
11. Pilot's intercom switchbox
12. Clock
13. Airspeed indicator
14. Throttle levers
15. Flap lever
16. Undercarriage selector
17. Starter switch, port
18. Starter switch, starboard
19. Emergency auto-pilot override
20. Rudder pedals
21. M.G. mounting
22. Bomb-sight
23. Signal flare pistol

SPITFIRE SPIRIT

IN THE DARK DAYS OF 1940, THE R.A.F. PILOTS WHO TOOK ON THE MIGHTY AIR ARMADAS OF THE LUFTWAFFE HAD PLENTY OF SPIRIT — FIGHTING SPIRIT. BUT THIS IS THE STORY OF ONE SQUADRON WHICH HAD A SECRET WEAPON ALL OF ITS OWN...

IN THESE EARLY DAYS, BOTH SIDES PRODUCED ACES — MEN WHO HAD THAT SPECIAL GIFT FOR COMBAT WHICH THE AVERAGE PILOT LACKED.

AND THIS SKILL SHOWED IN THE NUMBER OF KILLS THESE PILOTS EARNED.

ONE SUCH ACE WAS SQUADRON-LEADER HARRY "HANDLEBAR" HANLEY, A DEVIL-MAY-CARE CHARACTER WHO HAD AN EMBLEM OF A CROW ON HIS SPITFIRE WITH A MOUSTACHE ALMOST AS LARGE AS HIS OWN.

ON THE OTHER SIDE OF THE CHANNEL, THERE WAS ANOTHER ACE, MAJOR KURT KRANTZ OF THE LUFTWAFFE — LEADER OF THE NEWLY-FORMED "BLACK EAGLES" SQUADRON.

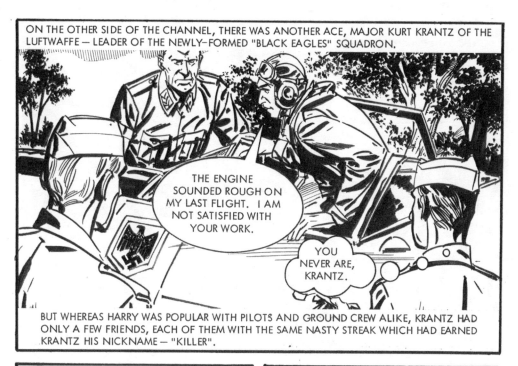

THE ENGINE SOUNDED ROUGH ON MY LAST FLIGHT. I AM NOT SATISFIED WITH YOUR WORK.

YOU NEVER ARE, KRANTZ.

BUT WHEREAS HARRY WAS POPULAR WITH PILOTS AND GROUND CREW ALIKE, KRANTZ HAD ONLY A FEW FRIENDS, EACH OF THEM WITH THE SAME NASTY STREAK WHICH HAD EARNED KRANTZ HIS NICKNAME — "KILLER".

THESE TWO HAD MET ONCE ALREADY, BUT NEITHER HAD GAINED THE UPPER HAND.

BLAST! HE'S DODGED ME.

HIMMEL, HE'S GOOD.

SCANT SECONDS LATER IT WAS HARRY'S TURN TO BE LUCKY.

CRIKEY, THAT TURN OF HIS NEARLY CAUGHT ME.

THE ENCOUNTER ENDED WITH HONOURS EVEN.

BUT HARRY WAS TOO EXPERIENCED TO BE PUT OFF SO EASILY. A DEFT TOUCH AT THE CONTROLS, AND HE WAS ON THE TAIL OF THE Me109.

SURPRISE, FRITZ! YOU'RE NOT HAVING IT ALL YOUR OWN WAY, OLD BOY.

ONLY THE GERMAN ACE'S SKILL THREW THE SPITFIRE OFF HIS TAIL — BUT NOT BEFORE HIS RUDDER HAD A FEW HOLES IN IT.

HIMMEL! HOW DID HE DO THAT? I THOUGHT I HAD HIM...

IT WAS FIRST BLOOD TO HARRY — AND THAT WAS A SITUATION KRANTZ DIDN'T LIKE AT ALL.

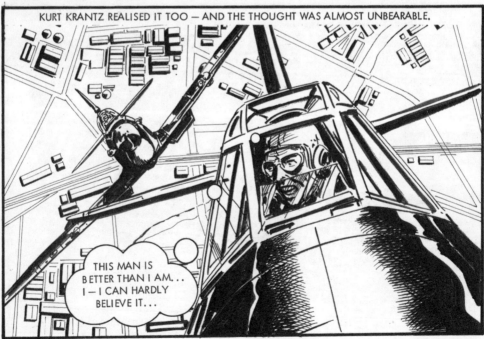

RELENTLESSLY HARRY WORE KRANTZ DOWN — UNTIL SUDDENLY HE SAW HIS CHANCE.

QUICKLY HARRY LINED UP ON THE DAMAGED GERMAN AIRCRAFT. IN A MATTER OF SECONDS, VICTORY WOULD BE HIS.

HIS THUMB JABBED DOWN, BUT HIS GUNS REMAINED SILENT.

UNAWARE OF THIS LATEST TRICK OF FATE, KRANTZ, UNABLE TO MANOEUVRE, WAITED FOR THE BURST OF FIRE WHICH WOULD CLAW HIS DAMAGED MACHINE FROM THE SKY.

HARRY WAS DISAPPOINTED, BUT HE KNEW HE'D WON. HE FLEW ALONGSIDE THE GERMAN AND GAVE HIM A WAVE BEFORE BREAKING OFF AND SETTING COURSE FOR BASE.

FIRE, THEN, BLAST YOU! GET IT OVER WITH!

BUT FOR NOW, LUCK WAS WITH KRANTZ.

MY, MY! HE DOES LOOK UPSET. BET HE NEVER MAKES IT HOME, THOUGH.

YOU CAN LAUGH NOW, BUT I SWEAR I'LL GET YOU, ENGLANDER!

ALMOST MAD WITH HATE AND FRUSTRATION, KRANTZ LIMPED AWAY, VOWING NEVER TO FORGET THE PILOT WHO HAD A CROW AS HIS EMBLEM.

He was lucky in one respect. At least he was over German-held France and not likely to end up as a P.O.W.

TOO LOW TO BALE OUT. MUST REACH THE AIRFIELD, AND TRY TO CRASH LAND HER...

Krantz did not know it, but his airfield had company — distinguished company, in the shape of Generaloberst Dieter Kruger.

MY FAVOURITE SQUADRON, GENTLEMEN. THERE IS A GREAT FUTURE FOR THE BLACK EAGLES.

IS IT TRUE WHAT THEY SAY ABOUT KURT KRANTZ — THAT HE IS INVINCIBLE IN THE AIR?

KRUGER WAS STILL BOASTING ABOUT HIS PET SQUADRON AS THEY ROLLED TO A HALT.

BUT AT THAT VERY MOMENT, THE INVINCIBLE HERO HIMSELF WAS FIGHTING JUST TO KEEP HIS CRIPPLED MACHINE IN THE AIR.

KRUGER'S PRAISES OF KRANTZ WERE SUDDENLY CUT SHORT BY THE STUTTERING ROAR OF A FAILING ENGINE.

HERR GENERAL! IT'S ONE OF OURS — AND IN TROUBLE!

SO DESPITE HARRY'S ASSESSMENT, KRANTZ MANAGED TO LAND ON HIS AIRFIELD. IT WAS, HOWEVER, MORE OF A CONTROLLED CRASH THAN A LANDING.

HIMMEL! I MUST HOLD HER, OR SHE WILL TURN OVER...

FINALLY THE MANGLED MACHINE SLEWED TO A HALT.

WHEN KRUGER LEFT, KRANTZ'S TEMPER WENT TOO — AS HIS BATMAN DISCOVERED.

GET OUT, FOOL — I WISH TO BE ALONE!

POOR OLD KRANTZ! HE HAD TO PICK THE DAY OF KRUGER'S VISIT TO GET SHOT TO BITS!

BUT THE BATMAN WASN'T THE ONLY ONE SMILING AT THE TAMING OF KILLER KRANTZ...

...THE GRIN WAS STILL ON HARRY'S FACE WHEN HE RETURNED FROM A COUPLE OF DAYS' LEAVE.

WHAT A BEAUTIFUL DAY. YOU'D HARDLY THINK THERE WAS A WAR ON. BET THAT JERRY ISN'T TOO HAPPY THOUGH — IF HE EVER MADE IT BACK!

HARRY'S THOUGHTS WERE INTERRUPTED WHEN HE SAW A FIGURE IN R.A.F. BLUE TRUDGING ALONG THE ROAD AHEAD OF HIM AND GOING IN THE SAME DIRECTION.

HELLO, HELLO! HE LOOKS ABOUT ALL IN. MUST BE HEADED FOR MY AIRFIELD AT WEST-CHURCH. HE'LL BE GLAD OF A LIFT, I'LL BET.

HOP IN, OLD CHUM. NOT THE WEATHER FOR WALKING, IS IT?

IT CERTAINLY ISN'T! THANKS A LOT.

SO IT WAS HARRY "HANDLEBAR" HANLEY, VETERAN ACE, MET PILOT OFFICER STEVE COBB, WHO HAD YET TO FLY HIS FIRST COMBAT SORTIE.

STEVE HAD NO IDEA WHO WAS GIVING HIM A LIFT. THE CIVILIAN CLOTHES GAVE NO CLUE AND HE HAD NO IDEA WHAT HARRY LOOKED LIKE.

HARRY GRINNED INWARDLY AS HE HEARD HIMSELF CLASSED AS "A BIT OF A CASE". STEVE CONTINUED, COMPLETELY UNAWARE THAT HE WAS TALKING ABOUT HIS COMPANION.

SUDDENLY STEVE CAUGHT THE AMUSEMENT IN HARRY'S EYES — AND EVERYTHING CLICKED INTO PLACE.

OH, I SAY — I MEAN. . . ARE YOU. . .?

RELAX, CHUM. YOU'RE LOOKING AT A REAL, LIVE ACE. BUT, YOU KNOW, I STILL FEEL FAIRLY HUMAN IN SPITE OF THAT!

STEVE'S EMBARRASSMENT SOON PASSED, FOR HARRY WAS THE KIND OF MAN IT WAS IMPOSSIBLE NOT TO BE FRIENDLY WITH.

MEANWHILE KRANTZ, STILL SMARTING WITH HUMILIATION AT HIS UNDIGNIFIED LANDING, WAS WALKING TO HIS NEW Me109, PREPARING FOR A MISSION HE WOULD ENJOY.

A STRIKE AGAINST WESTCHURCH! THE HEINKELS WILL SMASH THE BRITISH RIGHT ON THEIR OWN DOOR-STEP!

KRANTZ'S SQUADRON WAS TO PROVIDE FIGHTER COVER FOR A BOMBING FORCE DETAILED TO HIT THE VITAL R.A.F. FIGHTER BASE.

WITH ITS CARGO OF DESTRUCTION, THE GERMAN AIR ATTACK DRONED TOWARDS BRITAIN.

AND FOR ONE OF THE PILOTS AT LEAST, IT WAS MORE THAN JUST A TACTICAL TARGET.

KRANTZ'S MIND WAS NOW FILLED WITH A PERSONAL AND BITTER HATRED.

WITH LUCK WE'LL BLAST THAT ENGLANDER WHO MADE A FOOL OF ME RIGHT OUT OF EXISTENCE.

THE OBJECT OF THE GERMAN'S ANGER WAS NOW APPROACHING THE AIRFIELD — WITH THE MAN WHO WAS ALREADY A FIRM FRIEND.

FANCY YOU GOING TO THE SAME SCHOOL AS ME! OLD "STINKS" STILL THERE?

YES, SIR! HE WRECKED THE CHEMISTRY LAB THE WEEK I LEFT!

FOR A FEW SECONDS STEVE WAS DAZED. HE DIDN'T REALISE HARRY'S DANGER — TRAPPED AS HE WAS UNDER A CAR THAT COULD EXPLODE AT ANY SECOND.

WHAT HAPPENED? OH, MY HEAD...

GET OUT OF HERE, QUICK. SHE'S GOING TO BLOW!

THEN STEVE SAW THE FIX HARRY WAS IN AND IMMEDIATELY WENT TO HELP, DESPITE HARRY'S ANGRY YELL.

I TOLD YOU TO GET CLEAR, YOU YOUNG IDIOT!

I HEARD YOU, SIR. AND WITH ALL DUE RESPECT, PLEASE STOP YELLING. MY HEAD HURTS.

HEEDLESS OF HIS OWN SAFETY, STEVE STAYED TO RAISE THE CAR ENOUGH FOR HARRY TO GET CLEAR.

BOTH MEN GRINNED.   THEY WERE BRUISED AND SORE, BUT NOT SERIOUSLY HURT.

BUT WHEN THEY SLOWLY GOT TO THEIR FEET, HARRY'S FACE WAS GRIM.

IF YOU EVER DISOBEY ME AGAIN...

OK, SIR. BUT THOSE WERE EXCEPTIONAL CIRCUMSTANCES.

THEN SUDDENLY HE OFFERED HIS HAND TO THE YOUNG MAN WHOSE COURAGE HAD SAVED HIS LIFE.

OK, SON! BUT DON'T MAKE A HABIT OF IT.

DON'T WORRY, SIR!

THEIR FRIENDSHIP BECAME EVEN STRONGER OVER THE NEXT FEW DAYS. THEN, DURING A LULL IN THE AIR BATTLE, THEY WENT TO HELP THE LOCALS IN THE FIELDS.

WORKING US TO DEATH, YOU ARE, GEORGE!

WHAT, STRONG YOUNG FELLOWS LIKE YOU? YOU'RE GETTING LAZY, SITTING IN THOSE AEROPLANES ALL DAY!

BUT THE PEACEFUL SCENE WAS NOT TO LAST.   THERE WAS FEAR AND DEATH NEARBY — IN THE SHAPE OF KURT KRANTZ.

THE ENGLANDERS MUST NOT BE ALLOWED TO RELAX FOR A MOMENT. I'LL NEVER FORGET WHAT THAT CURSED SPITFIRE DID TO ME...

ALL EYES FLICKED SKYWARDS AS THE GERMAN AIRCRAFT DIVED IN.   THE MEN ON THE GROUND SAW WHAT WAS GOING TO HAPPEN — AND THEY COULD HARDLY BELIEVE IT.

HE'S — HE'S COMING IN FOR AN ATTACK... LOOK OUT!

GRIMLY HARRY MADE AN OATH. AS HE DID SO, THE STORM THAT HAD BEEN THREATENING ALL DAY SUDDENLY BROKE. A CHILL WIND SWEPT THE FIELD, AND EACH AIRMAN FELT A SHIVER RUN THROUGH HIM.

I'LL GET RID OF THOSE BLACK EAGLES IF I HAVE TO COME BACK FROM THE GRAVE TO DO IT!

THE NEXT DAY HARRY, STEVE AND ANOTHER NEW LAD, PILOT OFFICER BILL MARSHALL, TOOK OFF FOR A ROUTINE PATROL. BUT FATE DECIDED IT WAS TO BE FAR FROM ROUTINE.

IT'S USUALLY QUIET AROUND THIS TIME, LADS, BUT KEEP YOUR EYES PEELED.

HEADING FROM THE OPPOSITE DIRECTION, AND FLYING HIGHER THAN THE SPITFIRES, KRANTZ AND HIS BLACK EAGLES WERE LOOKING FOR A FIGHT.

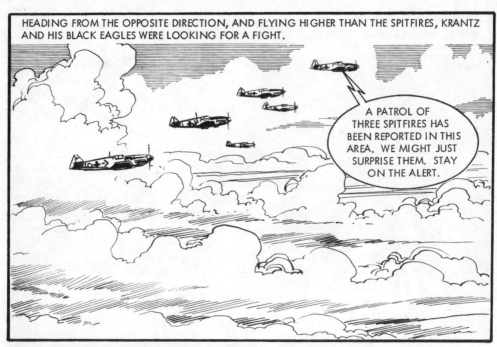

A PATROL OF THREE SPITFIRES HAS BEEN REPORTED IN THIS AREA. WE MIGHT JUST SURPRISE THEM. STAY ON THE ALERT.

BY THIS TIME STEVE WAS PRETTY BORED.

I'M FED UP — WHEN'S JERRY GOING TO APPEAR?

THE DEADLY, HARSH RATTLE OF Me109 MACHINE GUNS ANSWERED HIS QUESTION.

BLUE BLAZES!

THE FIRST THING STEVE KNEW ABOUT THE GERMANS WAS A TREMENDOUS CRASHING AS BULLETS RIPPED INTO HIS MACHINE. IN SECONDS THE SPITFIRE WAS ABLAZE.

THE SPITFIRES HAD BEEN WELL AND TRULY BOUNCED. ALMOST IMMEDIATELY BILL WAS ALSO HIT AND FOUND HIMSELF IN A FLYING WRECK LIKE STEVE.

HARRY WRENCHED HIS SPITFIRE OUT OF THE WAY AS STEVE AND BILL GOT OUT OF THEIR STRICKEN MACHINES.

THE LONE SPITFIRE SEEMED EASY MEAT FOR ONE OF THE BLACK EAGLES. BUT THEY SOON DISCOVERED HARRY WAS NO AMATEUR.

HIMMEL, WHERE HAS HE GONE — AAGH!

THAT NARROWS THE ODDS A BIT...

ONLY THEN DID KRANTZ RECOGNISE THE CROW ON HARRY'S FUSELAGE. ALL HIS HATE EMERGED ANEW, AND HE SCREAMED ORDERS AT HIS REMAINING AIRCRAFT.

IT'S THAT ACCURSED ENGLANDER AGAIN! ATTACK, ATTACK! HE MUST NOT BE ALLOWED TO ESCAPE.

STEVE, SWINGING ON THE END OF HIS CHUTE, FELT SUDDENLY HELPLESS. HE KNEW HARRY WAS NOW IN DIRE TROUBLE.

OLD HANDLEBAR IS REALLY UP AGAINST IT. AND WE CAN'T DO A THING TO HELP.

SUDDENLY STEVE AND HIS FELLOW PILOT REALISED THEY HAD TROUBLES OF THEIR OWN.   HEADING THEIR WAY WAS AN Me109 PILOT WITH MURDER IN MIND.

OH, NO! HE'S GOING TO RIDDLE US!

BUT THEN, WITH THE GERMAN PILOT ABOUT TO SEND DEATH SPRAYING AT THE TWO PILOTS, HARRY'S SPITFIRE ROARED IN BEHIND HIM.

ACH, THIS IS TOO EASY... AAAGH!

NO YOU DON'T, CHUM!

A SHORT BURST — AND THE GERMAN PILOT SLUMPED FORWARD. HARRY HAD SETTLED THE DEBT HE OWED TO STEVE.

THANKS TO HARRY, STEVE AND BILL REACHED FRIENDLY EARTH. BUT BOTH COULD THINK OF NOTHING BUT THEIR LEADER'S PLIGHT UP THERE IN A HOSTILE SKY.

WHEN THEY REACHED WESTCHURCH, THERE WAS NO NEWS AS YET OF HARRY. LIKE THE OTHERS, ALL THEY COULD DO WAS WAIT — AND HOPE.

HE'LL HAVE FOUGHT HIS WAY OUT. YOU'LL SEE.

THEY ALL HEARD IT TOGETHER. FAINT AT FIRST, BUT AT LAST THE SOUND OF A MERLIN ENGINE GREW LOUDER. THEN THE SPITFIRE APPEARED —

IT'S HIM — HE DID IT! WHAT DID I TELL YOU! THEY COULDN'T GET THE SKIPPER — NO NUMBER OF BLACK EAGLES!

THE SPITFIRE LANDED, AND ROLLED TO A HALT. BUT THEN THE CHEERS FADED OUT, FOR HARRY MADE NO EFFORT TO EMERGE. AND SUDDENLY EVERYONE WAS RUNNING TOWARDS THE AIRCRAFT.

SOME—THING'S WRONG! THE SKIPPER MUST BE HURT...

STEVE WAS THE FIRST TO REACH THE COCKPIT. WHAT HE FOUND MADE HIM GASP WITH SHOCK.

OH NO! THE SKIPPER... HE'S — HE'S DEAD!

RIDDLED WITH MACHINE—GUN FIRE, HARRY HAD SOMEHOW MANAGED TO BRING HIS PRECIOUS SPITFIRE HOME BEFORE HE DIED.

BY THAT NIGHT GLOOM HAD SPREAD OVER THE WHOLE OF WESTCHURCH, NORMALLY A BRIGHT, LIVELY STATION. HARRY'S DEATH HAD HIT EVERYONE HARD — ESPECIALLY STEVE.

THINGS WON'T BE THE SAME NOW WITH- OUT HANDLEBAR TO LEAD US, BILL. I LET HIM DOWN, NOT SEEING THOSE NAZIS.

DON'T BE STUPID, STEVE. NO ONE COULD HAVE SEEN THEM. DON'T BLAME YOUR- SELF.

IN THE EAGLES' MESS, HOWEVER, JUBILATION REIGNED. NEWS OF HARRY'S DEATH HAD REACHED THEM, AND KRANTZ FELT A DEEP GLOW OF SATISFACTION.

TO THE GREATEST OF THEM ALL — THE INVINCIBLE KILLER KRANTZ!

THIS RESTORES MY REPUTATION. EVEN IF I DIDN'T GET HIM ON MY OWN, I LED THE FLIGHT WHICH DID.

AFTER THAT, THE HEART SEEMED TO GO OUT OF THE SPITFIRE SQUADRON. THE NEXT DAY THEY GOT A MAULING FROM THE BLACK EAGLES, WHO REVELLED IN THEIR NEW-FOUND SUPERIORITY.

ACH, THESE ENGLANDERS ARE NO LONGER FIGHTERS. THIS IS TOO EASY...

PILOT OFFICER TED CARTER WAS A NEW ARRIVAL AT THE SQUADRON THAT DAY. TO ESCAPE THE AIR OF GLOOM, HE WENT OUT FOR A WALK WHICH TOOK HIM PAST THE HANGAR WHERE HARRY'S SPITFIRE STOOD, STILL UNDER REPAIR.

THE CHAPS SEEM REALLY DOWN IN THE MOUTH...HELLO, WHO'S THERE?

HE STROLLED INTO THE HANGAR...

THE SPITFIRES HAD BEEN IN THE AIR ONLY MINUTES WHEN STEVE HEARD THE URGENT VOICE IN HIS EARPHONES. AND IT WAS HARRY —

WATCH IT! BANDITS ABOVE! BREAK, YOU CHAPS.

RIGHT, SKIPPER! WHAT? BUT IT COULDN'T BE...

BUT EVERYONE HAD HEARD THE VOICE, AND PEELED OFF TO MEET THE ATTACK.

BUT THEN THERE WAS TIME ONLY FOR KILLING OR BEING KILLED.

AAGH!

THE BLACK EAGLES NO LONGER HAD THE ELEMENT OF SURPRISE THEY HAD HOPED FOR.

EVERY SECOND BROUGHT GREATER CONFIDENCE TO THE SPITFIRE PILOTS.

WE'RE HAMMERING 'EM. ALL BECAUSE OF THAT WARNING...

THE MESS WAS MORE CHEERFUL THAT EVENING. FOUR OF THE BLACK EAGLES HAD BEEN BROUGHT DOWN WITHOUT THE LOSS OF A SINGLE SPITFIRE. BUT STEVE STILL COULDN'T GET THE WARNING OUT OF HIS MIND.

IT SOUNDED LIKE HARRY'S VOICE — BUT THAT'S IMPOSSIBLE. IT MUST HAVE BEEN ONE OF THE CHAPS — BUT THEY ALL DENY IT...

THE DAY'S SETBACK HAD PUT KRANTZ IN NO MOOD TO LISTEN TO STORIES. BUT FRANZ WERNER CERTAINLY SEEMED TROUBLED WHEN THE FOUR NAZIS MET FOR A MEAL THAT NIGHT. IT APPEARED HE HAD SEEN SOME KIND OF VISION — NOT THAT ANYONE BELIEVED HIM, OF COURSE...

BUT I SAW IT, I TELL YOU...

LOOK, FRANZ — WHEN YOU SAY A SPITFIRE FLEW ALONGSIDE YOU, THEN SEEMED TO VANISH, I CANNOT TAKE YOU SERIOUSLY.

BUT THE YOUNG PILOT WAS INSISTENT, AND EVEN DESCRIBED AN INTERESTING DETAIL OF THE SPITFIRE —

IT HAD THAT EMBLEM ON IT, TOO. THE CROW WITH THE STUPID MOUSTACHE...

FRANZ, I FORBID YOU TO REPEAT THIS RIDICULOUS STORY. JUST SHUT UP!

POOR OLD KRANTZ IS GOING CRAZY. A GHOST SPIT-FIRE...RUBBISH!

NEXT DAY, THE BLACK EAGLES WERE PROVIDING ESCORT FOR A BOMBING RAID. WERNER STILL SEEMED TO CARRY A BURDEN OF WORRY. SCHULTZ TRIED TO REASSURE HIM.

SNAP OUT OF IT, FRANZ. IT WAS JUST YOUR IMAGINATION.

THAT'S EASY FOR YOU TO SAY. BUT YOU DIDN'T SEE THE SPITFIRE.

DURING THE RAID, WERNER'S GLOOMY FOREBODING SEEMED TO COME TRUE. A.A. FIRE SMASHED INTO HIS ENGINE, AND SUDDENLY HE WAS STRUGGLING TO LEAVE HIS DOOMED AIRCRAFT.

I KNEW IT...I HAD A FEELING. I MUST GET CLEAR!

BUT THIS TIME WERNER WAS LUCKY.

I MADE IT. MY FEELING MUST HAVE BEEN WRONG.

ALTHOUGH HE WAS OVER ENGLAND AND FACED CAPTURE, IT WAS PRE-FERABLE TO ROASTING ALIVE.

BUT WHEN HE REACHED THE GROUND, WERNER THOUGHT HE MIGHT YET AVOID CAPTURE.

PERHAPS I CAN STILL GET CLEAR. I'M NEAR THE COAST.

WERNER'S MIND WAS FULL OF ESCAPE PLANS AS HE HURRIED THROUGH THE WOOD — UNTIL HE TRIPPED OVER SOMETHING AND MEASURED HIS LENGTH ON THE GROUND.

I'LL STEAL A BOAT, AND — UGHHH!

THEN HE SAW WHAT HE HAD TRIPPED OVER — THE TAIL FIN OF A GERMAN DELAYED ACTION BOMB, OBVIOUSLY NEWLY DROPPED.

HIMMEL — A BOMB! AND ONE OF OURS! IS IT LIVE...

THEN THE BOMB DETONATED, ENDING THE LIFE OF FRANZ WERNER.

AAAGH!

BUT IN THE LAST SPLIT SECOND BEFORE DEATH OVERCAME HIM, HE THOUGHT HE HEARD A MOCKING CHUCKLE FROM THE WOOD...

BACK AT THE BLACK EAGLES' FIELD, NEWS CAME THAT WERNER'S Me109 HAD BEEN SEEN GOING DOWN IN FLAMES.

ACH! WELL, HE WAS A GOOD PILOT, EVEN IF HE WAS GOING CRAZY.

A GHOST SPITFIRE! POOR FRANZ. HE MUST HAVE HAD COMBAT NERVES.

BUT IT DIDN'T END THERE. ERICH SCHULTZ WAS NOT A MAN WITH A LOT OF IMAGINATION. BUT ON A LONE RECCE FLIGHT HE WAS AMAZED TO SEE A GHOSTLY SPITFIRE SLIDE IN BESIDE HIM...

WAS IST... A SPITFIRE! BUT HOW...?

SCHULTZ RUBBED HIS EYES IN DISBELIEF, AND WHEN HE LOOKED AGAIN, THE SPITFIRE HAD GONE.

HE BLURTED OUT HIS TALE TO KRANTZ AND BRANDT THAT NIGHT.

I KNOW THIS IS STUPID, BUT I SAW THAT LONE SPITFIRE THIS MORNING...

OH NO! NOT YOU TOO, SCHULTZ. I THOUGHT YOU HAD MORE SENSE.

SCORNFUL AS HE WAS, KRANTZ COULD SEE SCHULTZ WAS SHAKEN. BRANDT, TOO, SEEMED UNEASY, SO HE DECIDED TO ACT.

LOOK, SCHULTZ. I'M TAKING YOU OFF COMBAT DUTY FOR A WHILE. JUST UNTIL YOU GET THIS SPITFIRE RUBBISH OUT OF YOUR MIND.

WELL, I THOUGHT I SAW IT. IMAGINATION CAN PLAY FUNNY TRICKS AT TIMES.

THERE THE MATTER RESTED — KRANTZ HOPED. AND TO MAKE SURE SCHULTZ HAD LITTLE TIME TO BROOD HE WAS ASSIGNED TO HELP KRANTZ PASS ON SOME SKILLS TO NEW PILOTS.

SO THAT AFTERNOON, KRANTZ TOOK SCHULTZ AND A NEW EAGLE UP ON A FORMATION EXERCISE.

IT SEEMED NORMAL ROUTINE FLYING — FOR A WHILE.

BUT SUDDENLY SCHULTZ'S Me109 TOOK VIOLENT AVOIDING ACTION, WHICH LED TO DISASTER FOR HIMSELF AND HIS WINGMAN.

AAAH — LOOK OUT — A SPITFIRE!

SCHULTZ! WAS IST?

STEVE, DELIGHTED WITH HIS NEW SPITFIRE, STILL THOUGHT A LOT OF ITS PREVIOUS OWNER.

WELL, SIR, IF I CAN FLY IT WITH AS MUCH GALLANTRY AND SKILL AS YOU DID, I WON'T GO FAR WRONG.

EVEN WITHOUT HARRY'S VAST EXPERIENCE, STEVE STILL FLEW WITH ENOUGH SKILL TO GET HIM SIX KILLS IN A SINGLE WEEK.

GOT YOU! THAT'S ANOTHER ONE FOR THE SKIPPER.

BUT ON ONE ATTACK HIS VICTIM, CARRYING A FULL LOAD OF BOMBS, WENT UP IN AN EXPLOSION THAT SET STEVE'S SPITFIRE SPINNING AWAY WITH THE BLAST.

GOT HIM! HE'S ON FIRE, AND — UHHH!

DESPITE HIS RESTRAINING STRAPS, HE PITCHED FORWARD, BLACKNESS ENVELOPING HIM AS HIS HEAD STRUCK THE INSTRUMENT PANEL.

ANOTHER PILOT SAW STEVE'S SPITFIRE GO COMPLETELY OUT OF CONTROL AND THOUGHT THE WORST.

IT LOOKED LIKE THE END HAD COME FOR STEVE. UNCONSCIOUS, THERE WAS NO WAY HE COULD PULL OUT OF THE DIVE.

BUT THEN STEVE CAME TO, GROGGY AND SOMEWHAT SURPRISED TO FIND HIMSELF STILL ALIVE.

THE — THE SPIT MUST HAVE LEVELLED ITSELF OUT. THAT'S INCREDIBLE...

AFTER HIS ESCAPE, ANOTHER ODD INCIDENT MADE STEVE PONDER. A RAIDER WAS REPORTED JUST OFF THE COAST, AND STEVE WAS SENT TO INTERCEPT.

THERE IT IS — I'M RIGHT ONTO IT. I CAN'T MISS!

BUT STEVE'S INTENDED VICTIM WAS NO RAIDER. A LOST BLENHEIM HAD INADVERTENTLY FLOWN INTO GRAVE DANGER.

HECK! I THINK WE'RE WAY OFF COURSE, MATE, AND THE BLASTED RADIO IS ON THE BLINK.

ALL WE NEED NOW IS A JERRY ON OUR TAIL.

BUT IT WAS A SPITFIRE ON THEIR TAIL, AND AT THAT MOMENT IT WAS AS DANGEROUS TO THEM AS ANY GERMAN FIGHTER...

BUT, EVEN THOUGH STEVE DESPERATELY JABBED AT HIS GUNS, NO DEADLY STREAM OF TRACER APPEARED.

BLAST, THE GUNS ARE JAMMED...

THEN THE CLOUD SUDDENLY BROKE UP AND STEVE SAW WHAT IT WAS HE HAD ALMOST SHOT UP.

IT'S A BLENHEIM... BUT THERE'S THE JERRY FURTHER DOWN THERE! THANK GOODNESS MY GUNS ARE JAMMED, OR I'D HAVE NAILED OUR OWN CHAPS!

HE TURNED AWAY FROM THE BLENHEIM AND RACED AFTER THE HEINKEL WHICH WAS HEADING FOR MORE CLOUD.

MORE OUT OF SHEER FRUSTRATION THAN ANYTHING ELSE, STEVE MADE A DIVE AT THE RAIDER, JABBING WISTFULLY AT HIS GUNS. AMAZINGLY THEY SENT A STREAM OF HOT LEAD TEARING INTO THE HEINKEL.

THE GUNS HAVE CLEARED! BOY, I'M IN BUSINESS AGAIN.

A TRAGEDY HAD BEEN AVERTED BECAUSE THE GUNS HAD REFUSED TO FIRE AT FIRST. AND BECAUSE THEY HAD MYSTERIOUSLY CLEARED, HE'D GOT THE RAIDER. IT WAS ODD — VERY ODD.

I JUST CAN'T FIGURE IT OUT. THE CHANCES AGAINST THAT HAPPENING ARE FANTASTIC. BUT IT WORKED OUT OK...

BUT IF STEVE WAS HAVING GOOD FORTUNE, THE EAGLES WERE HAVING ANYTHING BUT. BRANDT, AFTER A SOLO FLIGHT, WALKED TOWARDS KRANTZ WITH A FACE DRAINED OF ALL COLOUR.

BRANDT — HE'S SEEN SOMETHING, OR THINKS HE HAS. AND I BET I KNOW WHAT IT IS...

KRANTZ WAS RIGHT. BRANDT, IN THE PRIVACY OF KRANTZ'S OFFICE, BLURTED OUT HIS STORY — THE SAME STORY AS THE OTHERS.

SO, THAT ACCURSED SPITFIRE AGAIN! ARE YOU GOING TO LET IMAGINATION PLAY TRICKS WITH YOU TOO, BRANDT?

I SAW IT, I TELL YOU! AND LOOK WHAT HAPPENED TO THE OTHERS. IT'S A JINX!

A COLD FURY WELLED UP IN KRANTZ — AND ALSO THE FIRST STIRRINGS OF FEAR AT THE TALE OF THE LONE SPITFIRE. BUT HE WOULDN'T ADMIT IT — EVEN TO HIMSELF.

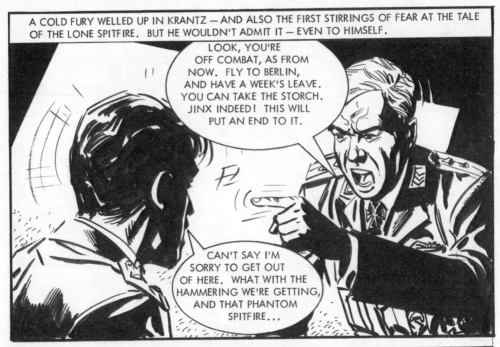

LOOK, YOU'RE OFF COMBAT, AS FROM NOW. FLY TO BERLIN, AND HAVE A WEEK'S LEAVE. YOU CAN TAKE THE STORCH. JINX INDEED! THIS WILL PUT AN END TO IT.

CAN'T SAY I'M SORRY TO GET OUT OF HERE. WHAT WITH THE HAMMERING WE'RE GETTING, AND THAT PHANTOM SPITFIRE...

IN SPITE OF HIMSELF, KRANTZ WAS SCARED.

EVER SINCE WE KILLED THAT ENGLANDER, WE'VE DONE NOTHING RIGHT. PERHAPS WE ARE INDEED JINXED.

BRANDT WAS SCARED TOO, BUT UNLIKE KRANTZ, HE ADMITTED IT.

THANK GOODNESS I'M GETTING AWAY. THAT SPITFIRE WOULD GIVE ME NIGHTMARES.

KRANTZ HEARD THE SPLINTERING, JUDDERING CRASH AS HE SAT DEEP IN THOUGHT. HE KNEW WHAT HAD HAPPENED EVEN BEFORE HE RUSHED OUTSIDE TO LOOK.

IT'S BRANDT! THE STORCH HAS CRASHED!

IT WAS OBVIOUS BRANDT WAS BEYOND HELP EVEN BEFORE KRANTZ REACHED THE STORCH.

WHAT HAPPENED HERE, LEUTNANT?

THE STORCH WAS ABOUT TO LIFT, WHEN HE SEEMED TO SWERVE, HERR MAJOR. AS IF TO AVOID SOMETHING...

KRANTZ FELT HIS BLOOD RUN COLD. SCHULTZ HAD ALSO DIED WHEN HE HAD TRIED TO AVOID SOMETHING...

BOTH MEN KNEW THAT SOMETHING IMPORTANT WAS ABOUT TO HAPPEN — THOUGH NEITHER KNEW WHAT OR WHY.

IT WAS AS IF SOME OUTSIDE FORCE WAS RESPONSIBLE FOR THEIR ACTIONS.

A LESS EXPERIENCED PILOT WOULD NOT HAVE SPOTTED THE SPITFIRE BREAK CLOUD ABOVE HIM, BUT KRANTZ DID.

ACH, SO — A SPITFIRE! A BURST OF BULLETS WILL PROVE THIS ONE IS NO PHANTOM!

THEN KRANTZ SAW, FOR THE FIRST TIME IN THIS COMBAT, THE EMBLEM WHICH HAD PLAGUED HIM FOR SO LONG.

WAS IST? IT — IT CAN'T BE YET IT IS. THAT CURSED SPITFIRE AGAIN!

STEVE KNEW HE HAD THE FIGHT OF HIS SHORT OPERATIONAL LIFE ON HIS HANDS. A LIFE THAT MIGHT ABRUPTLY BE TERMINATED IF HE MADE ONE ERROR.

THIS MUST BE THEIR LEADER. I'D BETTER REMEMBER ALL MY LESSONS THIS TIME — IF ONLY TO GET EVEN FOR HARRY...

THE NEXT MINUTES WERE A HECTIC TIME OF TURNING, TWISTING MANOEUVRES, WITH EACH PILOT STRIVING TO DEAL THE FINAL BLOW TO HIS ENEMY.

AT LEAST I KNOW THIS IS NO PHANTOM. THESE BULLETS ARE REAL ENOUGH.

AND WHILE KRANTZ WAS BY FAR THE MORE EXPERIENCED PILOT, STEVE FOUND THE SPITFIRE REACTING ALMOST BEFORE HE TOUCHED THE CONTROLS.

SUDDENLY KRANTZ FELT HIS MACHINE SHUDDER AS A LONG BLAST RIPPED INTO THE ENGINE. BUT AS HE PREPARED TO BALE OUT, HE KNEW THAT THE SPITFIRE TOO WAS NEARLY FINISHED.

I MUST GET OUT! BUT THAT SPITFIRE MUST ALSO BE IN BAD TROUBLE.

KRANTZ WAS RIGHT. HIS FINAL BURST HAD MADE THE CONTROLS OF THE SPITFIRE USELESS. STEVE TOO HAD TO BALE OUT.

WELL, I DOWNED HIM. EVEN IF I DID LOSE THE SKIPPER'S SPITFIRE TO DO IT.

STEVE HAD ILL LUCK ON LANDING. HIS PARACHUTE CAUGHT IN A TREE, AND HE WAS MOMENTARILY STUNNED — A FACT WHICH KRANTZ, WHO HAD LANDED NEARBY, NOTED WITH AN EVIL GRIN.

GUT! NOW TO FINISH THE JOB I BEGAN UP THERE. ONE SHOT SHOULD BE SUFFICIENT, I THINK.

THE STUTTERING ROAR OF A MERLIN ENGINE STOPPED KRANTZ IN HIS TRACKS. HE LOOKED ROUND TO SEE THE DAMAGED SPITFIRE BEARING DOWN ON HIM, SEEMINGLY OUT OF CONTROL.

HIMMEL! IT'S HEADING THIS WAY!

STEVE WENT ON FLYING WITH THE SQUADRON, PILOTING THE SPITFIRES THAT EVENTUALLY BROUGHT TO PASS HARRY "HANDLEBAR" HANLEY'S PREDICTION — THAT THE SKIES WOULD BE CLEARED OF THE ONCE PROUD, ONCE INVINCIBLE BLACK EAGLES.

THEY DID IT WITH FIGHTING SPIRIT. AND WHO CAN SAY THAT THERE WASN'T A GHOST SPITFIRE TO HELP WHEN THINGS GOT REALLY ROUGH?

Commando
THE END

FLY PAST

Commando

No. 7 – SUPERMARINE SPITFIRE Mk IX

Shown in the markings of 64 Squadron, R.A.F., its first squadron, in June, 1942.

DEATH of the COBRA

PEOPLE FIGHT IN WARS FOR DIFFERENT
REASONS — PERHAPS TO DEFEND THEIR
COUNTRY OR TO CONQUER AN ENEMY. BUT
THERE ARE ALSO MEN WHO REVEL IN KILLING
AND DESTRUCTION, ACTING LIKE MAD DOGS.
ONE OF THESE WAS KURT VON SCHLANGE —
FIGHTER PILOT, DEDICATED NAZI...AND COLD-
BLOODED MURDERER. HIS NAME MEANT
"SNAKE", AND HE REALLY LIVED UP TO IT!

SUMMER 1937. AT AN AIRFIELD IN ENGLAND THE INTERNATIONAL AIR RACES WERE IN FULL SWING. PILOTS FROM ALL OVER EUROPE CAME TO MATCH THEIR SKILLS IN THE VARIED PROGRAMME OF EVENTS.

MOST EXCITING OF ALL WAS THE CLOSED CIRCUIT RACE, THE SLEEK LITTLE MACHINES FLYING LAPS OF A SQUARE COURSE MARKED OUT BY PYLONS. THE CROWD WAS ON ITS TOES AS THE RACE ENTERED ITS CLOSING STAGE.

LEADING THE FIELD WAS KURT VON SCHLANGE, SON OF A MILLIONAIRE GERMAN INDUSTRIALIST. SCHLANGE'S AIRCRAFT HAD BEEN SPECIALLY BUILT, AND WAS FASTER THAN ANY OF THE OTHERS.

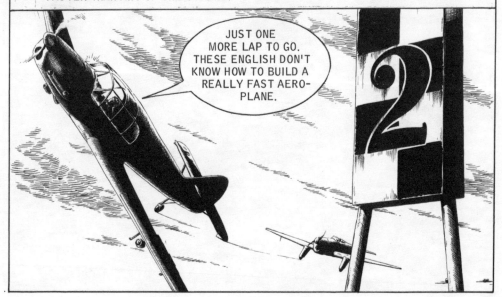

BUT IN THIS EVENT PURE SPEED WAS NOT ENOUGH. THE ART WAS TO TURN THE PYLONS AS TIGHTLY AS POSSIBLE, AND BRIAN CRAIG WAS A PAST-MASTER AT HAIR'S-BREADTH FLYING.

THAT'S A FINE AIRCRAFT YOU'VE GOT, CHUM, BUT YOU'RE NOT GETTING THE BEST OUT OF HER...

BRIAN HAD THAT TOUCH WHICH ENABLED HIM TO COAX MAXIMUM PERFORMANCE FROM ANY AIRCRAFT, AND HE COULD JUDGE HIS TURNS TO AN INCH. TRY AS HE MIGHT, SCHLANGE COULD NOT SHAKE OFF THE ENGLISHMAN'S MACHINE.

BLITZEN, THAT ACCURSED ENGLANDER IS STILL THERE! HOW DOES HE DO IT?

NOW IT WAS THE LAST LAP, AND BRIAN WAS THOROUGHLY ENJOYING HIMSELF. HE LOVED TO FLY, HAD SERVED BRIEFLY WITH THE R. A. F. AND WAS NOW ON THE RESERVE, WHILE MAKING A RATHER SHAKY LIVING AS A FREELANCE PILOT.

SCHLANGE HAD INCREASED HIS SPEED EVEN FURTHER TO TRY AND SHAKE BRIAN OFF. SO HE HAD TO SWING WIDE AT THE NEXT PYLON — WHICH WAS JUST WHAT BRIAN WANTED.

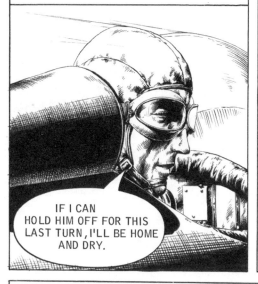

BOILING WITH RAGE AT LOSING THE LEAD, SCHLANGE OPENED HIS THROTTLE. BRIAN WATCHED HIM CLOSE THE GAP.

IF I CAN HOLD HIM OFF FOR THIS LAST TURN, I'LL BE HOME AND DRY.

THE LAST PYLON WOULD HAVE TO BE BRIAN'S TIGHTEST-EVER TURN IF HE WERE TO HOLD HIS LEAD. THEN A SHADOW FELL ACROSS HIS COCKPIT.

THAT IDIOT WILL RAM ME!

THE GERMAN'S PLANE EDGED CLOSER. BRIAN COULD SEE VON SCHLANGE SNEERING AT HIM, AND DESPERATELY PULLED HIS TURN TIGHTER. HIS WINGTIP TOUCHED THE PYLON...

TOUGH LUCK, ENGLANDER!

THE DIRTY RAT — HE FORCED ME RIGHT INTO THAT!

STILL TRAVELLING AT OVER A HUNDRED MILES AN HOUR THE LITTLE PLANE SKIDDED WILDLY, STARTED TO SPIN. ONLY BRIAN'S SKILL AVERTED A FATAL CRASH, BUT WHAT HAPPENED WAS BAD ENOUGH.

HANG ON, OLD CHAP!

A RACE STEWARD RAN UP AS THE WRECKED AIRCRAFT JUDDERED TO A HALT. HE FOUND BRIAN BRUISED, SHAKEN, BUT VERY MUCH ALIVE AND IN A TOWERING RAGE.

THE LOUSY RAT! COULDN'T WIN FAIRLY, SO HE FLIES ME INTO THE DECK. I'LL MURDER HIM...

STEADY, OLD MAN. I SAW IT ALL. COME ON, I'VE A CAR HERE. LET'S GET BACK TO THE DROME AND LODGE AN OBJECTION.

WHEN BRIAN PUT HIS OBJECTION, KURT VON SCHLANGE EYED THE DISHEVELLED FIGURE COLDLY. HE WAS NOT USED TO BEING SPOKEN TO IN THIS MANNER.

IF I HAD MY WAY I'D GIVE YOU THE HIDING OF YOUR LIFE!

WATCH YOUR TONGUE. REMEMBER MY FATHER IS A SENIOR MEMBER OF THE PARTY...

YOU'RE NOT IN GERMANY NOW, HERR VON SCHLANGE. WE HAVE DIFFERENT RULES. YOU ARE DIS-QUALIFIED.

SUDDENLY VON SCHLANGE REALISED THAT THE NAZI PARTY CUT NO ICE HERE. AT HOME EVERYBODY LOOKED UP TO HIM, BUT ENGLAND WAS A FREE COUNTRY. ANGRILY HE SPUN ON HIS HEEL AND STAMPED OFF.

ARROGANT YOUNG PUPPY. SERVE HIM RIGHT IF YOU DID GIVE HIM A PASTING. STILL, HE'S LOST THE TROPHY — NOT THAT THAT DOES YOU ANY GOOD.

NO. I DIDN'T FINISH THE COURSE, SO I GET NOTHING.

EVERY PENNY BRIAN COULD SCRAPE TOGETHER HAD GONE INTO THE LITTLE AIRCRAFT THAT WAS NOW A TOTAL WRECK. AS HE GLOOMILY SURVEYED THE SHAMBLES HE WAS JOINED BY HIS YOUNGER BROTHER, DAVID.

IT MAY NOT BE AS BAD AS IT LOOKS. WE COULD REBUILD HER...

NOT A CHANCE. MIGHT GET A FEW QUID FOR THE ENGINE, BUT THAT'S ALL. YOU GO ON BACK TO THE DIGS. I'LL SEE ABOUT MOVING THE BITS BACK TO THE AERODROME.

THIS TURNED OUT TO BE A LONG AND DIFFICULT TASK, AND NIGHT HAD FALLEN BEFORE BRIAN COULD LEAVE THE AIRFIELD.

BIT SPOOKY ALONG HERE – FEELS AS IF SOMEBODY'S WATCHING ME. OH, COME ON, CRAIG, YOU'RE TOO OLD TO BE SCARED OF BOGEY-MEN!

BUT HIS PREMONITION WAS CORRECT. HARDLY HAD HE GONE A FEW YARDS WHEN THREE SHADOWY FIGURES CONFRONTED HIM. VON SCHLANGE AND HIS FRIENDS WERE OUT FOR REVENGE.

HERE, WHAT ARE YOU DOING? LET GO!

NONE OF THE MEN SPOKE. TWO OF THEM HELD HIM WHILE THE THIRD BATTERED HIM UNMERCIFULLY.

UGH!

THE SILENT, SAVAGE BEATING WENT ON. THEN ONE OF THE FIGURES TURNED HIS HEAD. FOOTSTEPS WERE HURRYING DOWN THE LANE.

MAN KOMMT, SCHNELL!

NO YOU DON'T...

HALF-CONSCIOUS THOUGH HE WAS, BRIAN LUNGED FORWARDS. SOMETHING CAME AWAY IN HIS FINGERS, THEN THE ASSAILANTS WERE GONE. NEXT MOMENT DAVID ARRIVED.

BRIAN, WHAT HAPPENED?

THREE THUGS ROUGHED ME UP. GIVE ME A HAND...

WORRIED BY BRIAN'S LATENESS, DAVID HAD COME TO MEET HIM. BACK IN THEIR LODGINGS, HE SAW WHAT BRIAN HAD SNATCHED FROM HIS ATTACKER — A BLACK SCARF WITH A COBRA EMBROIDERED ON IT.

LAST TIME I SAW THIS SCARF WAS ROUND VON SCHLANGE'S NECK. SEEMS HE'S A BAD LOSER — A REAL SNAKE!

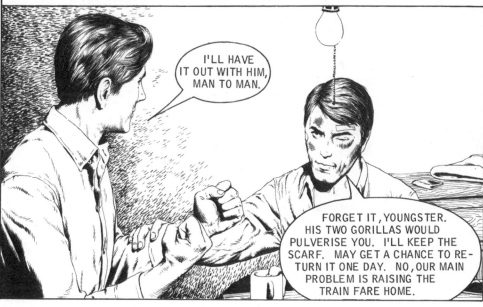

DAVID CRAIG SHARED HIS BROTHER'S FIERY TEMPER. HE WAS MORE THAN READY TO GO LOOKING FOR THE COWARDLY GERMAN AND AVENGE HIS BROTHER'S WOUNDS.

I'LL HAVE IT OUT WITH HIM, MAN TO MAN.

FORGET IT, YOUNGSTER. HIS TWO GORILLAS WOULD PULVERISE YOU. I'LL KEEP THE SCARF. MAY GET A CHANCE TO RE-TURN IT ONE DAY. NO, OUR MAIN PROBLEM IS RAISING THE TRAIN FARE HOME.

SADLY DAVID SAT DOWN.

THAT'S TRUE, WE'RE BROKE. BUT TO THINK A MAN COULD BEHAVE THAT WAY.

I'M AFRAID HE'S TYPICAL OF GERMANY THESE DAYS. THAT'S WHY THE R.A.F. IS EXPANDING. I EXPECT I'LL BE RE-CALLED ANY TIME, AND YOU'RE GOING UP TO CRANWELL IN THE AUTUMN, SO WITH LUCK WE WON'T STARVE.

BRIAN PUT THE SCARF IN HIS POCKET AND GRIMLY STARTED TO PACK HIS SUITCASE. WITHOUT FUNDS HIS RACING DAYS WERE OVER.

FRANCE, MAY 1940. THE "PHONEY WAR" WAS OVER. GERMAN TANKS HAD SMASHED THROUGH BELGIUM AND HOLLAND, SWEEPING ASIDE ALL OPPOSITION, AND RANGING ABOVE THEM WERE THE BLACK-CROSSED DIVE BOMBERS OF THE LUFTWAFFE.

THE ALL TOO FEW BRITISH AND FRENCH FIGHTERS ROSE TO MEET THE ONSLAUGHT. WHAT THEY LACKED IN NUMBERS THEY MADE UP FOR IN SKILL AND DAUNTLESS COURAGE.

IN THE THICK OF THE FRAY WAS FLIGHT LIEUTENANT BRIAN CRAIG, NOW A FLIGHT COMMANDER IN A HURRICANE SQUADRON. LOSSES WERE HEAVY, AND REPLACEMENT PILOTS WERE BEING RUSHED FROM ENGLAND, AMONG THEM PILOT OFFICER DAVID CRAIG.

SQUADRON LEADER GILCHRIST WAS A WELL-LIKED LEADER.

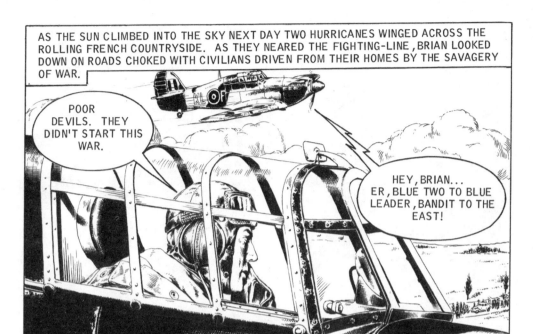

AS THE SUN CLIMBED INTO THE SKY NEXT DAY TWO HURRICANES WINGED ACROSS THE ROLLING FRENCH COUNTRYSIDE. AS THEY NEARED THE FIGHTING-LINE, BRIAN LOOKED DOWN ON ROADS CHOKED WITH CIVILIANS DRIVEN FROM THEIR HOMES BY THE SAVAGERY OF WAR.

POOR DEVILS. THEY DIDN'T START THIS WAR.

HEY, BRIAN... ER, BLUE TWO TO BLUE LEADER, BANDIT TO THE EAST!

BRIAN'S HEAD SNAPPED ROUND. A MESSERSCHMITT WAS CURVING DOWN TOWARDS THE CROWDED ROAD. EVEN AS HE WATCHED, ITS GUNS SPAT FLAME, AND DAVID GAVE CHASE AT ONCE.

HE'S SHOOTING AT THE REFUGEES! OF ALL THE FOUL...

STEADY ON, BLUE TWO, HE WON'T BE ALONE.

BRIAN HAD LEARNED HIS TRADE QUICKLY IN THE LAST FEW DAYS. HE GLANCED INTO THE SUN AND YELLED A WARNING.

TWO MORE OF THEM, IN THE SUN. BREAK LEFT, BLUE TWO, FOR PETE'S SAKE!

BUT HE WAS TOO LATE. CANNON SHELLS WERE ALREADY SLAMMING INTO DAVID'S HURRICANE. THROTTLE WIDE, BRIAN CHARGED INTO THE FRAY.

THESE CHAPS KNOW THEIR STUFF!

BRIAN BREATHED A SIGH OF RELIEF AS DAVID'S PARACHUTE BLOSSOMED. THEN THE TWO MESSERSCHMITTS WERE ON HIM, AND HE WAS FIGHTING TOOTH AND NAIL.

CAN'T HOLD OUT MUCH LONGER. SOON BE JOINING DAVID. OH, OH — HERE COMES THE OTHER HUN.

AND THIS Me109 CARRIED THE MARK OF THE COBRA — AND THE PILOT WAS KURT VON SCHLANGE.

BUT VON SCHLANGE IGNORED THE BATTLE. INSTEAD, HE FLEW TOWARDS DAVID WHO WATCHED CURIOUSLY AS THE SLEEK FIGHTER BANKED... THEN A COLD FEAR CLUTCHED AT HIS HEART.

HE'S NOT GOING TO... OH, NO!

A SECOND LATER THE MESSERSCHMITT'S GUNS FLAMED — AND DAVID DIED AS HE HUNG FROM HIS CHUTE.

THE CALLOUS, BRUTAL ACT DROVE BRIAN INTO A FRENZY OF RAGE AND HATE. HE FLUNG HIS BATTERED HURRICANE AT HIS ADVERSARIES. BUT NOW THE ENGINE WAS MISFIRING, THE CONTROLS NEARLY ALL SHOT AWAY.

COME ON, WHAT ARE YOU WAITING FOR? FINISH ME OFF AND HAVE DONE WITH IT! BUT WHERE ARE THEY GOING?

BRIAN LOST NO TIME IN WONDERING, BUT HEADED THE BATTLE-TORN HURRICANE FOR AN OPEN FIELD. BUT HIS RESPITE WAS BRIEF, FOR THE THIRD MESSERSCHMITT FASTENED ON TO HIS TAIL. A SUDDEN REALISATION STRUCK HIM.

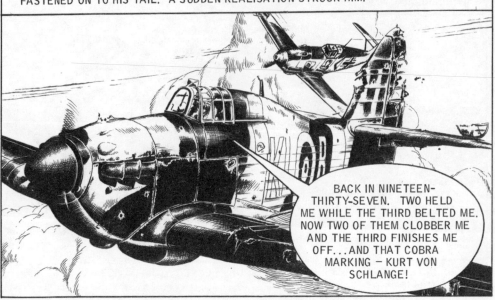

BACK IN NINETEEN-THIRTY-SEVEN. TWO HELD ME WHILE THE THIRD BELTED ME. NOW TWO OF THEM CLOBBER ME AND THE THIRD FINISHES ME OFF...AND THAT COBRA MARKING – KURT VON SCHLANGE!

AS BULLETS AGAIN HAMMERED THE TATTERED HURRICANE, BRIAN SLAMMED IT DOWN ON ITS BELLY IN THE FIELD. EVEN BEFORE IT GROUND TO A HALT, HE WAS OUT OF THE COCKPIT AND RUNNING.

IT'S HIM ALL RIGHT – CAN'T FIGHT MAN TO MAN. HERE HE COMES AGAIN!

BRIAN ZIG-ZAGGED FRANTICALLY AS BULLETS SNARLED ROUND HIM. GASPING FOR BREATH, HE HURLED HIMSELF INTO A DITCH AS THE COBRA-MARKED MESSERSCHMITT THUNDERED OVERHEAD.

THAT MAN IS NOT HUMAN, TO KILL A HELPLESS AVIATOR IN HIS PARA-CHUTE.

KEEP DOWN! HE'S STILL AFTER ME.

AT LAST VON SCHLANGE TIRED OF HIS FOUL SPORT AND TURNED AWAY, HIS BODY-GUARDS IN CLOSE ATTENDANCE. BRIAN RAN TO WHERE DAVID'S BODY LAY, THE LOOK OF DISBELIEF STILL FROZEN ON THE DEAD FEATURES.

YOU'LL ANSWER FOR THIS, VON SCHLANGE. I'LL HUNT YOU DOWN AND DE-STROY YOU IF IT TAKES THE REST OF MY LIFE. I'LL WEAR YOUR SCARF UNTIL I DO, THAT'S A PROMISE.

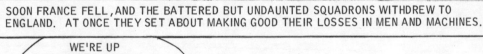

SOON FRANCE FELL, AND THE BATTERED BUT UNDAUNTED SQUADRONS WITHDREW TO ENGLAND. AT ONCE THEY SET ABOUT MAKING GOOD THEIR LOSSES IN MEN AND MACHINES.

WE'RE UP TO STRENGTH WITH AIRCRAFT NOW, AND THE LAST REPLACEMENT PILOTS ARE DUE THIS AFTER-NOON.

LET'S HOPE WE HAVE ENOUGH TIME TO LICK THEM INTO SHAPE BEFORE THE FIREWORKS START OVER HERE.

THE PILOTS ASSIGNED TO BRIAN'S FLIGHT WERE CURIOUS ABOUT THEIR SILENT, WITHDRAWN LEADER.

HE'S A QUEER FISH. HARDLY SAYS A WORD, AND AL-WAYS WEARS THAT SNAKE SCARF.

HE KNOWS HIS STUFF AND HATES THE GERMANS LIKE POISON. I'M GLAD HE'S ON OUR SIDE.

ONE FACT HAD BECOME ALL TOO PLAIN IN FRANCE. TRUSTY WARHORSE THOUGH SHE WAS, THE HURRICANE WAS NO MATCH FOR THE Me109.

WE ARE LUCKY TO HAVE SPITFIRES SHARING THIS BASE. WE'LL WORK TOGETHER. WE WILL GO AFTER THE BOMBERS, LEAVING THE ESCORTS TO THE SPITFIRES.

UNDER A BLAZING SUMMER SUN THE LUFTWAFFE HORDES SWARMED ACROSS THE CHANNEL, CONFIDENT THAT THEY WOULD QUICKLY BATTER ENGLAND TO HER KNEES. BUT THE GERMAN "EAGLES" FOUND THAT THE BRITISH LION HAD CLAWS AND TEETH.

GOTT IN HIMMEL!

NOT YOUR DAY, JERRY!

THE SPITFIRE-HURRICANE COMBINATION WORKED WELL. BRIAN LED HIS FLIGHT INTO THE MASSED RANKS OF BOMBERS. IN HIS HEADPHONES HE HEARD THE CALLS OF THE SPITFIRE PILOTS AS THEY TORE INTO THE MESSERSCHMITTS.

PHEW, WHAT A ROUGH-HOUSE. HULLO, WHAT ARE THOSE THREE DOING — WHY DON'T THEY GET STUCK IN?

I'VE STOPPED ONE, LEADER.

GET CLEAR THEN, HEAD FOR BASE. GOOD LUCK.

EVER ALERT, HE HAD SPOTTED THREE Me109s CIRCLING HIGH ABOVE.

BRIAN SAW A SPITFIRE WOBBLE AWAY FROM THE MELEE, VEERING FROM SIDE TO SIDE AS ITS WOUNDED PILOT STROVE TO CONTROL IT.   THEN A LEAN SHAPE CAME HURTLING DOWN FROM THE BLUE SKY ABOVE.

HATRED FLARED UP IN BRIAN.   SLAMMING HIS THROTTLE WIDE OPEN, HE BURST OUT OF THE BOMBER FORMATION AND BORE DOWN ON THE MESSERSCHMITT.   HE WAS ALREADY TOO LATE TO SAVE THE SPITFIRE PILOT.

BUT THE TWO GUARDIANS WERE ALREADY ON HIS TAIL. BRIAN FOUGHT LIKE A TIGER, RAKING THE MESSERSCHMITTS, TRYING TO GET PAST THEM.

THEY'RE TOO QUICK FOR ME. AND THERE'S HIS LORDSHIP WAITING TO POLISH ME OFF. OH, FOR A SPIT-FIRE...

BRIAN'S PRAYER WAS SWIFTLY ANSWERED. TWO SPITFIRES SAILED INTO HIS ATTACKERS, GUNS BLAZING.

NOW I'VE GOT YOU. COME ON, SCHLANGE THE SNAKE, LET'S HAVE IT OUT MAN TO MAN.

BUT THAT WAS NOT VON SCHLANGE'S WAY. NOSE DOWN, HE RACED FOR THE SAFETY OF THE FRENCH COAST. STRAINING HIS ENGINE TO THE LIMIT, BRIAN POUNDED AFTER HIM.

NO GOOD. HE'S GOT A BRAND-NEW KITE, AND THIS OLD BUS IS GETTING WORN OUT. FUEL LOW TOO. WELL, THERE'LL BE ANOTHER TIME.

BRIAN TURNED FOR BASE, LANDING ON HIS LAST GALLON OF PETROL. GILCHRIST WAS WAITING.

AREN'T THERE ENOUGH HUNS THAT YOU HAVE TO GO HARING OFF AFTER A PARTICULAR ONE? AND DIS-OBEY MY ORDERS TO DO IT.

SORRY, SIR. I'VE A SCORE TO SETTLE WITH THAT HUN. HE MURDERED MY BROTHER.

GILCHRIST SAW THE HATE STILL BURNING IN BRIAN'S EYES, AND REMEMBERED THAT TERRIBLE DAY IN FRANCE. BUT HE HAD THE WHOLE SQUADRON TO THINK OF.

LOOK, BRIAN, I KNOW HOW YOU FEEL, BUT WE'VE GOT OUR HANDS FULL ENOUGH WITHOUT PERSONAL VENDETTAS.

YES, SIR. BUT THAT SNAKE MARKING JUST MADE ME SEE RED.

DAY AFTER DAY THE BOMBERS CAME, BUT ALWAYS THE SPITFIRES AND HURRICANES WERE WAITING TO POUNCE AND HACK THEM OUT OF THE SKY. THE TIDAL WAVE THAT WAS TO HAVE ENGULFED BRITAIN SHATTERED ITSELF AGAINST THE COURAGE OF FIGHTER COMMAND.

STILL LOOKING FOR YOUR PET HUN, BRIAN?

NOT NOW, SIR. WE'RE GETTING ON TOP OF THEM. VON SCHLANGE ONLY SHOWS UP WHEN HE THINKS THE PICKINGS ARE EASY.

THE BATTLE WAS NOT OVER. BRITAIN SURVIVED THE TERRIBLE NIGHT BLITZ OF 1940-41, AND WITH THE NEW YEAR THE R.A.F. GATHERED STRENGTH TO HIT BACK. FASTER, MORE HEAVILY-ARMED AIRCRAFT WERE THERE TO GIVE THE PUNCH.

I WAS FOND OF THE OLD HURRICANE, BUT THIS NEW SPITFIRE IS A BEAUTY.

WITH THIS CANNON SHE'LL REALLY PACK A WALLOP. AND NOW WE CAN GO LOOKING FOR THE HUNS, NOT WAIT FOR THEM TO COME TO US.

BOMBER COMMAND POUNDED GERMANY BY NIGHT, WHILE BY DAY WHOLE WINGS OF FIGHTERS CROSSED THE CHANNEL, DARING THE LUFTWAFFE TO COME AND DO BATTLE, STRAFING THEM ON THEIR AIRFIELDS IF THE CHALLENGE WAS NOT MET.

NOBODY WANTS TO PLAY. LET'S STIR THEM UP A BIT. WE'LL HIT THAT AIRFIELD JUST SOUTH OF HERE.

ONE SQUADRON PLAYED HAVOC WITH THE INSTALLATIONS AND PARKED AIRCRAFT WHILE THE OTHER TWO CIRCLED PROTECTIVELY OVERHEAD.

BANDITS COMING IN FROM THE NORTH. SWARMS OF THEM!

MINUTES LATER THE TWO FORCES CLASHED. THE MARK V SPITFIRES AND THE MESSERSCHMITT 109F WERE EVENLY MATCHED, BUT THE GERMANS OUTNUMBERED THE BRITISH. IN A VERY SHORT TIME THE SPITFIRES HAD TAKEN CARE OF THAT.

WHAT A SHINDIG! HULLO, WHAT HAVE WE HERE?

FROM FORCE OF HABIT BRIAN HAD GLANCED UP-SUN. LURKING IN THE BLINDING ORB WERE THREE MORE MESSERSCHMITTS.

THREE OF THEM, SITTING UP THERE, NOT JOINING IN – THAT'LL BE MISTER YELLOW-BELLY SCHLANGE. LET'S SEE...

JUGGLING HIS MIXTURE CONTROL, BRIAN MADE THE ENGINE COUGH AND MISFIRE AND VEERED AWAY FROM THE FLIGHT.

HE'S FALLEN FOR IT. COME ON, CHUM, JUST A BIT CLOSER.

THE MESSERSCHMITT CAME ON CONFIDENTLY, TAKING ITS TIME. WHEN IT WAS RIGHT ON HIS TAIL, BRIAN KICKED THE RUDDER. THE SPITFIRE SPUN ROUND LIKE A TOP, GUNS BLAZING.

HOLD THAT, JERRY – GOOD GRIEF, THE MAN'S AN AMATEUR!

FROM THE CLUMSY WAY VON SCHLANGE AVOIDED BRIAN'S FIRE, IT WAS PLAIN HE HAD NO REAL ABILITY. AS ALWAYS HE TURNED TO FLEE, BUT BRIAN WAS ON HIM.

THAT'S WINGED HIM, BUT HERE COME HIS BULLY BOYS. SOMEBODY GET THESE TWO OFF MY BACK!

THERE WERE NOW SPITFIRES TO SPARE , AND BRIAN'S CALL WAS SWIFTLY ANSWERED.
GRIMLY HE CLOSED ON VON SCHLANGE.

NOW , MY FINE
FRIEND , IT'S JUST YOU
AND ME.

AS ALWAYS WHEN FACED WITH A FAIR FIGHT , VON SCHLANGE HAD TAKEN TO HIS HEELS.
THROTTLE WIDE OPEN , BRIAN SLOWLY BUT SURELY CUT DOWN THE GERMAN'S LEAD.

I MUST HAVE HIT
SOMETHING , HE'S LOSING
HEIGHT. I'LL BE IN RANGE
ANY MINUTE
NOW...

AGAIN BRIAN'S GUNS CRACKLED. THE MESSERSCHMITT JERKED, SWAYED, THEN SIDE-SLIPPED TOWARDS THE GROUND.

HE'S PUT HER DOWN TOO FAST. STONE ME, HE CAN'T EVEN CRASH A PLANE PROPERLY.

THE MESSERSCHMITT SKATED WILDLY OVER THE TURF, DEMOLISHED A FENCE AND PLUNGED FULL-TILT INTO A DEEP, SLIMY DUCKPOND.

BLITZEN, THE STENCH!

BRIAN COULD NOT SUPPRESS A GRIN AS HE SAW THE NAZI FLOUNDERING IN THE FOUL SLIME.

GASPING FOR BREATH, VON SCHLANGE TURNED HIS HEAD AS A SWELLING ROAR BATTERED HIS EARDRUMS. LOOMING OVER HIM LIKE A GIANT BIRD OF PREY WAS THE SPITFIRE, ONE WING SCYTHING TOWARDS HIM.

WHO IS THIS MADMAN? WHAT DOES HE WANT WITH ME?

THE RAKING WINGTIP MISSED THE GROVELLING NAZI BY INCHES, THEN BRIAN HAD TO WRENCH AT HIS CONTROLS TO AVOID SMASHING INTO THE FARMHOUSE. HE WAS JOLTED OUT OF HIS ORGY OF HATE BY BULLETS STRIKING HIS WING.

OH, CRUMBS, NOW I'M REALLY IN THE SOUP!

ONE OF SCHLANGE'S BODYGUARDS HAD FOUGHT HIS WAY CLEAR OF THE SPITFIRES. KNOWING HE WOULD BE IN SERIOUS TROUBLE FOR LETTING HIS MASTER BE SHOT AT, HE HAD HURRIED TO THE RESCUE.

HE REALLY MEANS TO GET ME. I CAN'T SHOOT BACK, SO LET'S SEE IF HE'S EVER DONE ANY AIR RACING...

AVOIDING THE GERMAN'S WILD RUSHES, BRIAN HEADED FOR THE COAST, NOT AT TREE-TOP LEVEL, BUT NEARLY AT GROUND LEVEL.

NOT BAD, CHUM, BUT NOT GOOD ENOUGH.

THE MAD CHASE WENT ON, THE GERMAN DESPERATELY TRYING TO CLOSE WITH THE FLEEING SPITFIRE.

YOU'RE BETTER THAN SCHLANGE, I'LL SAY THAT FOR YOU.

GOTT IN HIMMEL!

BUT THE GERMAN LACKED BRIAN'S EXPERIENCE OF LOW-LEVEL FLYING AND ABOVE ALL, HIS HAIR'S-BREADTH JUDGEMENT.

THERE'S THE COAST, AND NOT BEFORE TIME. I'M RUNNING OUT OF TRICKS, AND PETROL.

THE SPITFIRE WING HAD ROUNDED OFF THE DAY'S WORK BY PLASTERING A COASTAL ANTI-AIRCRAFT GUN BATTERY. THE GUNNERS WERE JUST CRAWLING OUT OF THEIR SLIT TRENCHES, THANKFUL TO BE ALIVE.

I THOUGHT THEY'D NEVER GO. WHAT A MESS...

HIMMEL, LOOK OUT!

WITH A ROAR LIKE AN EXPRESS TRAIN, BRIAN'S SPITFIRE BORE DOWN ON THE HAPLESS GERMANS.

EVERYBODY DOWN!

BRIAN'S TUMULTUOUS ARRIVAL WAS OBSERVED BY THE OTHER PILOTS, PARTICULARLY SQUADRON LEADER GILCHRIST. HE WAS UNIMPRESSED.

WHO'S THAT NUT-CASE?

ONE OF MY MOB. I'LL HAVE A FEW WORDS TO SAY TO HIM WHEN WE GET BACK.

ONCE AGAIN BRIAN FOUND HIMSELF ON THE CARPET.

YOUR PET HUN AGAIN, I SUPPOSE?

YES, SIR. I NEARLY GOT HIM — NEXT TIME I SHALL. THIRD TIME LUCKY.

DON'T BE TOO SURE. IT MIGHT BE THIRD TIME UNLUCKY.

THAT'S A RISK I'M PREPARED TO TAKE, SIR. I'LL GET HIM, NO MATTER WHAT!

IN WESTERN EUROPE THE NAZI JUGGERNAUT HAD BEEN HALTED, BUT ELSEWHERE THE SITUATION WAS VERY DIFFERENT. AND NEXT DAY THE SQUADRON RECEIVED ITS POSTING ORDERS.

WE'RE HEADING FOR THE MED. MALTA IS HANGING ON BY THE SKIN OF HER TEETH. THEY'RE BEING BOMBED ALL DAY, EVERY DAY. WE'RE GOING OUT THERE TO GIVE THEM A HAND. YOU'LL TAKE ONLY THE MINIMUM OF KIT, AS WE'LL BE FLYING THE LAST LEG OF THE TRIP IN OUR SPITFIRES.

AIRCRAFT AND MEN EMBARKED ON AN AIRCRAFT CARRIER AND SAILED FOR THE MEDITERRANEAN. NEAR MALTA THE SPITFIRES FLEW OFF THE SHIP, WHERE THEY WERE MET AND GUIDED IN BY ONE OF THE "RESIDENTS". A FULL SCALE AIR-RAID WAS GOING ON AS THEY ARRIVED.

IS IT ALWAYS LIKE THIS?

NO, THIS IS ONE OF THE QUIET DAYS.

IN ONE OF THE CAVES GROUP CAPTAIN MAYNARD WELCOMED THE NEW ARRIVALS. HE WAS MORE THAN GLAD TO SEE THEM. UP UNTIL NOW THE AIR DEFENCE OF MALTA HAD RESTED ON A HANDFUL OF OVER-WORKED HURRICANES AND AGED GLADIATOR BIPLANES.

THE BOMBERS CAME FROM SICILY, ONLY A FEW MINUTES' FLYING TIME FROM MALTA. EVEN WITH RADAR WARNING, THERE WAS VERY LITTLE TIME FOR THE DEFENDERS TO TAKE OFF AND GAIN HEIGHT. BUT FOR THE SPITFIRES IT WAS ENOUGH.

THAT SHOOK THEM UP. RED LEADER TO RED FLIGHT —LEAVE THOSE THAT HAVE DUMPED THEIR BOMBS. THEY CAN'T DO ANY DAMAGE.

THE STIFFENED DEFENCE HAD ITS EFFECT. THE RAIDS WERE LESS FREQUENT AND NOT SO HEAVY, BUT THE ITALIANS NEVER GAVE UP.

THEY'RE SENDING MORE FIGHTERS NOW, BUT WE'RE HOLDING THEM.

ONLY JUST. THE MECHANICS WORK WONDERS TO KEEP US FLYING, BUT THE AIRCRAFT ARE FEELING THE STRAIN. WHAT WE NEED ARE MORE NEW KITES, AND THERE JUST AREN'T ANY.

REGULAR RECONNAISSANCE FLIGHTS WERE MADE OVER THE SICILIAN AIRFIELDS. THEY BROUGHT BACK OMINOUS NEWS.

THE GERMANS ARE PILING IN WITH A VENGEANCE. THE AIRFIELDS ARE STIFF WITH HEINKELS, STUKAS AND MESSER-SCHMITTS.

NOW WE'RE REALLY GOING TO HAVE OUR WORK CUT OUT.

ONCE AGAIN BRIAN SAW THE EVIL, CROOKED-WINGED DIVE-BOMBERS. SUPERBLY FLOWN, THEY DIVED HELL FOR LEATHER THROUGH THE STORM OF ANTI-AIRCRAFT FIRE THROWN UP AT THEM.

THESE JERRIES REALLY KNOW THEIR STUFF. BANDITS ABOVE, CHAPS. LEAVE THE STUKAS TO THE HURRICANES.

EVERYTHING THAT COULD FLY AND CARRY A GUN WAS THROWN INTO THE BATTLE. EVEN THE ANCIENT GLADIATORS DID THEIR BIT, HOVERING LOW DOWN TO CATCH THE STUKAS AS THEY PULLED OUT OF THE DIVES.

WELL DONE, THE BOX-KITE BRIGADE. SOONER THEM THAN ME IN THOSE OLD RELICS.

THEN BRIAN JUMPED AS THREE MESSERSCHMITTS FLASHED BY HIM, TWO CLOSE TOGETHER, A THIRD FOLLOWING. PAINTED ON THE SIDE OF THE LAST ONE WAS A SYMBOL HE HAD COME TO KNOW AND HATE.

VON SCHLANGE! I THOUGHT HE'D TURN UP SOONER OR LATER, WHEN HIS SIDE ARE ON TOP.

SCHLANGE WAS RUNNING TRUE TO FORM, LOOKING FOR THE OLDEST, SLOWEST AIRCRAFT TO ADD TO HIS SCORE. BRIAN WAS ON HIS TAIL IN A FLASH.

PICK ON SOMEONE YOUR OWN SIZE, NAZI!

AS ALWAYS THE NAZI SPED AWAY TO SAFETY. BRIAN'S HARD-USED SPITFIRE COULD NO LONGER MATCH HIS SPEED.

HE ALWAYS HAS A BRAND-NEW KITE TO GET HIM OUT OF TROUBLE. THIS TIME I'M NOT RISKING MY NECK AGAINST HIS TWO GORILLAS.

NEARLY EVERY DAY VON SCHLANGE WAS THERE, LURKING ON THE SIDELINES, WAITING FOR EASY PREY. BRIAN COULD ONLY GRIND HIS TEETH IN FRUSTRATION. THEN HIS CHANCE CAME.

JUST HEARD FROM THE GROUP CAPTAIN THAT SOME NEW AIRCRAFT ARE DUE, LATE MODEL SPITFIRES.

ABOUT TIME. THE MECHANICS ARE RUNNING OUT OF STRING AND STICKY TAPE!

THE NEW SPITFIRES FLEW IN, TIMING THEIR ARRIVAL BETWEEN THE ALMOST CONTINUOUS GERMAN RAIDS. THEY WERE MARK NINES, WITH A MORE POWERFUL ENGINE THAN THE OLD MARK FIVE.

THIS ONE'S YOURS, BRIAN. THE PILOT WHO FLEW HER IN KICKED UP QUITE A FUSS WHEN I TOLD HIM HE'D HAVE TO HAND IT OVER AND TAKE YOUR OLD BUS.

I CAN BELIEVE THAT, SIR. SHE'S A BEAUTY.

THE CLASSIC SPITFIRE LINES WERE STILL THERE, BUT THE LONGER NOSE GAVE HER A DEADLY, SHARK-LIKE APPEARANCE. MOST IMPORTANT, SHE WAS FASTER THAN THE Me109...

RIGHT, VON SCHLANGE... NEXT TIME WE MEET, YOU WON'T BE ABLE TO RUN AWAY.

THE NEW MACHINES WENT INTO ACTION THAT SAME EVENING, LEADING THE ATTACK.

THESE NEW BABIES ARE JUST THE JOB!

BUT EVEN AS HE FLUNG HIMSELF INTO THE BATTLE BRIAN WAS ALWAYS ON THE LOOKOUT FOR HIS ARCH-ENEMY. AND SURE ENOUGH...

BRIAN OPENED THE THROTTLE, AND THE SPITFIRE WENT UP LIKE A LIFT. GUESSING HIS PURPOSE, VON SCHLANGE'S TWO GUARDIANS POUNCED.

THE CHASE WAS ON. BRIAN LEFT THE TWO BODYGUARDS BEHIND AND SET OFF AFTER VON SCHLANGE, FIERCE ELATION FILLING HIS MIND. AND THE NAZI WAS COMPLETELY AT A LOSS.

BRIAN WAS STILL OUT OF RANGE WHEN THE SICILIAN COAST APPEARED ON THE HORIZON, BUT HE WAS CUTTING DOWN THE GERMAN'S LEAD EVERY SECOND.

AT LOW LEVEL VON SCHLANGE TORE ACROSS THE COAST. HARD BEHIND HIM CAME BRIAN, RIGHT ON TO THE WAITING ANTI-AIRCRAFT GUNS.

A STORM OF BULLETS AND SHELLS RIPPED INTO THE SPITFIRE. SMOKE BELCHED FROM THE ENGINE, A SEARING PAIN TORE THROUGH BRIAN'S LEG.

FIGHTING THE WAVES OF PAIN THAT ENGULFED HIM, BRIAN SIDESLIPPED, STRIVING TO KEEP THE HUNGRY FLAMES AWAY. THEN THE SPITFIRE SHUDDERED AS FRESH BULLETS SLAMMED INTO IT.

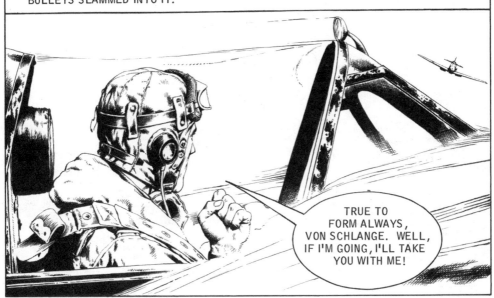

TRUE TO FORM ALWAYS, VON SCHLANGE. WELL, IF I'M GOING, I'LL TAKE YOU WITH ME!

SUMMONING UP HIS FAILING STRENGTH, BRIAN DRAGGED THE BLAZING SPITFIRE ROUND AND CHARGED AT THE COBRA-MARKED MESSERSCHMITT. BUT VON SCHLANGE AVOIDED HIM EASILY.

NO GOOD. CAN'T GET NEAR HIM...HAVE TO DITCH...

SOMEHOW BRIAN SET HIS TATTERED PLANE DOWN IN THE SEA. WITH THE LAST OF HIS STRENGTH HE SCRAMBLED CLEAR AS SHE SANK LIKE A STONE. BUT HIS ORDEAL WAS NOT OVER...

NO, HE CAN'T BE...

BULLETS AND SHELLS LASHED THE SEA TO FOAM AROUND BRIAN. WHITE-HOT AGONY SEARED THROUGH HIS CHEST... THEN BLACKNESS ENGULFED HIM.

AH! YOU WIN... SNAKE...

AS NIGHT CLOSED IN, H.M. SUBMARINE VIXEN, RETURNING TO MALTA, CAUTIOUSLY POKED HER PERISCOPE ABOVE THE SURFACE. AT THE EYEPIECE HER CAPTAIN GAVE A CRY OF SURPRISE.

WHAT'S UP, SIR?

A BODY, PRACTICALLY LOOKING DOWN THE SCOPE AT ME! SURFACE, AND MAKE IT SNAPPY.

THE CAPTAIN EDGED HIS BOAT AS CLOSE AS HE DARED, AND BRIAN'S LIMP FORM WAS DRAGGED ABOARD.

IS HE DEAD, NUMBER ONE?

NOT FAR OFF IT, SIR. LET'S GET HIM TO MALTA.

IN ONE OF THE CAVERNS OF MALTA A MAKESHIFT OPERATING THEATRE HAD BEEN SET UP. HERE, AN ARMY SURGEON REMOVED FIVE BULLETS FROM BRIAN'S BODY.

BY ALL THE RULES HE SHOULD BE DEAD. HEAVEN ALONE KNOWS WHAT'S KEEPING HIM ALIVE. BUT THOSE WOUNDS AND BURNS NEED SPECIALIST TREATMENT THAT I CAN'T GIVE HERE.

H.M.S. CLANSMAN IS DUE TONIGHT, SIR. IF HE CAN STAND THE VOYAGE TO GIBRALTAR HE MAY HAVE A CHANCE.

FAST MINELAYERS, CAPABLE OF FORTY KNOTS, RAN THE ESSENTIAL SUPPLIES TO THE BELEAGURED ISLAND, AND EVACUATED SERIOUS CASUALTIES.

THE SURGEON STRAIGHTENED UP.

HE'LL DIE FOR SURE IF HE STAYS HERE. GET HIS THINGS TOGETHER. OH, AND PUT THIS SCARF IN. HE ALWAYS WEARS IT. SOME SORT OF MASCOT, I BELIEVE.

HASN'T BROUGHT HIM MUCH LUCK, HAS IT, SIR?

AND SO THAT NIGHT WHEN THE GALLANT MINELAYER RAN THE GAUNTLET BETWEEN MALTA AND GIBRALTAR AT FORTY KNOTS, BRIAN WENT WITH HER, UNDER CONSTANT WATCH IN THE SICK-BAY.

TWO HOURS TO GIB AT PRESENT SPEED, SIR.

FIRST CLASS... BUT LET'S KEEP OUR FINGERS CROSSED ALL THE SAME.

ONCE IN GIBRALTAR, BRIAN WAS RUSHED TO THE BASE HOSPITAL. FOR A WEEK HE HOVERED BETWEEN LIFE AND DEATH. THEN THE TINY SPARK OF LIFE REKINDLED.

ANY CHANGE, NURSE?

HE'S BEEN SEMI-CONSCIOUS OFF AND ON, SIR. KEEPS MUMBLING ABOUT "FIND THE SNAKE", WHATEVER THAT MEANS.

AS SOON AS HE WAS STRONG ENOUGH, BRIAN WAS FLOWN TO ENGLAND. THERE SPECIALISTS SET TO WORK TO RESTORE THE TORN, BURNED BODY. HE MADE STEADY PROGRESS.

GOOD TO SEE YOU SITTING UP AND TAKING NOTICE. WE THREW YOUR UNIFORM AWAY, IT WAS RUINED. BUT I WASHED THAT SCARF, THOUGH IT'S ALL FRAYED AND TORN.

THANKS A LOT, SISTER. I'VE RATHER AN ATTACHMENT FOR IT.

BRIAN PICKED UP THE PIECE OF BLACK SILK. A BULLET HAD PASSED THROUGH IT, NEATLY TAKING THE HEAD OFF THE COBRA.

COULD THIS BE A SIGN? WE'LL HAVE TO WAIT AND SEE. FIRST JOB IS TO GET BACK ON OPS, THOUGH...

MONTHS PASSED, AND HE OFTEN MET OTHER AIRCREW RECOVERING FROM THEIR WOUNDS.

...WE WERE DAMAGED, ANYWAY, THEN THREE FOCKE-WULFS JUMPED US.

THREE? DON'T THEY USUALLY WORK IN PAIRS?

BRIAN WAS AT ONCE ALL ATTENTION. THIS PATTERN SOUNDED OMINOUSLY FAMILIAR.

TWO OF THEM SET ABOUT US UNTIL THE OLD CRATE WAS IN PIECES, THEN THE THIRD CAME IN TO FINISH US OFF. WAIT A MINUTE – HE HAD A SNAKE PAINTED ON HIS KITE, JUST LIKE THE ONE ON YOUR SCARF.

SO VON SCHLANGE IS STILL AROUND, BUT WITH AN FW NOW. THE DEVIL LOOKS AFTER HIS OWN, SURE ENOUGH.

IF BRIAN NEEDED FURTHER CONFIRMATION THAT HIS OLD ENEMY WAS STILL AT HIS VILE GAME, THE PILOT SUPPLIED IT AS HE CONTINUED HIS STORY.

I MANAGED TO DITCH HER IN THE SEA, BUT THIS RAT CAME DOWN AND STRAFED US. KILLED MY NAVIGATOR. HE WOULD HAVE HAD ME TOO, ONLY A RESCUE LAUNCH TURNED UP AND HE HOPPED IT. I'D LIKE TO MEET THAT PERISHER AGAIN.

SO WOULD I.

TWO YEARS HAD PASSED BEFORE BRIAN WAS DECLARED FIT FOR DUTY, BUT NOT FOR FLYING. HE WAS POSTED AS OPERATIONS OFFICER TO A CONVERSION UNIT WHERE PILOTS FRESH FROM TRAINING LEARNED TO HANDLE THE AIRCRAFT THEY WOULD TAKE INTO BATTLE.

LOOKS LIKE I'VE A LOT OF GROUND TO MAKE UP.

TWO YEARS OF WAR HAD PASSED HIM BY. NOW THERE WERE NEW AIRCRAFT, NEW METHODS. BUT HE FULLY INTENDED TO RETURN TO OPERATIONAL FLYING AND HUNT DOWN HIS BROTHER'S MURDERER. THIS WAS THE IDEAL PLACE TO START.

HE KNEW HE WOULD ALMOST HAVE TO LEARN TO FLY AGAIN, FOR TWO YEARS WAS A LONG TIME FOR A FIGHTER PILOT.

I'D LIKE TO GET MY HAND IN AGAIN, SIR, IF YOU'VE NO OBJECTION.

NONE AT ALL. BUT DON'T HARE OFF IN A TEMPEST OR SOMETHING AND BREAK YOUR NECK. START OFF GENTLY.

BUT BRIAN HAD ALREADY LEARNED TO BE PATIENT. FIRST HE PERSUADED AN INSTRUCTOR TO CHECK HIM OUT ON THE STATION "HACK", AN OLD PERCIVAL PROCTOR.

SEE, IT'S ALL COMING BACK. YOU NEVER REALLY FORGET.

THANKS, TOMMY. A FEW HOURS ON THIS OLD BOX, THEN I'LL TRY SOMETHING FIERCER.

BRIAN FOUND THAT HE HAD NOT LOST HIS OLD TOUCH. SOON HE WAS FLYING THE LATEST FIGHTERS WITH AN EASE AND CONFIDENCE THAT DREW COMMENT FROM TRAINEES AND INSTRUCTORS ALIKE.

ONE DAY I MAY BE ABLE TO FLY LIKE THAT. WHO IS IT?

FLIGHT LIEUTENANT CRAIG, THE OPS. OFFICER. WHY HE'S KEPT MUCKING ABOUT ON A GROUND JOB IS BEYOND ME. THE MAN'S A NATURAL PILOT.

BESIDES HIS FLYING, BRIAN INSTITUTED A FITNESS PROGRAMME TO GET HIMSELF INTO SHAPE PHYSICALLY. EVERY MORNING HE WAS TO BE SEEN JOGGING AROUND THE PERIMETER TRACK.

FOR PETE'S SAKE GET DRESSED AND COME AND HAVE BREAKFAST. YOU'VE BEEN GALLOPING AROUND THE AIRFIELD WEARING OUT THE TARMAC SINCE SIX O'CLOCK.

BE WITH YOU IN A MINUTE, SIR. BY THE WAY, COULD I SIT IN ON THE TACTICS LECTURE THIS AFTERNOON? MY WORK'S UP TO DATE.

FIT AS A FIDDLE, THOROUGHLY VERSED IN THE LATEST COMBAT TECHNIQUES, BRIAN ALSO FLEW AND MASTERED EACH NEW TYPE AS IT ARRIVED AT THE UNIT. HE BEGAN TO SEND IN APPLICATIONS FOR RETURN TO OPERATIONS – WITHOUT MUCH SUCCESS.

SAME OLD EXCUSE, "UNFAMILIAR WITH LATEST AIRCRAFT AND TECHNIQUES". FIDDLE-STICKS! I'VE FLOWN THEM ALL AND SAT THROUGH ALL THE LECTURES.

THAT'S OFFICIALDOM FOR YOU. BUT I'VE SOME-THING HERE THAT MAY INTEREST YOU.

THE CAREFULLY WORDED LETTER ASKED FOR SKILLED PILOTS TO TAKE PART IN A "SPECIAL TEST PROGRAMME". NOTHING MORE, AND THE LETTER WAS MARKED "HIGHLY CONFIDENTIAL".

WHAT YOU'LL BE TESTING I DON'T KNOW. THE WHOLE THING IS VERY HUSH-HUSH. WHAT I DO KNOW IS THAT THEY WANT EXPERIENCED PILOTS WHO CAN FLY BY THE SEAT OF THEIR PANTS. MEN LIKE YOU.

THANKS FOR THE COMPLIMENT, SIR. NEVER COULD RESIST A MYSTERY, AND I RECKON THERE'S SOMETHING EXTRA SPECIAL IN THE WAY OF AIRCRAFT BEHIND ALL THIS. PUT MY NAME DOWN.

WING COMMANDER NEILL, WHO COMMANDED THE MYSTERY STATION, LED BRIAN TO A LOCKED, GUARDED HANGAR. ONLY AFTER NEILL HAD BEEN POSITIVELY IDENTIFIED AND VOUCHED FOR BRIAN WERE THEY ALLOWED IN. NEILL SWITCHED ON THE LIGHTS.

THERE YOU ARE, THE GLOSTER METEOR. WORTH KEEPING LOCKED UP, AREN'T THEY?

THEY'RE JET-PROPELLED! I HEARD RUMOURS, BUT I DIDN'T REALISE DEVELOPMENT HAD REACHED THIS STAGE.

THE SPECIAL UNIT WAS CONDUCTING TRIALS TO SHAKE OUT THE LAST 'BUGS' BEFORE THE METEORS WENT INTO SQUADRON SERVICE. AND ONE WEEK LATER, BRIAN CLIMBED INTO THE COCKPIT OF ONE OF THE SLEEK FIGHTERS.

NOW TAKE THINGS GENTLY. YOU'VE GOT AN AWFUL LOT OF POWER TO HANDLE.

I WILL, SIR. STAND BY TO START UP.

THE ROLLS ROYCE WELLAND TURBINES WOKE TO LIFE WITH THEIR EERIE WHISTLING ROAR. HE TAXIED TO THE HEAD OF THE RUNWAY, PUT THE BRAKES HARD ON AND OPENED THE THROTTLES. THE METEOR BEGAN TO TREMBLE LIKE A LIVE THING. THEN HE KICKED OFF THE BRAKES...

JUST LIKE A BIRD!

UP, UP INTO THE SPARKLING BLUE DOME OF THE SKY SHE SPED. TEN THOUSAND, TWENTY THOUSAND, THIRTY THOUSAND FEET, AND STILL CLIMBING!

THIS IS THE AIRCRAFT I'VE DREAMED ABOUT!

ALL TOO SOON IT WAS TIME TO RETURN. BRIAN LANDED AND TAXIED BACK TO THE HANGARS, BREATHLESS AND ELATED.

JUST LIKE RIDING A MAGIC CARPET.

I KNEW YOU'D ENJOY IT. YOU'VE HAD YOUR FUN, FROM NOW ON IT'S HARD WORK.

SO IT PROVED — BUT TO BRIAN IT WAS A LABOUR OF LOVE. HE HAD A MAGNIFICENT AIRCRAFT TO FLY, ALL DAY, EVERY DAY. HE WAS IN HIS ELEMENT, SO MUCH SO THAT HE ALMOST FORGOT VON SCHLANGE.

WELL, THAT'S SORTED OUT THE GUN JAMMING PROBLEM. BY THE WAY, WHERE DID YOU GET THAT TATTY OLD SCARF? YOU'RE NEVER WITHOUT IT.

I CAME BY IT BEFORE THE WAR, SIR. I WEAR IT AS A SORT OF REMINDER.

NEILL SAW THE LOOK OF BITTERNESS COME INTO THE YOUNGER MAN'S EYES AND ASKED NO MORE QUESTIONS.

AND JUST A LITTLE WHILE LATER, THE METEOR TEST PROGRAMME ENTERED ITS FINAL STAGES.

NOW WE HAVE TO SEE HOW OUR NEW TOYS BEHAVE UNDER COMBAT CONDITIONS. AIR FIRING TRIALS ARE LAID ON FOR TOMORROW MORNING. WE SHALL FLY TO THE FIRING AREA AT MAXIUM HEIGHT, THEN DIVE TO SHOOT AT A TOWED TARGET.

NEXT DAY THE METEORS ROSE INTO THE CRYSTAL-CLEAR MORNING AIR AND HEADED OUT TO SEA. FAR BELOW THEM THE TUG AIRCRAFT WAS RELEASING THE CANVAS DROGUE THAT WOULD BE THEIR TARGET. BUT THEY WERE NOT ALONE IN THE DAWN SKY.

THREE BANDITS TO THE EAST.

THEY'RE ATTACKING THE TARGET PLANE. NOW WE CAN HAVE SOME REAL COMBAT PRACTICE. TALLY-HO!

A FIERCE ELATION FILLED BRIAN. TWO FOCKE-WULFS WERE FIRING ON THE HELPLESS TARGET TUG, THE THIRD HOLDING OFF. THAT WAS THE TRADE-MARK OF ONLY ONE MAN – VON SCHLANGE. THE METEORS HURTLED DOWN LIKE BOLTS FROM THE BLUE.

THE THIRD ONE'S RUNNING FOR IT. GET HIM, CRAIG.

YOU BET!

BRIAN WAS ALONGSIDE THE FLEEING FOCKE-WULF IN SECONDS. THERE WAS THE LOATHSOME SYMBOL BLAZONED ON ITS SIDE. BRIAN TORE OFF HIS SCARF AND HELD IT UP FOR VON SCHLANGE TO SEE.

AT LAST IT'S JUST YOU AND ME. YOU DON'T DESERVE IT, BUT WE'LL HAVE THIS OUT MAN TO MAN.

BRIAN SAW THE STARK FEAR IN THE NAZI'S EYES. THEN HE KICKED THE RUDDER AND JABBED HIS GUN BUTTON.

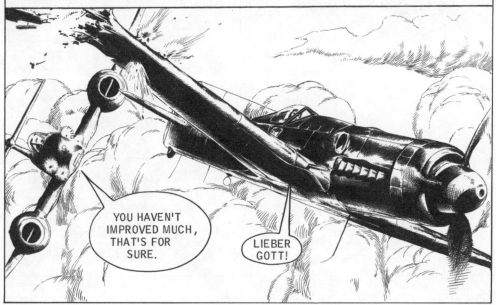

YOU HAVEN'T IMPROVED MUCH, THAT'S FOR SURE.

LIEBER GOTT!

TRUE TO FORM, VON SCHLANGE TRIED TO FLEE, BUT NOW BRIAN HAD THE WHIP HAND. HIS MACHINE WAS A HUNDRED MILES AN HOUR FASTER.

NO, YOU CAN'T GET AWAY, NAZI. COME ON, CURSE YOU, FIGHT!

FINALLY, LIKE A CORNERED RAT, VON SCHLANGE TURNED ON HIS TORMENTOR. BUT BRIAN EASILY EVADED THE ILL-TIMED, WILD RUSHES.

THAT'S MORE LIKE IT! BUT AS I SAID BEFORE, YOU'RE AN AMATEUR.

IN COMPETENT HANDS, THE FOCKE-WULF WAS A DANGEROUS ADVERSARY, EVEN TO A METEOR. BRIAN GAVE THE GERMAN EVERY CHANCE OF A FAIR FIGHT, BUT KURT VON SCHLANGE HAD NEITHER THE ABILITY NOR THE GUTS. THERE COULD ONLY BE ONE ENDING.

THIS IS FOR DAVID, AND FOR ALL THE OTHER POOR HELPLESS WRETCHES YOU'VE BUTCHERED, YOU MURDERER!

STONY-FACED, BRIAN WATCHED THE FOCKE-WULF, BLAZING FROM END TO END, HURTLE DOWN LIKE A FIERY COMET TO SHATTER ITSELF ON THE ROCKY COASTLINE BELOW.

THAT'S THE LAST FAREWELL, NAZI — BUT THERE'S ONE MORE THING...

THE COVERS

No. 1594
16p

Commando

WAR STORIES IN PICTURES

THE FLYING AVENGERS